Security/
Fire-Alarm
Systems

Security/ Fire-Alarm Systems

Design, Installation, Maintenance

John E. Traister

Second Edition

McGraw-Hill

New York   San Francisco   Washington, D.C.   Auckland   Bogotá
Caracas   Lisbon   London   Madrid   Mexico City   Milan
Montreal   New Delhi   San Juan   Singapore
Sydney   Tokyo   Toronto

Library of Congress Cataloging-in-Publication Data

Traister, John E.
   Security/fire-alarm: design, installation, maintenance /
John E. Traister—2nd ed.
      p.   cm.
   Includes index.
   ISBN 0-07-065296-1.
   1. Burglar alarms. 2. Fire alarms. I. Title.
TH9739.T73   1996
621.389-28—dc20   95-35183
                                        CIP

McGraw-Hill

A Division of The McGraw-Hill Companies

1 2 3 4 5 6 7 8 9 0   AGM/AGM   9 0 0 9 8 7 6 5

ISBN 0-07-065296-1

National Electrical Code® and *NEC*® are registered trademarks of the National Fire Protection Association, Inc., Quincy, MA 02269.

Cover design: Keeler Chapman.
Printed and bound by Quebecor/Martinsburg.

 This book is printed on recycled, acid-free paper containing a minimum of 50% recycled, de-inked fiber.

Contents

Preface

In general, an alarm system is used for the protection of life and property, as well as anything else of value. Therefore, any company or person who owns something of value has a valid interest in security/fire-alarm systems.

There are security/fire-alarm systems designed for every application imaginable — for structures as small as homes and roadside produce stands to large hotels and factories; security alarms for guarding automobiles to large national defense installations.

This book is designed to review the various security systems currently available to help the reader select the most appropriate system for the job. Installation methods are also covered, using the latest installation techniques and requirements to comply with the 1996 National Electrical Code. Finally, a review of printreading and troubleshooting techniques makes this book invaluable to anyone involved with security/fire-alarm systems in any capacity.

John E. Traister
1995

Chapter 1
Basic Considerations

The use of security/fire-alarm systems is not only advisable, but is also mandated in most populated towns and cities by national codes and local ordinances. This chapter introduces the basic types of security-system equipment and components.

SIGNALING SYSTEMS

Signaling techniques are not new. Methods were devised more than 5000 years ago to signal individuals and tribes of danger and of oncoming strangers; Indians used smoke signals for communicating with each other; other tribes used drums, animal horns, and other natural objects of sight or sound; bells were used extensively during the early settling of the United States to announce meetings and warn of fires and other dangers. And, of course, military troops have for years used flags and horns (bugles) to communicate and to signal orders, like "charge," "retreat," and "assemble."

When electricity was put to practical use around the latter part of the last century, methods were devised to use electrical buzzers and bells, such as doorbells, entrance detectors, and manually operated fire-alarm signals, for signaling devices. However, at that time, electrical and electronic devices were usually limited to certain specialized applications, such as banks and school buildings.

Today, all apartment buildings and town houses in almost every section of the United States must have an adequate number of smoke detectors installed to warn occupants of fire. Buildings such as nursing homes, schools, hospitals, and hotels are required to have an approved fire-alarm system installed, as well as sprinkler systems. The latter is usually designed to operate in conjunction with the fire-alarm system. Banks and similar institutions would not think of opening their doors without adequate security systems installed on the premises.

The cases are almost endless, and great opportunities await the trained security technician. To verify this, look in the Yellow Pages of any city phone directory under Alarm Systems, Burglar Alarm Systems & Monitoring, and Fire-Alarm Systems and see the number of businesses listed. Each one probably has a dozen or more employees, and are eager to hire several more trained technicians.

CLASSIFICATION OF SIGNAL CIRCUITS

A signal circuit used for security or fire-alarm system may be classified as open circuit or closed circuit. An *open circuit* is one in which current flows only when a signal is being sent. A *closed circuit* is one in which current flows continuously, except when the circuit is opened to allow a signal to be sent.

All security systems have three functions in common:

- Detection

- Control

- Annunciation (or alarm) signaling

Many systems incorporate switches or relays that operate when entry, movement, pressure, infrared-beam interruption, and other intrusions occur. The control senses the operation of the detector with a relay and produces an output that may operate a bell, siren, silent alarm such as telephone dialers to law enforcement agencies, or other signals. The controls frequently contain ON/OFF switches, test meters, time delays, power supplies, standby batteries, and terminals for connecting the system together. The control output usually provides power on alarms to operate signaling devices or switch contacts for silent alarms. See Figure 1-1.

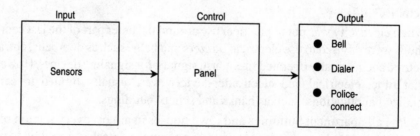

Figure 1-1: Basic subdivisions of an alarm system.

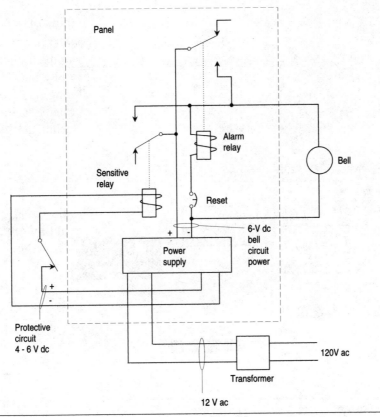

Figure 1-2: Basic closed-circuit security alarm system.

An example of a basic closed-circuit security system is shown in Figure 1-2. The detection (or input) subdivision in this drawing shows exit/entry door or window contacts. However, the detectors could just as well be smoke or heat detectors, switch mats, ultrasonic detectors, and the like.

The control subdivision for the system in Figure 1-2 consists of switches, relays, a power supply, a reset button, and related wiring. The power supply shown is a 6-V nickel-cadmium battery that is kept charged by a plug-in transformer unit. Terminals are provided on the battery housing to accept 12-V ac charging power from the plug-in transformer which provides 4- to 6-V power for the detection (protective) circuit and power to operate the alarm or output subdivision.

Figure 1-3 shows another closed-circuit system. The protective circuit consists of a dc energy source, any number of normally closed intrusion-detection contacts (wired in series), a sensitive relay (R_1) and interconnecting wiring. In operation, the normally closed intrusion contacts are connected to the coil of the sensitive relay. This keeps the relay energized, holding its normally closed contacts open against spring pressure — the all-clear condition of the protective circuit. The opening of any intrusion contact breaks the circuit, which deenergizes the sensitive relay and allows spring force to close the relay contacts. This action initiates the alarm.

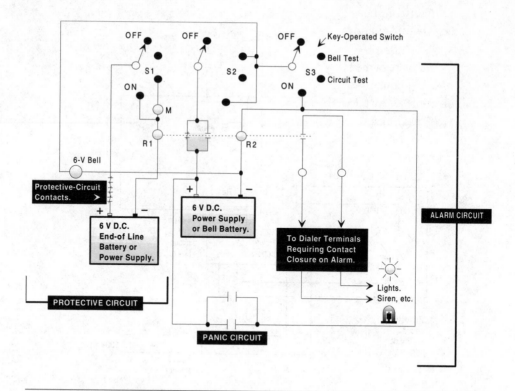

Figure 1-3: Closed-circuit security alarm system.

The key-operated switch shown in the circuit in Figure 1-3 is provided for opening the protective circuit for test purposes. A meter (M) is activated when the switch is set to CIRCUIT TEST. The meter gives a current reading only if all intrusion contacts are closed. All three sections of the switch (S_1, S_2, S_3) make contact simultaneously as the key is turned.

Opening of intrusion contacts is not the only event that causes the alarm to activate. Any break in protective-circuit wiring or loss of output from the energy source has the same effect. The circuit is broken which deenergizes the sensitive relay and allows spring force to close the relay contacts, thus sounding the alarm. Any cross or short circuit between the positive and negative wires of the protective circuit also keeps current from reaching the relay coil and causes dropout which again sounds the alarm.

Other components of the alarm circuit in Figure 1-3 include a second energy source, an alarm bell, and a drop relay (R_2). When the keyed switch is at ON, dropout of the sensitive relay (R_1), and closing of its contacts completes a circuit to energize the coil of drop relay (R_2). Closing of the drop relay's normally open contacts rings the bell and latches in the drop-relay coil so that R_2 stays energized even if the protective circuit returns to normal and opens the sensitive relay's contacts. As a result, the bell continues to ring until the key switch is turned away from ON to break the latching connections to the R_2 coil.

Drop relays often have additional contacts to control other circuits or devices. The extra contacts in the circuit in Figure 1-3 are for turning on lights, triggering an automatic telephone dialer, etc. But the main two functions of the drop relay are actuation of the alarm and latching the coil to keep the circuit in the alarm condition.

Almost all burglar systems use a closed-loop protective circuit. In general, the system consists of an annunciator connected to a special design contact on each door and window and a relay so connected that when any window or door is opened it will cause current to pass through the relay. The relay, in turn, will operate to close a circuit on a bell, horn, or other type of annunciator which will continue to sound until it is shut off, thereby alerting the occupants or law enforcement agencies.

The wiring and connections for the open-circuit system are shown in Figure 1-4. This diagram shows three contacts, but any number can be added as needed. Closing any one of the contacts completes the power circuit through the winding of the proper annunciator drops, the constant-ringing switch, the constant-ringing relay, the alarm bell, and the bell-cutoff switch. The current through the winding of the constant-ringing relay operates to complete a circuit placing the alarm bell directly across the battery or other power source so the bell continues to ring until the cutoff switch is opened. At the same time, current in another set of wires operates a relay that closes an auxiliary circuit to operate other devices, such as lights and automatic telephone dialer.

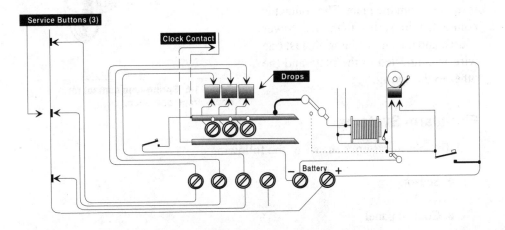

Figure 1-4: Open-circuit security alarm system.

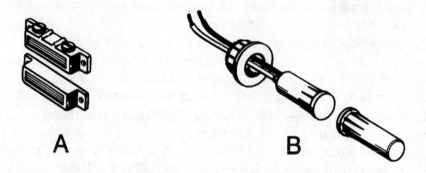

Figure 1-5: Spring-type contact for closed-circuit operation.

Contacts for closed-circuit operation are shown in Figure 1-5A. The contacts are surface-mounted opposite each other, one on a stationary window or door frame; the other on the movable part of the window or door. When the window is raised, or the door is opened, the contacts break and sound the alarm. Contacts for recessed mounting are shown in Figure 1-5B and operate the same way as described for the surface-mounted contacts.

A spring-type contact for open-circuit operation is shown in Figure 1-6. This device is recessed in the window frame or a door jamb so that the cam projects outward. When the window is raised, the cam pivots and is pressed in and makes contact with a spring that is insulated from the plate. The contact is connected in series with the power source and the annunciator; that is, one wire is connected to the plate and the other to the spring.

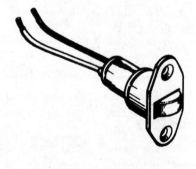

Figure 1-6: Spring-type contact for open-circuit operation.

Fire-alarm Systems

A fire-alarm system consists of the following:

- Sensors

- Control panel

- Annunciator

- Related wiring

They are generally divided into the following four types:

- Noncoded

- Master-coded

- Selective-coded

- Dual-coded

Each of these four types has several functional features so designed that a specific system may meet practically any need to comply with local and state codes, statutes, and regulations.

In a noncoded system, an alarm signal is sounded continuously until manually or automatically turned off.

In a master-coded system, a common-coded alarm signal is sounded for not less than three rounds. The same code is sounded regardless of the alarm-initiating device activated.

In a selective-coded system, a unique coded alarm is sounded for each firebox or fire zone on the protected premises.

In a dual-coded system, a unique coded alarm is sounded for each firebox or fire zone to notify the building's personnel of the location of the fire, while noncoded or common-coded alarm signals are sounded separately to notify other occupants to evacuate the building.

Figure 1-7 represents a riser diagram of a fire-alarm system. If the detector senses smoke or if any manual striking station is operated, all bells within the building will ring. At the same time, the magnetic door switches will release the smoke doors to help block smoke and/or drafts. This system is also connected to a water-flow switch on the sprinkler system. If the sprinkler valves are activated causing a flow of water in the system, the fire-alarm system will again go into operation energizing all bells and closing smoke doors.

Smoke and Fire Detectors

Any product of a fire that changes the ambient conditions is called a *fire signature* and is potentially useful for detection purposes. The principle fire signature used in residential smoke detectors is aerosol. *Aerosols* are particles suspended in air. The process of combustion releases into the atmosphere large numbers of such solid and liquid particles that may range in size from 10 μm [a micron (μm) is one thousandth of a millimeter] down to 0.001 μms. Aerosols resulting from a fire represent two different fire signatures. Those particles less than 0.3 μms do not scatter light efficiently and are classified as visible. The invisible aerosol signature is usually

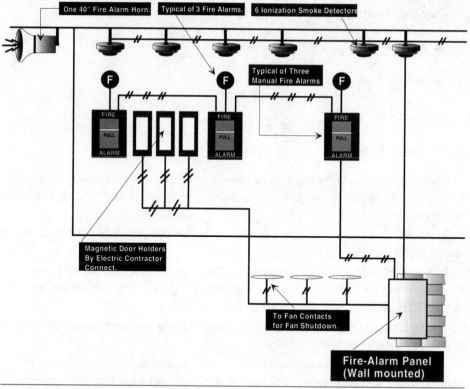

Figure 1-7: Riser diagram of a fire-alarm system.

referred to as the "products of combustion" and the visible aerosol signature as "smoke." Invisible aerosol is the earliest appearing fire signature.

Types of Fire Detection Devices

Thermal Detectors: Thermal detectors are devices that operate on high heat — typically 135°F. These units consist of a bimetallic element which bends to complete a circuit under high heat conditions. Since these units do not detect smoke or products of combustion, they are not recommended for living areas of a residence. They do have value for use in attics, unheated garages and furnace rooms.

Flame Detectors: Flame detectors detect actual flames by sensing the ultraviolet emissions. These devices would not be used in residential applications.

Gas Detectors: These units respond to certain gases (propane, carbon monoxide, liquid petroleum, butane, gasoline vapors, etc.) that would not be detected by a smoke and fire detector. While these detectors do have some uses, they should not be a substitute for a smoke and fire detector. They will not respond to aerosols produced by the majority of residential fires.

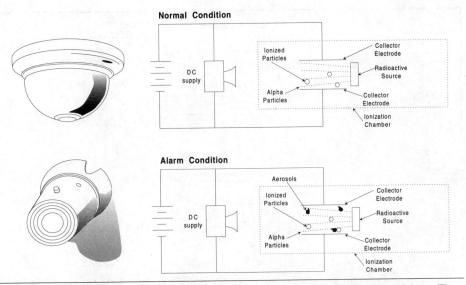

Figure 1-8: Diagrams of ionization detectors. The top diagram shows normal conditions. The bottom diagram shows aerosols, such as products of combustion or smoke, entering the sensor. In the latter condition, the alarm is activated.

Ionization Detectors: Inside the ionization chamber, the radioactive source emits radiation, main alpha particles, which bombard the air and ionize the air particles, which, in turn, are attracted by the voltage on the collector electrodes. This action results in a minute current flow. If aerosols, such as products of combustion or smoke, enter the chamber, the ionized air particles attach themselves to the aerosols and the resultant particles, being of larger mass than ionized air, move more slowly, and thus, per unit of time, fewer reach the electrodes. A decrease in current flow, therefore, takes place within the chamber whenever aerosols enter. The decrease in current flow is electronically converted into an alarm signal output. See Figure 1-8.

An ionization type of detector responds best to invisible aerosols where the particles from burning materials are in the range of 1.0 µm in size down to 0.01 µm. A tremendous amount of these particles are produced by a flaming fire as opposed to a smoldering fire which produces large and small particles, but, because of low heat, the low thermal lift tends to allow particles to agglomerate into larger particles if the detector is some distance from the fire.

High air flows will affect the operation of this type of unit by reducing the ion concentration in the detector chamber. In fact, with a high enough air flow, the unit will respond and alarm even though a fire does not exist. For this reason, locations near windows, direct air flows from air vents and comparable areas should be avoided.

Ionization smoke detectors (Figure 1-9) may be used in place of conventional smoke detectors or may be used in combination with standard smoke detectors. They are more sensitive than the conventional smoke detectors.

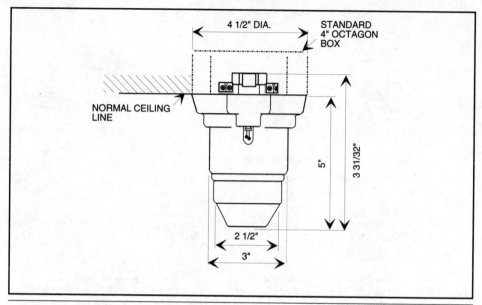

Figure 1-9: Ionization smoke detector.

Photoelectric Detectors: A beam from the light source is projected across a chamber into a light catcher. The chamber is designed to permit access of smoke, but not access of external light. A photo-resistive cell or light sensitive device is located in a recessed area perpendicular to the light beam. When smoke enters the chamber, smoke particles will scatter or reflect a small portion of the light beam to the light receiving device, which, in turn, will provide a signal for amplification to the alarm. This description of operation is the basic operating principle of photo-electric detectors. Some variations in design are used.

Some photoelectric detectors are adversely affected by dirt films. Any accumu-lated dirt, dust, film, or foreign matter collecting on either or both lenses of the light source or the photocell will cause an opaque effect and the detector will then become less and less sensitive. It, therefore, will require more smoke in order to respond.

While latest photoelectric models utilize solid state light emitting and receiving devices which have a longer life than previous light devices, the problem of failure of the light source still exists. Underwriters' Laboratories requires an audible alarm if light failure occurs.

Photoelectric units respond best to fires producing visible aerosols where the particles range from 10 µm down to 0.3 µm. These particles would be produced by a smoldering fire where very little heat is produced. See Figure 1-10.

Ionization and Photoelectric Devices: The diagram in Figure 1-11 can be used to illustrate both types of devices — the difference is the use of either an ionization sensor or a photoelectric sensor in the reference chamber and detector portions of the circuit. Under normal conditions, the voltage across the reference chamber and the detection chamber is the same. However, when fire occurs, the detection

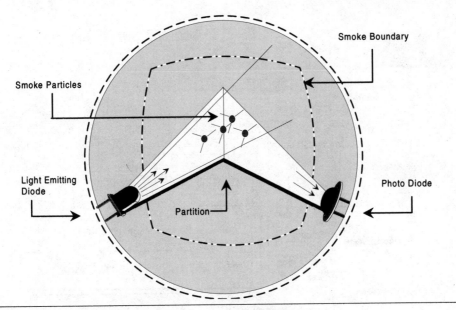

Figure 1-10: Basic operating principles of photoelectric detectors.

chamber then functions as described in the previous explanation. Thus, when there is sufficient voltage difference between the two chambers, the alarm is activated through the switching circuit.

Complete descriptive information and practical applications of smoke detectors are covered later in this chapter.

Components of Security/Fire-Alarm Systems

Wire sizes for the majority of low-voltage systems range from No. 22 to No. 18 AWG. However, there are some situations where it may be necessary to use larger wire sizes (such as where larger-than-normal currents are required and longer distance between outlets) to prevent excessive voltage drop. *NOTE:* Voltage-drop

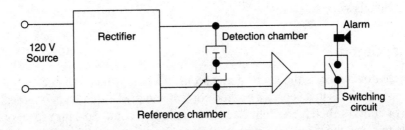

Figure 1-11: Diagram of ionization and photoelectric devices.

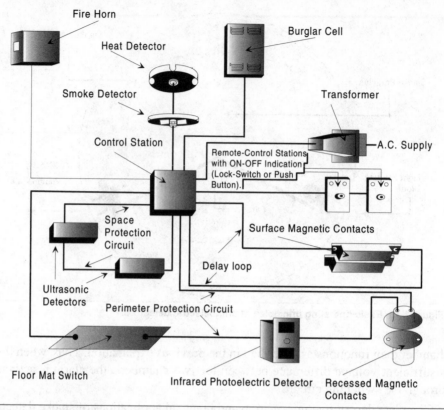

Fire Horn

Heat Detector

Burglar Cell

Smoke Detector

Transformer

Control Station

A.C. Supply

Remote-Control Stations
with ON-OFF Indication
(Lock-Switch or Push
Button).

Space
Protection
Circuit

Surface Magnetic Contacts

Delay loop

Ultrasonic
Detectors

Perimeter Protection Circuit

Floor Mat Switch

Infrared Photoelectric Detector

Recessed Magnetic
Contacts

Figure 1-12: Components for a typical security/fire-alarm system.

calculations should be made to determine the correct wire size for a given application. See Chapter 2.

Most closed systems use two-wire No. 22 or No. 24 AWG conductors and are color-coded to identify them. A No. 18 pair normally is adequate for connecting bells or sirens to controls if the run is 40 ft or less. Many, however, prefer to use No. 16 or even No. 14 nonmetallic cable.

A summary of the various components for a typical security/fire-alarm system is shown in the riser diagram in Figure 1-12. Notice the varying types of sensors or detectors in this system.

Control Station

The control station is the heart of any security system since it is the circuitry in these control panels that senses a broken contact and then either sounds a local bell or horn or omits the bell for a silent alarm. Most modern control panels use relay-type controls to sense the protective circuits and regulate the output for alarm-sounding devices. They also contain contacts to actuate other deterrent or reporting devices and a silent holdup alarm with dialer or police-connected reporting mechanism.

Power Supplies

Power supplies vary for different systems, but in general they consist of rechargeable 6-V dc power supplies for burglar alarm systems. The power packs usually contain nickel-cadmium batteries that are kept charged by 12-V ac input from a plug-in or otherwise connected transformer to a 120-V circuit. The better power supplies have the capability of operating an armed system for 48 hours or more without being charged and still have the capacity to ring an alarm bell for 30 minutes or longer. Power supplies are obviously used in conjunction with a charging source and supply power for operation of the alarm system through the control panel.

Contacts and Conductive Foil

Recessed Magnetic Contacts in Door (Figure 1-13): Holes are drilled in the door and in the casing, one directly across from the other, and a pair of wires from the positive side of the protective circuit is run out through the switch hole. The switch and magnet are then installed with no more than a ⅛-in gap between them.

Recessed Magnetic Contacts in Casement Window (Figure 1-14A): A switch and magnet are installed as in the door, preferably in the top of the window and underside of the upper window casing, where they will be least noticeable.

Surface-Mounted Magnetic Contacts on Double-Hung Window (Figure 1-14B): A switch is mounted on the window casing with a magnet on the window casing and a magnet on the window. As long as the switch and magnet are parallel and in close proximity when the window is shut, they may be oriented side-to-side, top-to-side, or top-to-top.

Conductive Foil on Glass Doors (Figure 1-15): A self-adhesive foil block (terminator) on the door is connected to a similar unit on the door frame by a short length of flexible cord to allow for door movement. The foil is connected in the positive conductor of the protective circuit and is adhered to the glass parallel to and about 3 in from the edge of the glass, using recommended varnish. Breaking the glass breaks the foil and opens the circuit. To provide more coverage, a double

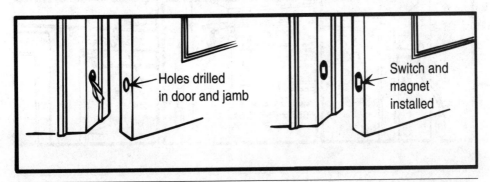

Figure 1-13: Recessed magnetic contacts installed in edge of door and also in door jamb.

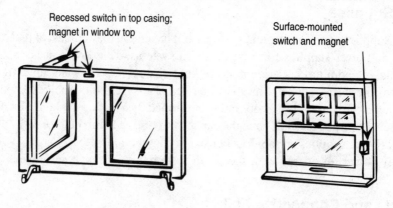

Figure 1-14: Magnetic contacts used on casement windows.

circuit of foil may be taken from the foil block. Coiled, retractable cords are available for use between foil blocks to allow for sliding-door travel.

Complete Glass-Door Protection (Figure 1-16A): A glass door with a glass transom may be protected by a combination of magnetic contacts and foil.

Surface-Mounted Magnetic Contacts on Door (Figure 1-16B): Where appearance is not the most important consideration, the use of a surface mounted switch (on the door frame) and a magnet (on the door) will simplify installation.

Conductive Foil on Picture Windows (Figure 1-16C): Where a window does not open, a single run of foil is connected to a foil block on the glass, frame, or wall. When the foil crosses over a frame member, a piece of plastic electrical tape should be used to provide an insulated crossover surface for the foil.

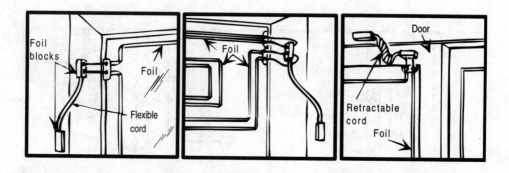

Figure 1-15: Conductive foil on glass doors.

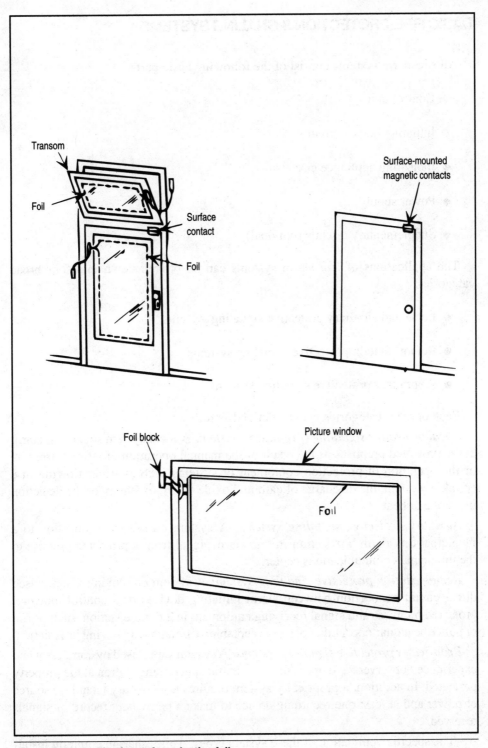

Figure 1-16: Applications of conductive foil.

BASIC FIRE-PROTECTION SIGNALING SYSTEMS

All fire alarm systems consist of the following basic parts:

- Control unit

- Initiating device circuits

- Indicating appliance circuits

- Power supply

- Supplementary circuits (optional)

The applications of fire alarm systems can be broken down into four broad categories:

- Local and auxiliary protective signaling systems

- Remote station protective signaling systems

- Proprietary protective signaling systems

Each of these categories may be defined as follows:

Local protective signaling (fire-alarm) system: A local system sounds an alarm at the protected premises as the result of the manual operation of a fire-alarm box or the operation of protection equipment or systems such as water flowing in a sprinkler system, the discharge of carbon dioxide (CO_2) or Halon, or the detection of smoke or heat.

Auxiliary protective signaling systems: A system utilizing a connection to a municipal fire-alarm box to transmit an alarm signal from a protected premise to the municipal communications center.

Remote station protective signaling system: A system employing a supervised direct circuit connection between alarm initiating devices or a control unit in a protected premises and signal receiving equipment in a remote station, such as fire or police headquarters or other places acceptable to the authority having jurisdiction.

Proprietary protective signaling systems: A system supervised by competent and experienced observers and operators in a central supervising station at the property protected. In addition, a proprietary system requires a secondary (standby) source of power and at least one recording device to make a permanent record of signals received.

The specific application of these system types, while sharing common installation requirements, should be selected to meet the requirements of one or more authorities having jurisdiction. In addition, care should be taken to install equipment in accordance with manufacturer's instructions.

Control unit: The control unit is the brain of the system. It provides power to the system and electrically supervises its circuits. In general, the control unit contains the logic circuits to receive signals from alarm initiating devices and transmit them to alarm indicating devices and supplement equipment. Depending on system design, the fire-alarm signaling function may provide for one or more of the following:

- Notify all building occupants simultaneously

- Notify occupants in certain portions of the building who are in immediate danger

- Notify key building personnel

- Notify the fire department

- Perform supplementary functions as required

The fire-alarm signaling function falls into two broad categories:

- Coded

- Noncoded

A coded system is one in which not less than three rounds of coded fire-alarm signals are transmitted after which the fire-alarm system may be manually or automatically restored to normal.

A noncoded system is one in which a continuous fire-alarm signal is transmitted for a predetermined period of time after which the alarm indicating devices may be manually or automatically restored to normal.

Both coded and noncoded systems are further broken down into several different types as follows:

- Zoned noncoded

- Master-coded system

- March time-coded system

- Selective-coded system

- Zoned coded system

Control Unit Operation

A fire-alarm control may be a simple, single-zone panel providing for one alarm initiating circuit and one or two alarm indicating circuits. However, most control units are modular in construction and are designed to accommodate multiple zones of detection and alarm signaling, as well as the selection of other modular components to perform any of the system functions listed previously.

Fire-alarm systems must perform in an emergency. For this reason, the control panel constantly monitors the integrity of the primary power supply and the installation wires and the connections of the alarm initiating devices. The control unit will sound a trouble signal to alert operating personnel when a fault condition on any of the supervised circuits exists.

The trouble signal normally will sound to indicate any of the following types of faults which could interfere with the proper transmission or receipt of an automatic or manual alarm signal:

@BULLET = Loss of primary power

- An open or ground in a supervised wire

- Loss of an audio amplifier, tone generator, or preamplifier

- Loss of connection between any installation wire and any alarm initiating device (or indicating appliance) wire or terminal necessary to sense an alarm

The trouble signal is an audible appliance with a distinctive sound. A visible indication (pilot light/LED) may be provided also.

Most problems encountered during the start-up of a fire-alarm system are traced to errors made in the installation wiring or connections, or both. It is, therefore, extremely important to follow manufacturer's instructions when installing a fire-alarm system.

The control panel is usually installed in a wall-mounted cabinet which may be either surface- or flush-mounted, a floor-mounted cabinet, or a desk-type console, depending upon the size of the system and the manufacturer. Normally, a lock is provided for security of the controls.

Alarm Initiating Devices

Alarm initiating devices for fire-alarm systems are either manual stations or automatic detectors and are used to initiate an alarm on a fire-alarm system.

Manual stations may be of the following types:

- Noncoded or coded

- Presignal or general alarm

- Breakglass or nonbreakglass

- Single-action or double-action

The single-acting devices may be initiated with one motion while the double-acting devices require two motions. For example, a device that requires lifting the cover and then pulling the handle requires two motions. Double-acting devices are designed to prevent false alarms.

As the name implies, manual stations must be operated by hand, and are seldom, if ever, used alone in a fire-alarm system. Rather, they are used to supplement the automatic detection devices.

Automatic Alarm Initiating Devices

Automatic alarm initiating devices may be actuated by various factors that may be present as the result of a fire. These factors may be direct effects such as heat, smoke, flame radiation, or combinations of these effects. Devices sensing these direct effects of fire are generally referred to as automatic fire detectors. Automatic initiating may also be accomplished as the result of detecting flow of water in a sprinkler pipe, either by a vane deflected by the water or a pressure-operated switch mounted on a sprinkler system dry pipe valve. In addition, pressure switches may be mounted on fixed fire suppression systems that suppress fires by releasing such agents as halon, carbon dioxide, dry chemicals, or foam. These devices are generally referred to by their direct function; that is, flow switch, pressure switch, and the like.

Automatic fire detectors fall under several different categories:

- By combustion product detected

- By physical arrangement of detector

- By operating modes

Heat-sensing fire detectors: A heat detector detects abnormally high temperature or rate-of-temperature rise. A fixed-temperature detector responds when its operating element becomes heated to a predetermined level. Its operating element usually consists of a bimetallic, snap-action disc located in the center of the detector, although thermistors and fusible alloys are also used to trigger heat-sensing devices.

Heat-sensitive cable: A line-type device whose sensing element comprises, in one type, two current-carrying conductors held separated by a heat-sensitive insulation which softens at the rated temperature. See Figure 1-17. When the insulation softens, this action allows the wires to make electrical contact. In another type, a single wire is centered in a metallic tube and the intervening space filled with a substance which, at a critical temperature, becomes conductive, thus establishing electrical contact between the tube and the wire.

Rate compensating detector: A rate compensation detector is a device that will respond when the temperature of the air surrounding the device reaches a predetermined level, regardless of the rate of temperature rise. See Figure 1-18.

Rate-of-rise detector: A rate-of-rise detector is a device that will respond when the temperature rises at a rate exceeding a predetermined amount (usually 15° F/min).

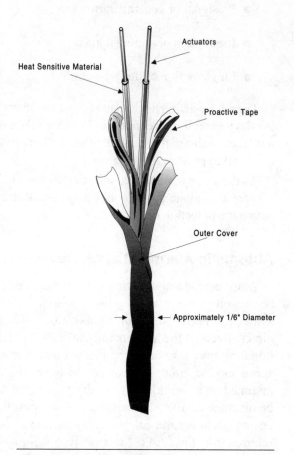

Figure 1-17: Heat-sensitive cable.

Pneumatic rate-of-rise tubing: A line-type detector comprising small diameter tubing, usually copper, which is installed on the ceiling or high on the walls throughout the protected area. The tubing is terminated in a detector unit, containing diaphragms and associated contacts set to actuate at a predetermined pressure. The system is sealed except for calibrated vents which compensate for normal changes in ambient temperature. See Figure 1-19.

In referring to Figure 1-19, note that the copper tubing (A) is fastened to ceilings or walls in a continuous loop and terminates at both ends in chambers (B) having flexible diaphragms (C) which control electrical contacts (D). When air in the tubing expands under the influence of heat, pressure builds within the chambers causing

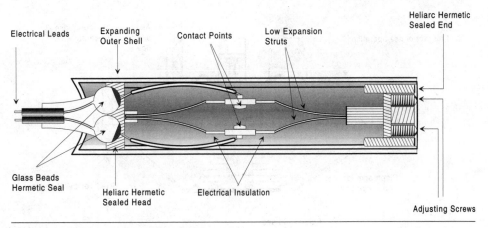

Electrical Leads
Expanding Outer Shell
Contact Points
Low Expansion Struts
Heliarc Hermetic Sealed End
Glass Beads Hermetic Seal
Heliarc Hermetic Sealed Head
Electrical Insulation
Adjusting Screws

Figure 1-18: Rate-compensation detector.

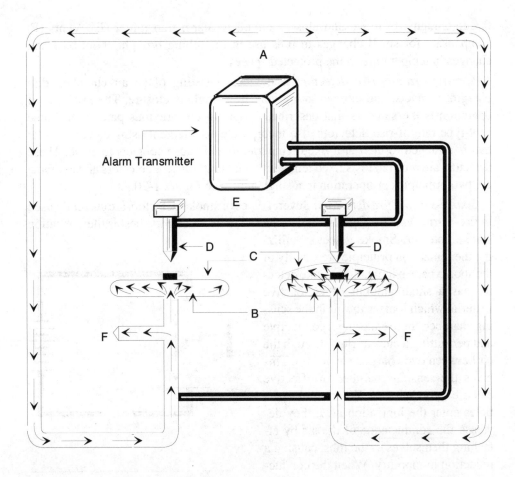

A
Alarm Transmitter
E
D
C
D
B
F
F

Figure 1-19: Pneumatic rate-of-rise tubing.

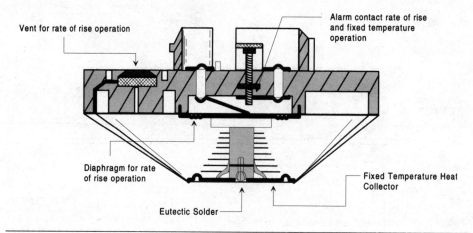

Vent for rate of rise operation

Alarm contact rate of rise and fixed temperature operation

Diaphragm for rate of rise operation

Fixed Temperature Heat Collector

Eutectic Solder

Figure 1-20: Combination spot-type rate-of-rise fixed temperature detector.

the diaphragms to move and close a circuit to alarm transmitter (E). Vents (F) compensate for small changes in pressure in the tubing brought about by small changes in temperature in the protected spaces.

Spot-type-rate-of-rise detector: A device consisting of an air chamber, diaphragm, contacts, and compensating vent in a single enclosure. The principle of operation is the same as that described in (A) in the previous paragraph. Some spot-type rate-of-rise detectors also incorporate an element using eutectic solder that is arranged to melt at a fixed temperature and cause contacts to close. These detectors are referred to as fixed temperature and rate-of-rise detectors and combine the two principles of operation in a single unit. See Figure 1-20.

Smoke-sensing fire detectors: Several types of smoke detectors are currently used in fire-alarm systems. One that is considered to be among the best is the ionization smoke detector. Smoke detectors utilizing the ionization principle are usually of the spot-type. An ionization smoke detector has a small amount of radioactive material which ionizes the air in the sensing chamber, thus rendering it conductive and permitting a current flow through the air between two charged electrodes. This gives the sensing chamber an effective electrical conductance. When smoke particles enter the ionization area, they decrease the conductance of the air by attaching themselves to the ions, causing a reduction in mobility. When the conductance is less than a predetermined level, the detector responds. See Figure 1-21.

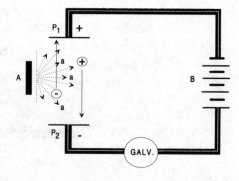

Figure 1-21: Current flow through ionization detector sensing chamber.

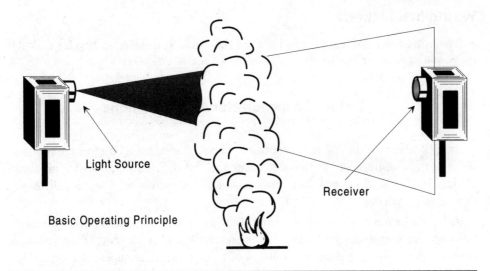

Figure 1-22: Projected-beam smoke detector.

Photoelectric light obscuration smoke detectors: Smoke detectors utilizing the photoelectric light obscuration principle consist of a light source which is projected onto a photosensitive device. Smoke particles between the light source and the photosensitive device reduce the light reaching the device, causing the detector to respond.

Projected beam smoke detector: A line type light obscuration smoke detector where the light beam is projected across the area to be protected. See Figure 1-22.

Photoelectric light-scattering smoke detectors: Smoke detectors utilizing the photoelectric light scattering principle are usually of the spot-type. They contain a light source and a photosensitive device so arranged that light rays do not normally fall onto the photosensitive device. When smoke particles enter the light path, light strikes the particles and is scattered onto the photosensitive device, causing the detector to respond. See Figure 1-23.

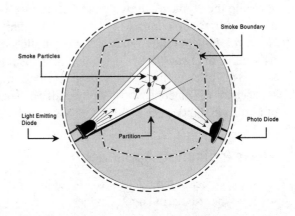

Figure 1-23: Photoelectric light-scattering detector.

Wiring Installations

The primary rule of installing wiring for fire-alarm systems, and also for making the required connections is:

Follow the manufacturer's instructions

To do otherwise is asking for trouble. This rule cannot be overemphasized because the requirement for fire-alarm circuits and their connections to initiating devices and indicating appliances makes fire-alarm system wiring very different from general wiring.

A manufacturer's installation wiring drawing routes wires and makes connections in a certain manner because of the supervision requirements. Any variance from the drawings might cause a portion of a circuit to be unsupervised and, if an open or short occurred, prevent the circuit from performing its intended function, and possibly lead to loss of life.

The rules of supervision are complex. Unless an installer specializes in fire-alarm system installations, he is not likely to be familiar with them. It is possible that hardware that appears to be identical in two different buildings is wired radically differently.

Fire-alarm system installation drawings take two forms. One form is where the manufacturer of a control panel or a qualified installer creates an installation wiring diagram for a particular building. The other form is where a manufacturer of the control panel or other components in the system furnishes "typical" installation drawings.

An installer that uses the "typical" drawings takes on the responsibility of applying the "typical" drawings in accordance with local code requirements. The manufacturer's drawings will show how the unit is to be connected into a system. However, how to interconnect devices on the same floor but served by a different riser may not always be shown. Generally, installers using typical drawings should be well qualified in fire-alarm system installation requirements or be under the direct supervision of someone who is well qualified. See Figures 1-24 and 1-25 for samples of correct and incorrect wiring methods.

Alarm Indicating Appliances

Alarm indicating devices provide audible or visible signals, or both. There are several types of alarm signal devices:

- Audible alarm signal

- Visible alarm signal

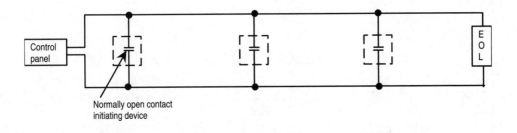

Normally open contact
initiating device

Figure 1-24: Initiating devices incorrectly wired.

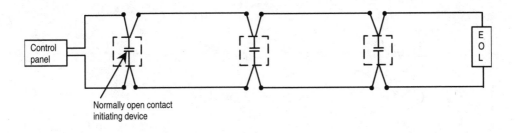

Normally open contact
initiating device

Figure 1-25: Initiating devices correctly wired.

- Visible alarm signal annunciators

- Audible/visible (combination) alarm signal

All alarm indicating devices should be installed in the protected property in accordance with local codes, architect's plans and specifications, requirements of authorities having jurisdiction, the manufacturer's recommendations, and the basic requirements of the National Fire Protection Association (NFPA) Standards insofar as they apply to the installation.

A wire-to-wire short on an alarm signal appliance installation wiring circuit should sound a trouble signal. A description of some of the audible alarm signal appliances follows. See Figure 1-26.

Bells: Bells may be used for fire-alarm signals where their sound is distinctive and will not be confused with similar audible signals used for other purposes. Single-stroke bells are used to provide audible coded signals. Continuous vibrating types are used primarily for noncoded, continuous-ringing applications. They also may be used to provide coded audible signals.

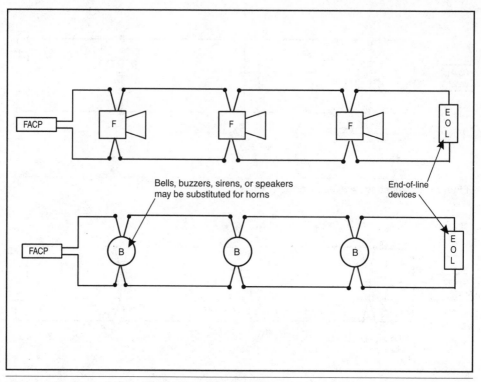

Figure 1-26: Correct wiring method for typical audible signal circuits.

Horns: Horns are provided for applications requiring louder or more distinctive signals, or both. They may be operated by either alternating or direct current and may be connected in series or parallel. They are usually of the continuous vibrating type and may be used either coded or noncoded audible alarm signals. They may also be of the surface, flush, semiflush, single projector, or trumpet type.

Chimes: Chimes are soft-toned appliances. They normally are used in applications where panic or other undesirable actions might result from the use of loud audible alarm signals such as in nurses' stations in hospitals. They may be operated by either alternating or direct current.

Buzzers: Buzzers also may be operated from an ac or dc supply. They are used for trouble signals, rather than alarm signals.

Sirens: Sirens usually are limited to outdoor applications but are sometimes used in extremely noisy indoor areas. They are motor-driven and may be either alternating or direct current.

Speakers: Speakers are frequently used as fire-alarm signaling appliances. Since they reproduce electronic signals, they can be made to sound like any mechanical signaling device and have the capability of reproducing unique sounds that are not practical on mechanical appliances. The speakers are driven by an electronic tone generator, microphone, tape player, or voice synthesizer and an electronic amplifier. A typical fire-alarm riser diagram appears in Figure 1-27.

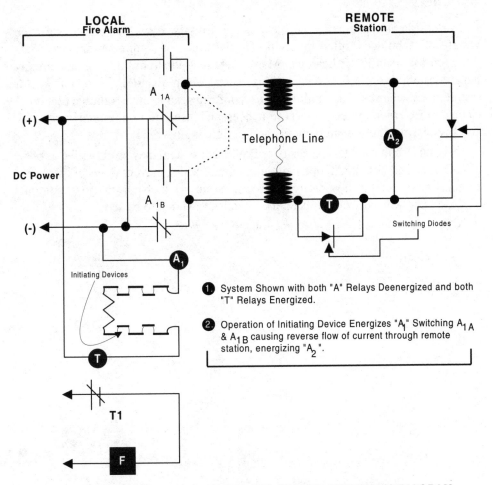

1. System Shown with both "A" Relays Deenergized and both "T" Relays Energized.

2. Operation of Initiating Device Energizes "A_1" Switching A_{1A} & A_{1B} causing reverse flow of current through remote station, energizing "A_2".

REMOTE STATION PROTECTIVE SIGNALING SYSTEM SCHEMATIC DIAGRAM

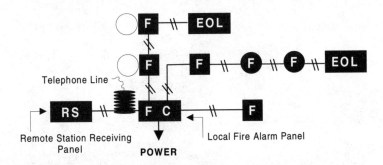

REMOTE STATION PROTECTIVE SIGNALING SYSTEM RISER DIAGRAM

Figure 1-27: Typical fire-alarm wiring diagram and riser diagram.

Summary

The design and installation of security and fire-alarm systems employs a wide variety of techniques, often involving special types of equipment and materials designed for specific applications. Many systems operate on low-voltage circuits but are installed similarly as conventional electrical circuits for light and power. All installations, when used in buildings, must conform to applicable National Electrical Code® (NEC) requirements, local ordinances, and instructions provided by security and fire-alarm system manufacturers and design engineers.

A signal circuit used for a security or fire-alarm system may be classified as open circuit or closed circuit. An open circuit is one in which current flows only when a signal is being sent. A closed-circuit system in one in which current flows continuously, except when the circuit is opened to allow a signal to be sent.

All alarm systems have three functions in common:

- Detection

- Control

- Signaling

Chapter 2
Electric Circuits

The material covered in this chapter is the "rock" on which all electrical/electronic security-system circuits are built. The laws and equations will be used on a daily basis by security technicians.

Electricity is basically the flow of electrons — tiny atomic particles. These particles are found in all atoms. Atoms of some metals such as copper and aluminum have electrons that are easily pushed and guided into a stream. When a coil of metal wire is turned near a magnet, or vice versa, electricity will flow in the wire. This principle is made use of in generating plants; water or steam is used to turn turbines which rotate electromagnets that are surrounded by huge coils of wire. The push transmitted to the electrons by the turbine/magnet setup is measured in units called *volts*. The quantity of the flow of electricity is called *current* and it is measured in *amperes* or *amps*.

Multiply volts by amps and you get *volt-amperes* or *watts* — the power or amount of work that electricity can do. Electrical appliances and motors have certain wattage requirements depending on the task they are expected to perform. For convenience, we can use *kilowatts*, (1 kW equals 1000 W) when speaking of power production or power needs. A power plant produces kilowatts which are sold to users by the *kilowatt-hour*. For example, a 100-W lamp left on for ten hours uses 1 kWh of electricity.

Resistance, or the opposition to the flow of electricity, is another term that will be covered in this chapter. In general, a conductor enhances the flow of electricity while resistance impedes or stops the flow of electricity. Therefore, insulators are constructed of materials offering a high resistance to the flow of electricity.

The relationship between current, voltage, resistance, and power in a basic dc circuit are common to many types of electrical circuits. Consequently, this chapter covers direct current (dc) fundamentals, including the following:

- Matter

- Energy

- Electricity

- Batteries

- dc series circuits

- dc parallel circuits

- Ohm's law

- Kirchoff's laws

ELECTRICAL ESSENTIALS

Matter is defined as anything that occupies space and has weight; that is, the weight and dimensions of matter can be measured. Examples of matter include air, water, clothing, automobiles, and even our own bodies. Matter may therefore be found in any one of three states:

- Solid

- Liquid

- Gaseous

ELEMENTS AND COMPOUNDS

An *element* is a substance that cannot be reduced to a simpler substance by chemical means. Examples of elements — to name a few — include iron, gold, silver, copper, and oxygen. But there are other elements. In fact, there are over 100 known elements and all of the substances on earth are composed of one or more of these elements.

When two or more elements are chemically combined, the resulting substance is called a *compound*. A compound is a chemical combination of elements that can be separated by chemical but not by physical means. For example, water consists of hydrogen and oxygen (H_2O), while common table salt consists of sodium and chlorine. Neither of two compounds can be separated physically.

A *mixture*, on the other hand, is a combination of elements and compounds, not chemically combined, and mixtures can therefore be separated by physical means. Examples of mixtures include air, which is made up of nitrogen, oxygen, carbon dioxide, and small amounts of several rare gases. Sea water is another mixture that consists of salt and water.

Molecules

A *molecule* is a chemical combination of two or more atoms and is the smallest particle in a compound that has all the characteristics of the compound itself.

Consider water, for example. Water is matter since it occupies space and has weight. Depending on the temperature, it may exist as a liquid (water), a solid (ice), or a gas (steam). Regardless of the temperature or its physical form, it will still have the same composition. However, if we start with a certain quantity of water, divide this and pour out one half, and continue this process a sufficient number of times, we will eventually end up with a quantity of water that cannot be further divided without ceasing to be water. Once this point is reached, it becomes a molecule of water. If this molecule of water is further divided in the same way as before, instead of two parts of water, there will be one part of oxygen and two parts of hydrogen (H_2O), and the resulting elements will no longer be water if they are divided.

Atoms

If it were possible to view the flow of electrons through a highly powerful microscope, at first glance the viewer may think he or she is studying astronomy rather than electricity. According to our present understanding, the atom is believed to consist of a central nucleus composed of protons and neutrons, surrounded by orbiting electrons as shown in the illustration in Figure 2-1 on page 42. The nucleus is relatively large when compared with the orbiting electrons, the same as our sun is large when compared to its orbiting planets; also the orbiting satellites are small in comparison to the satellites' planet.

In the case of an atom, the orbiting electrons are held in place by the attractive electric force between the electron and the nucleus — similar to how the earth's gravity keeps its satellite (the moon) from drifting off into space. The law of charges states that opposite charges attract and like charges repel (Figure 2-2). The positive charge of the protons in the nucleus, therefore, attracts the negatively charged electrons. If this force of attraction were the only one in force, the electrons would be pulled closer and closer to the nucleus and eventually be absorbed into the nucleus. However, this force of attraction is balanced by the centrifugal force that

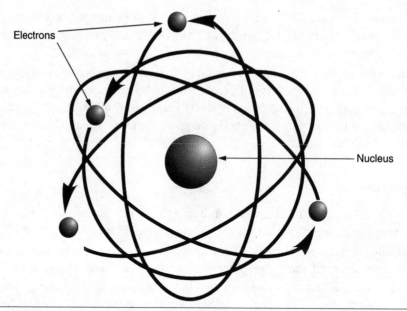

Figure 2-1: Nucleus consisting of protons and neutrons with orbiting electrons.

results from the motion of the electron around the nucleus as shown in Figure 2-3. The law of centrifugal force states that a spinning object will pull away from its center point. The faster an object spins, the greater the centrifugal force becomes.

Figure 2-4 shows an example of this principle. If an object is tied to a string, and the object is spun around, it will try to pull away from you. Compare the spinning object with a spinning electron. Compare the string — held securely by your hand — as the force of gravity. The faster the object spins, the greater the force tries to pull the object away, but the securely held string (similar to the force of gravity)

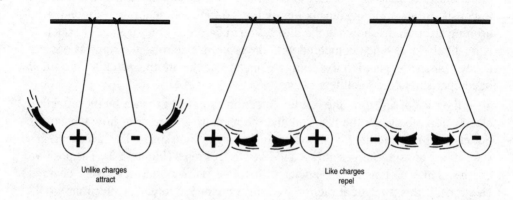

Unlike charges
attract

Like charges
repel

Figure 2-2: Reaction between charged bodies.

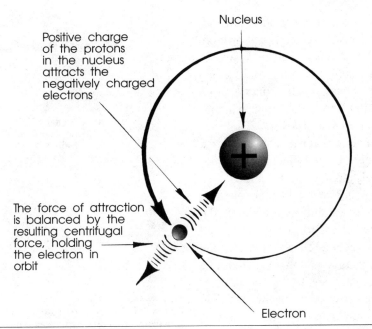

Nucleus

Positive charge
of the protons
in the nucleus
attracts the
negatively charged
electrons

The force of attraction
is balanced by the
resulting centrifugal
force, holding
the electron in
orbit

Electron

Figure 2-3: A combination of gravity and centrifugal force keeps electrons in orbit around the nucleus.

keeps the object spinning the same distance (the length of the string) from your body. If the object is spun still faster, the force becomes even greater, and perhaps the string will slip slightly through your hand, and the object spins farther away from your body. Similarly, the faster an electron spins, the farther away from the nucleus it will be.

If the string holding the object being spun should slip out of your hand (similar to the absence of gravity), the object will fly off into space in a straight line. The same is true of the earth's satellite. Were it not for the earth's gravity, the moon would follow a straight line through space. Centrifugal force results from the combined effects of gravitational force and the tendency of a moving body to travel in a straight line.

Since the protons and orbital electrons of an atom are equal in number and equal and opposite in charge, they neutralize each other electrically. Consequently, each atom is normally electrically neutral — exhibiting neither a

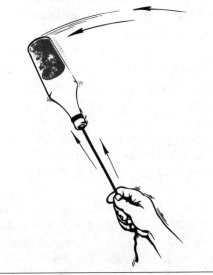

Figure 2-4: Centrifugal force causes an object to pull away.

positive nor a negative charge. However, under certain conditions, an atom
can become unbalanced by losing or
gaining electrons. If an atom loses a
negatively charged electron, the atom
will exhibit a positive charge, which is
then referred to as a *positive ion*. Similarly, an atom that gains an additional
negatively charged electron becomes
negatively charged itself and is then
called a *negative ion*. In either case, an
unbalanced condition is created in the
atom causing the formerly neutralized
atom to become charged. When one
atom is charged and there is an unlike
charge in another nearby atom, electrons can flow between the two. We
have already learned what the flow of
electrons is called. It's electricity!

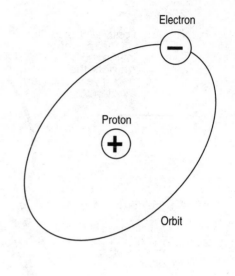

**Figure 2-5: The hydrogen atom consists of only
one electron in orbit around one proton.**

The hydrogen atom is the simplest of all atoms since it consists of only one
electron and one proton as shown in Figure 2-5.

Atoms of other materials are more complex. They are made up of protons and
neutrons in the nucleus with different number of electrons in multiple orbits or shells
rotating around the nucleus. The copper atom, for example, has 29 protons, 35
neutrons, and a total of 29 electrons. One electron is in the outer orbit by itself as
shown in Figure 2-6. The electrons are organized into several different orbits, or
shells, surrounding the nucleus.

Atoms have a set number of electrons that can be contained in one orbit or shell.
The outer shell of an atom is known as the *valence shell*. Any electrons located in
the outer shell of an atom are known as valence electrons. These valence electrons
in some materials, especially metals, can be easily knocked out of their orbits. Such
electrons are referred to as free electrons, and materials with free electrons are called
conductors. It is the valence electrons that are of primary concern in the study of
electricity, because it is these electrons that explain much of electrical theory. A
conductor, for instance, is made from a material that contains one or two valence
electrons. When an atom has only one or two valence electrons, they are loosely
held by the atom and are easily given up for current flow. Silver, copper, and
aluminum all contain one valence electron, but silver is a better conductor than
copper, and copper is a better conductor than aluminum. The reason for this is that
an atom of silver is larger than an atom of copper, and an atom of copper is larger
than an atom of aluminum. Since an atom of silver is larger than an atom of copper,
it contains more orbits than an atom of copper. This means that the valence electron

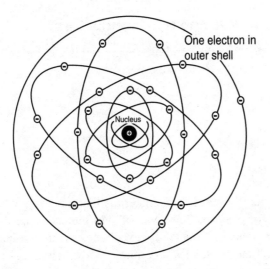

Figure 2-6: A copper atom has 29 protons, 35 neutrons, and 29 electrons.

of silver is farther away from the nucleus than an atom of copper. Since the speed an electron spins is decided by its distance from the nucleus, the valence electron of silver is spinning around the nucleus at a faster speed than the valence electron of copper. Therefore, the valence electron of silver contains more energy than the valence electron of copper. When the valence electron of silver is knocked out of orbit, it simply contains more energy than the valence electron of copper, and therefore, makes a better conductor of electricity. Copper is a better conductor of electricity than aluminum for the same reason. Figure 2-7 shows an atom of silver and an atom of copper for comparison.

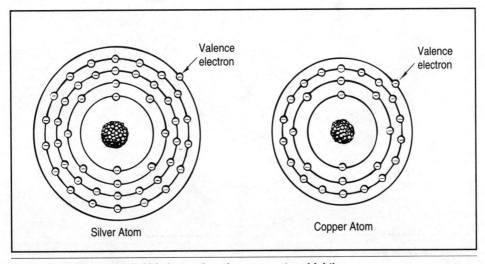

Figure 2-7: Silver atom (left) is larger than the copper atom (right).

Conductors, Insulators, and Semiconductors

Materials used in the electrical and electronic fields can be classified in three groups, according to their electrical properties:

- Conductors

- Insulators

- Semiconductors

Conductors are generally made from materials that have large, heavy atoms to provide an easy path for electron flow. A variety of materials are used to transmit electrical energy, but copper — due to its excellent cost-to-conductivity ratio — still remains the basic and most ideal conductor. Other electrical conductors are made from aluminum. Sometimes materials are silver-plated to provide an even better flow of electrons.

Theoretically, conductors are materials that have only one or two valence electrons in their atom as shown in Figure 2-8. An atom that has only one valence electron makes the best electrical conductor because the electron is loosely held in orbit and is easily given up for current flow.

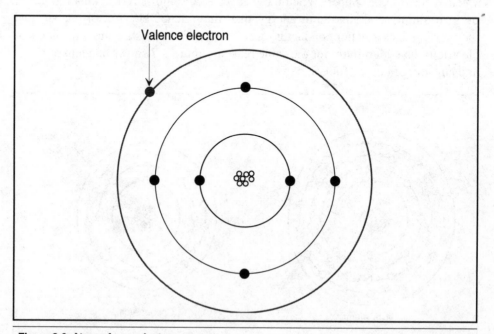

Figure 2-8: Atom of a conductor.

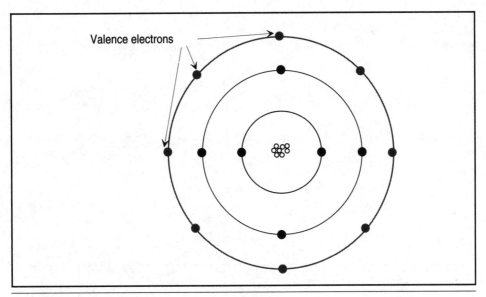

Figure 2-9: Atom of an insulator.

Insulators

Insulators are generally made from lightweight materials that have small atoms. Materials such as glass, rubber, and certain plastics have practically no free electrons. This makes it very difficult for current to flow through them. The atoms of an insulating material have their outer orbits filled or almost filled with valence electrons; this means an insulator will have seven or eight valence electrons as shown in Figure 2-9. Since an insulator has its outer orbit filled or almost filled with valence electrons, they are tightly held in orbit and not easily given up for current flow. Insulators are used in a variety of applications ranging from the covering on conductors to the dielectric in capacitors.

Semiconductors

Semiconductors, as the name implies, are materials that are neither good conductors nor good insulators. Semiconductors are made from materials that have some free electrons — more than an insulator, but fewer than a conductor and have four valence electrons in their outer orbit as shown in Figure 2-10.

ELECTRICITY

Electricity, as stated previously, is the flow of electrons. Mostly, however, all atoms tend to remain neutral because the outer orbits of electrons repel other electrons, which prevent their movement or flow between atoms. To have electricity,

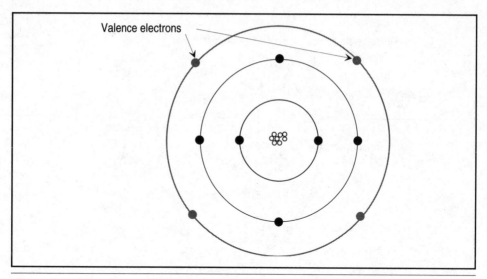

Figure 2-10: Atom of a semiconductor.

these atoms must be charged by knocking the one or more of its electrons out of orbit by another electron. There are several known ways to accomplish this:

- Friction — Voltage produced by rubbing certain materials together.

- Chemical action — Voltage produced by chemical reaction in a battery cell.

- Magnetism — Voltage produced in a conductor when the conductor moves through a magnetic field, or a magnetic field moves through the conductor in such a manner as to cut the magnetic lines of force of the field.

- Light — Voltage produced by light striking photosensitive (light-sensitive) substances.

- Heat — Voltage produced by heating the joint (junction) where two unlike metals are joined.

- Pressure — Voltage produced by squeezing crystals of certain substances.

Static Electricity

Friction or static electricity can be produced by walking across a carpet with leather soles on a dry winter day. After doing so, the next metal object you touch will probably cause a spark and perhaps a shock. Sliding across car seat covers during the winter will do the same thing; or quickly pulling off a sweater. Static electricity may also be experienced by combing your hair on a dry cold day that will probably result in sparks and a crackling sound.

Lightning is another form of static electricity. Air currents striking the face of clouds causes condensation of the moisture in them. When the wind strikes the cloud, these small particles of moisture are blown upward, carrying negative charges to the top of the cloud and leaving the bottom with positive charges. As very heavy rain or other forms of heavy condensation fall through a part of the cloud, one side of the cloud becomes charged positively and the other side negatively, with millions of volts difference in potential.

When clouds (under the condition described) come near enough to the ground or to another cloud with opposite charges, they will discharge to the ground or to another cloud with explosive violence. Since there is a strong tendency for lightning discharges to strike trees, structures, and other objects and travel on any metal parts that extend in the general direction of the discharge, lightning rods and properly grounded electrical systems can prevent much of the damage.

Static electricity, even in the small charges obtained from combing your hair will often damage the "memory" of computer software and hardware along with other types of electronic equipment.

Static electricity, however, whatever its source, has little use in practical applications because the flow of electrons is temporary and erratic; that is, one brief transfer of electrons from one material to another, and the effect is over. To make electricity useful for practical applications, a constant and steady flow of electrons must be produced.

Chemical Electricity

Chemical action, contained in electric cells and batteries, is another source of electricity.

In general, a typical basic battery consists of a container filled with liquid that is called *electrolyte*. Into this liquid are placed two plates of different metals, which in turn are separated from each other. The purpose of the chemical (electrolyte) is to push electrons onto one plate while at the same time, take them off from the other. This action results in an excess of electrons or a negative charge on one of the plates, called the negative terminal. The other plate loses electrons and becomes positively charged to provide the positive terminal. See Figure 2-11.

The action of the electrolyte in carrying electrons from one plate to the other is actually a chemical reaction between the electrolyte and the two plates. This action changes chemical energy into electrical charges on the cell plates and terminals.

With no load connected to the battery terminals, such as an electric lamp, electrons would be pushed or transferred onto the negative plate until there is room

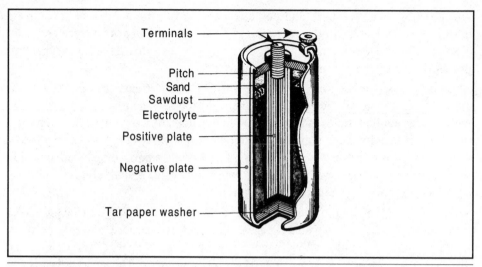

Figure 2-11: Components of a typical primary cell battery.

for no more. The electrolyte would take from the positive plate enough electrons to make up for those it pushed onto the negative plate. Both plates would then be fully charged and no electrons would be moving between the plates.

Now when a load is connected to the terminals of the battery, the electrons will leave the negative plate, travel through the load, and back to the positive plate in the battery. During this process, the electrolyte will carry more electrons across from the positive plate to the negative plate. As long as electrons leave the negative plate and travel through the load to the positive plate, the battery will produce electricity.

In a primary cell, during the above use of electricity, the negative plate is being used up as the electrons are being transferred. Eventually the negative plate will be completely dissolved in the electrolyte by the chemical action, and the cell would become "dead," or unable to furnish a charge, until the negative plate is replaced. Consequently, this type of cell is called a primary cell, meaning that once it is completely discharged, it cannot be charged again except by using new materials.

Plates in primary cells can be made from carbon and most other metals, while acids or salt compounds can be used for the electrolyte. Flashlight dry cell batteries are examples of primary cells.

A storage battery of secondary cells can furnish more power than a primary cell battery, and can be recharged. Most are of the lead-acid type whereas the electrolyte is sulfuric acid, the positive plate is lead peroxide, and the negative plate is lead. During discharge of the cell, the acid becomes weaker and both plates change chemically to lead sulfate. See Figure 2-12.

The housing or cases of lead-acid cells are made of hard rubber or glass, which prevents corrosion and acid leaks. A space at the bottom of the cell collects the sediment formed as the cell is used. The top of the case is removable and acts as the

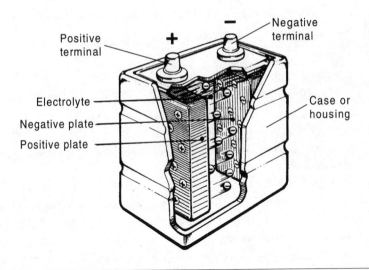

Positive terminal

Negative terminal

Electrolyte

Negative plate

Positive plate

Case or housing

Figure 2-12: Components of a secondary cell.

support for the plates. Two or more cells connected together make up a storage battery as used in cars or for emergency standby power. This type of battery stores electricity and can be recharged after discharge by reversing the current flow into the battery.

The active materials of most secondary cells are not rigid enough to be mounted independently. Therefore, a special grid structure of inactive metal is normally used to hold them. For maximum chemical action, a large plate area is needed, so each positive plate is interlaced between two negative plates. Separators, made of wood or porous glass, hold each positive and negative plate apart but let the electrolyte pass through.

Although the cells are constructed somewhat differently, the chemical action of both types is the same; that is, electrons are pushed onto the negatively charged plates by the electrolyte and are discharged through the load to the positive plates. In secondary cells, it is the electrolyte that becomes weaker, and not the dissolving of the negative plate as in primary cell batteries.

Magnetism

Magnetism is one of the most commonly used methods to produce voltage. Vast quantities of electric power are produced daily from mechanical sources. The mechanical power may be provided by a number of different sources, such as gasoline or diesel engines, and water or steam turbines. However, the final conversion of these source energies to electricity is accomplished by generators employing the principle of electromagnetic induction.

There are three fundamental conditions that must exist before a voltage can be produced by magnetism.

1.   There must be a conductor in which the voltage will be produced.
2.   There must be a magnetic field in the conductor's vicinity.
3.   There must be relative motion between the field and conductors. The conductor must be moved so as to cut across the magnetic lines of force, or the field must be moved so that the lines of force are cut by the conductor.

Therefore, when a conductor or conductors move across a magnetic field so as to cut the lines of force, electrons within the conductor are propelled in one direction or another. Thus, an electric force, or voltage, is created.

Figure 2-13 shows the three basic conditions needed for creating an induced voltage.

1.   A magnetic field exists between the poles of the C-shaped magnet.
2.   There is a conductor (copper wire).
3.   There is a relative motion. The wire is moved back and forth across the magnetic field.

A voltage will also be produced by holding the wire stationary and moving the magnetic field back and forth.

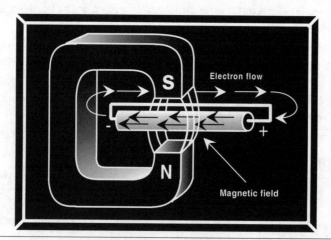

Figure 2-13: Voltage produced by magnetism.

Electricity Produced by Light

When light strikes the source of a substance, it may dislodge electrons from their orbits around the surface atoms of the substance. This occurs because light has energy, the same as any moving force.

Some substances — mostly metallic ones — are far more sensitive to light than others. That is, more electrons will be dislodged and emitted from the surface of a highly sensitive metal, with a given amount of light, than will be emitted from a less sensitive substance. Upon losing electrons, the photosensitive (light-sensitive) metal becomes positively charged, and an electric force is created. Voltage produced in this manner is referred to as a *photoelectric voltage*.

The photosensitive materials most commonly used to produce a photoelectric voltage are various compounds of silver oxide or copper oxide. A complete device that operates on the photoelectric principle is referred to as a "photoelectric cell." There are many different sizes and types of photoelectric cells in use, and each serves the special purpose for which it is designed. Nearly all, however, have some of the basic features of the photoelectric cells shown in Figure 2-14.

The cell in Figure 2-14 has a curved light-sensitive surface focused on the central anode. When light from the direction shown strikes the sensitive surface, it emits electrons toward the anode. The more intense the light, the greater the number of electrons emitted. When a wire is connected between the filament and the back, or dark side of the cell, the accumulated electrons will flow to the dark side. These electrons will eventually pass through the metal of the reflector and replace the electrons leaving the light-sensitive surface. Thus, light energy is converted to a flow of electrons, and a usable current is developed.

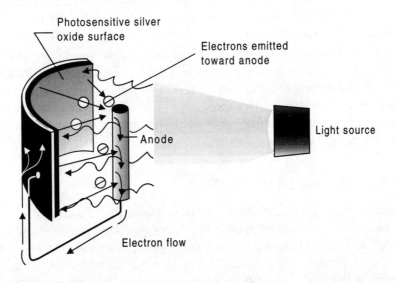

Figure 2-14: Photocell with curved surface.

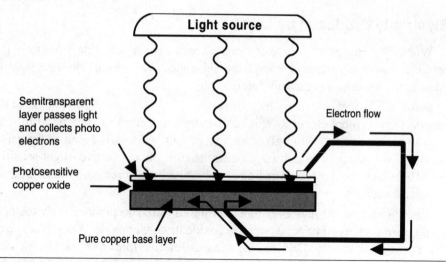

Figure 2-15: Photoelectric cell constructed in layers.

Another type of cell is shown in Figure 2-15. This cell is constructed in layers; that is, a baseplate of pure copper is coated with light-sensitive copper oxide. An extremely thin semitransparent layer of metal is placed over the copper oxide. This additional layer serves two purposes:

- It permits the penetration of light to the copper oxide.

- It collects the electrons emitted by the copper oxide.

An externally connected wire completes the electron path, the same as in the reflector-type cell. The photocell's voltage is used as needed by connecting the external wires to some other device, which amplifies (enlarges) it to a usable level.

The power capacity of a photocell is very small. However, it reacts to light-intensity variations in an extremely short time. This characteristic makes the photocell very useful in detecting or accurately controlling a great number of operations. For instance, the photoelectric cell, or some form of the photoelectric principle, is used in television cameras, automatic manufacturing process controls, door openers, burglar alarms, and so forth.

Electricity Produced By Heat

When a length of metal, such as copper, is heated at one end, electrons tend to move away from the hot end toward the cooler end. This is true of most metals. However, in some metals, such as iron, the opposite is true; that is, electrons tend to move toward the heat or hot end. These characteristics are shown in Figure 2-16. The negative charges (electrons) are moving through the copper away from the heat

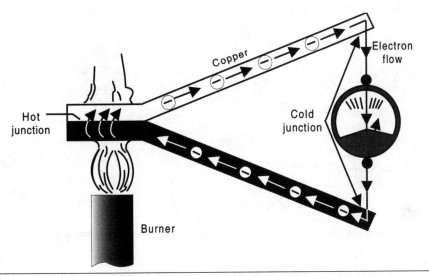

Figure 2-16: Electricity produced by heat; the device shown is called a *thermocouple*.

and through the iron toward the heat. They cross from the iron to the copper through the current meter to the iron at the cold junction. This device is generally referred to as a *thermocouple* and such a device will be frequently encountered in HVAC temperature controls and controls for electrical appliances.

The thermoelectric voltage in a thermocouple depends mainly on the difference in temperature between the hot and cold juntions. Consequently, they are widely used to measure temperature, and as heat-sensing devices in automatic temperature control equipment. Thermocouples generally can be subjected to much greater temperatures than ordinary thermometers, such as the mercury or alcohol types.

Electricity Produced By Pressure

One specialized method of generating a voltage utilizes the characteristics of certain ionic crystals such as quartz, Rochelle salts, and tourmaline. These crystals have the remarkable ability to generate a voltage whenever stresses are applied to their surfaces. Consequently, if a crystal of quartz is squeezed, charges of opposite polarity will appear on two opposite surfaces of the crystal. If the force is reversed and the crystal is stretched, charges will again appear, but will be of the opposite polarity from those produced by squeezing. If a crystal of this type is given a vibratory motion, it will produce a voltage of reversing polarity between two of its sides. Quartz or similar crystals can therefore be used to convert mechanical energy into electrical energy. This phenomenon, called the *piezoelectric effect*, is shown in Figure 2-17. Some of the common devices that make use of piezoelectric crystals are microphones, phonograph cartridges, and oscillators used in radio transmitters, radio receivers, and sonar equipment. This method of generating voltage is not

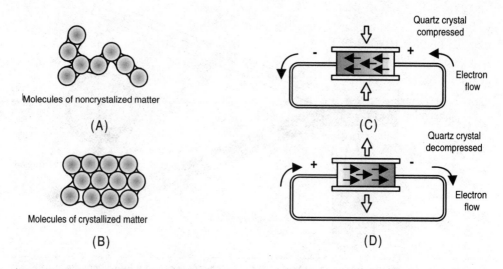

Figure 2-17: Principles of producing electricity by pressure.

suitable for applications having large voltage or power requirements, but is widely used in sound and communications systems where small signal voltages can be effectively used.

Crystals of this type also possess another interesting property: the converse piezoelectric effect. That is, they have the ability to convert electrical energy into mechanical energy. A voltage impressed across the proper surface of the crystal will cause it to expand or contract its surfaces in response to the voltage applied.

MEASURING ELECTRICITY

The three basic terms used to measure electricity are:

- Electromotive force — measured in volts

- Current — measured in amperes

- Resistance — measured in ohms

In general, *electromotive force* or *voltage* is the force that causes electrons to flow. The unit of measurement of voltage is volts. In equations, voltage is represented by the letter E which stands for electromotive force. Voltage is measured with a *voltmeter*. This and other measuring instruments are discussed in detail in Chapter 8.

Current is the rate at which electrons flow in a circuit. A current of 1 A is said to flow when 1 C of charge passes a point in 1 second. One coulomb is equal to the charge of 6.28×10^{18} electrons. Current is measured in units called amperes or amps. In equations, current is represented by the letter *I* which stands for intensity of current.

NOTE

The rate of electron flow is not the speed at which the electrons are moving. Rather, it is the amount of electrons that flows past a given point in a given period of time.

In many cases, the ampere is too large a unit for measuring current. Therefore, the *milliampere* (mA) or the *microampere* is used. A milliampere equals one-thousandth of an ampere, while the microampere (μA) equals one-millionth of an ampere. The device used to measure current is called an *ammeter*.

Resistance is the opposition to the flow of current in a circuit. All circuits have some resistance and the amount of resistance is measured in ohms. In equations, resistance is represented by the letter *R* or the Greek letter omega (Ω). A conductor has one ohm of resistance when an applied potential of one volt produces a current of one ampere.

Resistance, although an electrical property, is determined by the physical structure of a material. The resistance of a material is governed by many of the same factors that control current flow.

Factors that Affect Resistance

The magnitude of resistance is determined in part by the number of free electrons available with the material. Since a decrease in the number of free electrons will decrease the current flow, it can be said that the opposition to current flow (resistance) is greater in a material with fewer free electrons. Consequently, the resistance of a material is determined by the number of free electrons available in a material.

Depending upon their atomic structure, different materials will have different quantities of free electrons. Therefore, the various conductors used in electrical applications have different values of resistance.

Effect of Cross-sectional Area

Cross-sectional area greatly affects the magnitude of resistance. If the cross-sectional area of a conductor is increased, a greater quantity of electrons are available for movement through the conductor. Therefore, a larger current will flow for a given amount of applied voltage. An increase in current indicates that when the cross-sectional area of a conductor is increased, the resistance must have decreased. If the cross-sectional area of a conductor is decreased, the number of available electrons decreases and, for a given applied voltage, the current through the conductor decreases. A decrease in current flow indicates that when the cross-sectional area of a conductor is decreased, the resistance must have increased.

The diameter of many electrical conductors is often only a fraction of an inch. Therefore, the diameter of conductors is usually expressed in mils (thousandths of an inch). It is also standard practice to assign the unit circular mil to the cross-sectional area of a conductor (*See* Figure 2-18). The circular mil is found by squaring the diameter, when the diameter is expressed in mils. Consequently, if the diameter of a conductor is, say, 35 mils (0.035 in), the circular mil area is equal to:

$$(35)2 = 1225 \text{ circular mils}$$

NOTE

Resistance of a conductor is inversely proportional to its cross-sectional area.

Effect of Conductor Length

The length of a conductor is also a factor which determines the resistance of a conductor. If the length of a conductor is increased, the amount of energy given up increases. As free electrons move from atom to atom, some is given off as heat. The longer a conductor is, the more energy is lost to heat. The additional energy loss is subtracted from the energy being transferred through the conductor, resulting in a decrease in current flow for a given applied voltage. A decrease in current flow indicates an increase in resistance, since voltage was held constant. Therefore, if the length of a conductor is increased, the resistance of that conductor increases.

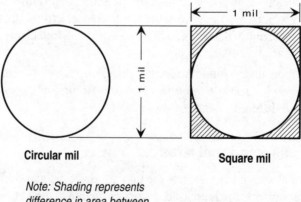

Circular mil   Square mil

Note: Shading represents
difference in area between
circular and square mils.

Figure 2-18: Comparison between a square mil and a circular mil.

Effect of Temperature

Temperature changes affect the resistance of materials in different ways. In some materials, an increase in temperature causes an increase in resistance, whereas in others, an increase in temperature causes a decrease in resistance. The amount of change of resistance per unit change in temperature is known as the temperature coefficient. When the resistance of a material increases with an increase in temperature, the material is said to have a positive temperature coefficient. When the resistance of a material decreases with an increase in temperature, the material is said to have a negative temperature coefficient. Most conductors used in electrical applications have a positive temperature coefficient. However, carbon — a frequently used material — is a substance having a negative temperature coefficient.

NOTE

The resistance of a conductor is directly proportional to its length.

Some materials, such as the alloys constantan and manganin, are considered to have a zero temperature coefficient because their resistance remains relatively constant for changes in temperature.

Conductance

Conductance is the ability of a material to pass electrons, and is the opposite of resistance. The factors that affect the magnitude of resistance are exactly the same for conductance, but they affect conductance in the opposite manner. Therefore, conductance is directly proportional to area, and inversely proportional to the length of the material. The unit of conductance is the MHO, which is ohm spelled backward. Another term for mho is *siemans*.

DIRECT CURRENT

The common flashlight is an example of a basic electric circuit. It contains a source of electrical energy (the dry cells in the flashlight), a load (the bulb) which changes the electrical energy into light energy, and a switch to control the energy delivered to the load.

The technician's main aid in studying circuits is the schematic diagram. In general, a schematic diagram is a "picture" of the circuit that uses symbols to represent the various circuit components and lines to connect these components. Basic symbols used in schematic diagrams are shown in Figure 2-19. Refer to this symbol list frequently as you study the various schematic diagrams in the remaining

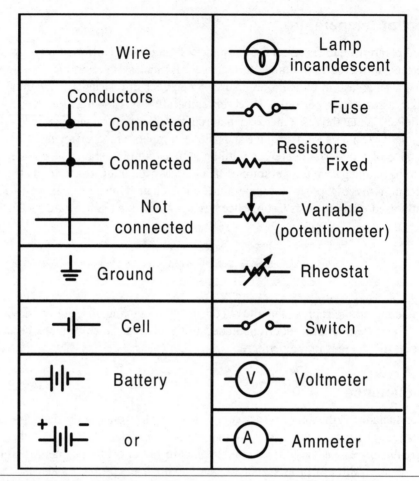

Figure 2-19: Symbols commonly used in electrical schematic diagrams.

pages of this chapter. In doing so, you will have these symbols memorized by the time you have completed Chapter 2.

Figure 2-20 shows a pictorial representation of a common flashlight (A), along with the appropriate symbols, at the approximate locations, for the bulb, switch, and battery. A line is used to connect these components. In actual practice, drafters would not draw the flashlight since we are concerned only with the electrical circuit. Consequently, schematic diagrams are used as shown in (B) and (C) below the pictorial drawing. These are actually simplified representations of the drawing in (A).

Refer again to Figure 2-20 and note the schematic in (B). This drawing shows the flashlight in the OFF or deenergized state. The switch (S1) is open. There is no complete path for current (I) through the circuit, and the bulb (DSI) does not light. In Figure 2-20C, however, switch S1 is closed (moved to the ON position) and current flows in the direction of the arrows from the negative terminal of the battery,

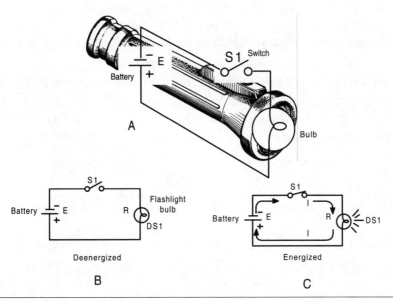

Figure 2-20: Basic electric circuit in a common flashlight.

through the switch (S1), through the lamp (DS1), and back to the positive terminal of the battery. With the switch closed, the path for current is complete and current will continue to flow until the switch (S1) is moved to the open (OFF) position, or the battery is completely discharged.

Ohm's Law

In the early part of the nineteenth century, George Ohm proved by experiment that a precise relationship exists between current, voltage, and resistance. This relationship is called *Ohm's law* and is stated as follows:

> *The current in a circuit is directly proportional to the applied voltage and inversely proportional to the circuit resistance.*

Ohm's law may be expressed as an equation:

$$I = \frac{E}{R}$$

where: I = current in amperes

E = voltage in volts

R = resistance in ohms

As stated in Ohm's law, current is inversely proportional to resistance. This means, as the resistance in a circuit increases, the current decreases proportionately.

Refer again to Figure 2-20C — the schematic of the flashlight in the ON state. If the battery supplies a voltage of 1.5 V and the lamp (DS1) has a resistance of 5 Ω, then the current in the circuit can be determined by substituting values in the equation previously described:

$$I = \frac{E}{R} = \frac{1.5\ V}{5\ \Omega} = .3\ A$$

NOTE

In using Ohm's law, if any two quantities are known, the third one can be determined.

If the flashlight contained two 1.5-V batteries, the voltage would double and 3 V would be applied to the circuit. Using this voltage in the equation:

$$I = \frac{3.0\ V}{5\ \Omega} = .6\ A$$

In comparing these two sample equations, you can see that both the voltage and current has doubled in the latter example. This demonstrates that the current is directly proportional to the applied voltage.

If the value of resistance of the lamp is double, the equation will be:

$$I = \frac{E}{R} = \frac{3.0\ V}{10\ \Omega} = .3\ A$$

The current has been reduced to one-half of the value of the previous equation, or .3 A. This demonstrates that the current is inversely proportinal to the resistance. Doubling the value of the resistance of the load reduces circuit current value to one-half of its former value.

Application of Ohm's Law

In using Ohm's law, if any two of the variables are known, the unknown can be found. For example, if current (I) and voltage (E) are known, resistance (R) can be determined as follows:

Step 1. Use the basic equation:

$$I = \frac{E}{R}$$

Step 2. Remove the divisor by multiplying both sides by R:

$$R \times I = \frac{E}{R} \times \frac{R}{I}$$

Step 3. Note result of Step 2: $R \times I = E$

Step 4. To get R alone (on one side of the equation), divide both sides by I:

$$\frac{RI}{I} = \frac{E}{I}$$

Step 5. The basic equation, transposed for R, is:

$$R = \frac{E}{I}$$

Now let's put this equation to practical use. Refer to Figure 2-21 and note that the voltage (E) is 10 V, and the current (I) equals 1 A. Solve for R, using the equation just explained.

Step 1. Insert the known values in the equation:

$$R = \frac{10\ V}{1\ A} = 10\ \Omega$$

The basic Ohm's law equation can also be used to solve for voltage (E).

Step 1. Use the basic equation:

$$I = \frac{E}{R}$$

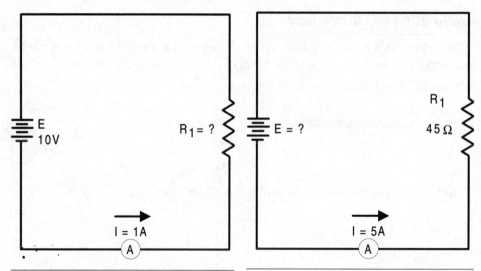

Figure 2-21: dc circuit with unknown resistance.

Figure 2-22: dc circuit with unknown voltage.

Step 2. Multiply both sides by R:

$$I \times R = \frac{E}{R} \times \frac{R}{1}$$

Step 3. Note the results of Step 2.

$$E = I \times R$$

Now let's use this equation to find the voltage in the circuit shown in Figure 2-22, where the amperage equals .5 A, and the resistance equals 45 Ω.

$$E = I \times R$$

$$E = .5 A \times 45 \Omega$$

$$E = 22.5 V$$

The Ohm's law equation and its various forms may be readily obtained with the aid of the circle in Figure 2-23. Note that the circle is divided into three parts with each part containing *E*, *I*, and *R* respectively. The letter *E* is above the horizontal line, while *I* and *R* are below the horizontal line. To determine the unknown quantity, first cover that quantity with a finger. The position of the uncovered letters in the circle will indicate the mathematical operation to be performed. For example, to find current (*I*), cover the letter *I* with a finger. The uncovered letters indicate that E is to be divided by R, or $I = \frac{E}{R}$. To find the equation for *E*, cover *E* with your finger.

The result indicates that I is to be multiplied by R, or $E = IR$. To find the equation for R, cover R. The result indicates that E is to be divided by I, or $R = \dfrac{E}{I}$.

Although some shortcut methods are great time-saving devices when used on the job or in practical applications, the technician should have a basic knowledge of how these shortcut methods are obtained. The diagram in Figure 2-23 should be used to supplement your knowledge of the algebraic method, not as a substitution for the algebraic method. Algebra is a basic tool in the solution of electrical problems.

Power

Power, whether electrical or mechanical, pertains to the rate at which work is being done. Work is done whenever a force causes motion. When a mechanical force is used to lift or move a weight, work is done. When voltage causes electrons to move, work is done. The instantaneous rate at which this work is done is called the electric power rate, and is measured in watts or volt-amperes. Power in watts is equal to the voltage across a circuit multiplied by current through the circuit. This represents the rate at any given instant at which work is being done. The symbol P indicates electrical power, and the basic power equation is:

$$P = E \times I$$

where: E = voltage and I = current

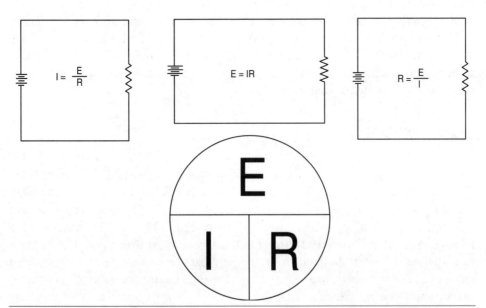

Figure 2-23: Ohm's law in diagram form.

The amount of power changes when either voltage or current, or both voltage and current, are caused to change. The power equation also has variations similar to those discussed previously for determining either voltage, current, or resistance in a circuit.

Electrical components are often given a power rating. The power rating, in watts, indicates the rate at which the device converts electrical energy into another form of energy, such as light, heat, or motion.

As with other electrical quantities, prefixes may be attached to the word *watt* when expressing very large or very small amounts of power. Some common examples of these are the kilowatt (1000 W), the megawatt (1,000,000 W), and the milliwatt ($1/1000$ of a watt). The National Electrical Code® is now referring to watts as "volt-amperes" in most NEC Articles and Sections, so the technician should be aware that power may be expressed in either watts or volt-ampers (VA).

Four of the most important electrical quantities have been discussed thus far:

- Voltage (E)

- Current (I)

- Resistance (R)

- Power (P)

Anyone involved in the electrical industry in any capacity must understand the relationships that exist among these quantities because they are used throughout this book and will be used throughout the technician's career. Figure 2-24 is a summary of 12 basic equations that you should know. The four quantities E, I, R, and P are at the center of the circle. Adjacent to each quantity are three segments. Note that in each segment, the basic quantity is expressed in terms of two other basic quantities, and no two segments are alike.

SERIES DC CIRCUITS

A series circuit is defined as a circuit that contains only one path for current flow. To compare the basic flashlight circuit (discussed previously) with a more complex series circuit, refer to Figure 2-25. Remember that our basic flashlight circuit had only one lamp, while the more complex series circuit in Figure 2-25 contains three lamps connected in series. The current in this circuit must flow through each lamp to complete the electrical path in the circuit. Each additional lamp offers added resistance. Consequently, in a series circuit, the total circuit resistance (R_T) is equal to the sum of the individual resistances.

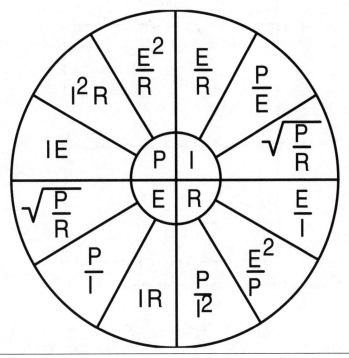

Figure 2-24: Summary of basic electrical equations.

$$R_T = R_1 + R_2 + R_3 + \ldots + R_n$$

The series circuit in Figure 2-26 consists of three resistors; one rated at 10 Ω, one at 15 Ω, and one at 30 Ω. A voltage source provides 120 V. What is the total resistance?

Step 1. Use the basic equation for finding resistance in a series circuit.
Step 2. Substitute known values in the equation.

$$R_T = 10\ \Omega + 15\ \Omega + 30\ \Omega$$

$$R_T = 55\ \Omega$$

In some applications, the total resistance is known and the value of one of the circuit resistors has to be determined. The former equation for finding resistance in a series circuit can be transposed to solve for the value of the unknown resistance.

NOTE

The subscript n in the above equation denotes any number of additional resistances that might be in the equation.

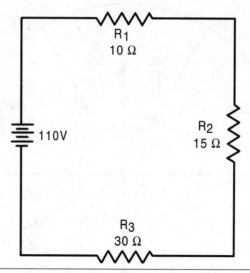

Figure 2-26: Solving for total resistance in a series circuit.

For example, the series circuit in Figure 2-27 has a total resistance of 40 Ω. Two of the resistors are rated at 10 Ω each, while the rating of resistor R_3 is unknown. Here's how to find the value of the unknown resistor.

Step 1. Use the basic equation.
Step 2. Subtract $R_1 + R_2$ from both sides of the equation.
Step 3. Continue solving for R_3 as follows:

$$R_T - R_1 - R_2 = R_3$$

$$R_3 = R_T - R_1 - R_2$$

$$R_3 = 40\ \Omega - 10\ \Omega - 10\ \Omega$$

$$R_3 = 40\ \Omega - 20\ \Omega$$

$$R_3 = 20\ \Omega$$

Current in a Series Circuit

Since there is only one path for current in a series circuit, the same current must flow through each component of the circuit. To determine the current in a series circuit, only the current through one of the components need be known. Ohm's law may be used to calculate the current in a series circuit if the voltage and resistance quantities are known.

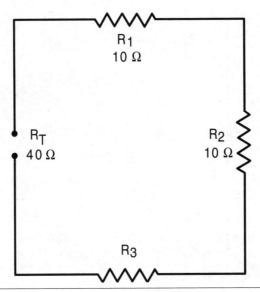

Figure 2-27: Calculating the value of one unknown resistance in a series circuit.

The current flow through each component of a series circuit can be verified by inserting meters into the circuit at various points, as shown in Figure 2-28. Upon examining these meters, each meter would be found to indicate the same value of current.

Voltage in a Series Circuit

The voltage drop across the resistor in a circuit consisting of a single resistor and a voltage source is the total voltage across the circuit and is equal to the applied voltage. The total voltage across a series circuit that consists of more than one resistor is also equal to the applied voltage, but consists of the sum of the individual resistor voltage drops.

In any series circuit, the sum of the resistor voltage drops must equal the source voltage. This statement can be proven by examining the series circuit in Figure 2-29. In this circuit, a source voltage (E_T) of 20 V is dropped across a series circuit consisting of two 5-Ω resistors. The total resistance of the circuit (R_T) is equal to the sum of the two individual resistances, or 10 Ω. Using Ohm's law, the circuit current may be calculated as follows:

$$I_T = \frac{E_T}{R_T}$$

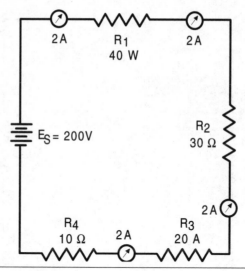

Figure 2-28: Current in a series circuit.

$$I_T = \frac{20\ V}{10\ \Omega}$$

$$I_T = 2\ A$$

Since the value of the resistors is known to be 5 Ω each, and the current through the resistors is known to be 2 A, the voltage drops across the resistors can be calculated as follows:

$$E_1 = I_1 \times R_1$$

$$E_1 = 2\ A \times 5\ \Omega$$

$$E_1 = 10\ V$$

Since R_2 is the same ohmic value as R_1, and carries the same current, the voltage drop across R_2 also equals 10 V. Then, adding the voltage drops for R_1 and R_2, we obtain (10 + 10 =) 20 V, which is equal to the applied voltage in the circuit. From the previous explanation, we see that the total voltage in a dc series circuit may be obtained by using the following equation:

$$E_T = E_1 + E_2 + E_3 + \ldots + En$$

To use the above equation on a practical application, let's assume that a circuit has three resistors connected in series of 20, 30 and 50 Ω, respectively. An ammeter shows that 2 A of current flows through the circuit. What is the total applied voltage?

Step 1. Draw a circuit diagram as shown in Figure 2-30.

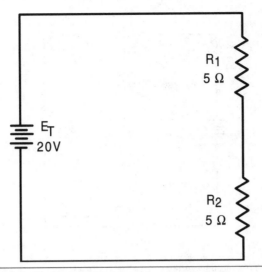

Figure 2-29: Calculating indivudual voltage drops in a series circuit.

Step 2. Solve for the voltage drop across resistor R_1.

$$E_1 = R_1 \times I$$

$$E_1 = 20\ \Omega \times 2\ A = 40\ V$$

Step 3. Solve for the voltage drop across resistor R_2.

$$E_2 = R_2 \times I$$

$$E_2 = 30\ \Omega \times 2\ A = 60\ V$$

Step 4. Solve for the voltage drop across resistor R_3.

$$E_3 = R_3 \times I$$

$$E_3 = 50\ \Omega \times 2\ A = 100\ V$$

Step 5. Add the three voltage drops.

$$E_T = 40\ V + 60\ V + 100\ V$$

$$E_T = 200\ V$$

Power in a Series Circuit

Each of the resistors in a series circuit consumes power which is dissipated in the form of heat. Since this power must come from the source, the total power must be equal to the power consumed by the circuit resistances. In a series circuit, the total

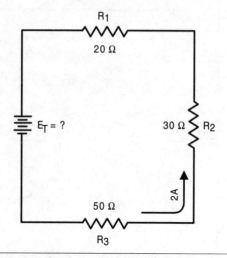

Figure 2-30: Solving for applied voltage in a series circuit.

power is equal to the sum of the power dissipated by the individual resistors. The equation to find the total power in a series circuit follows:

$$P_T = P_1 + P_2 + P_3 + \ldots + P_n$$

Let's determine the total power in watts for the series circuit in Figure 2-31. Note that this circuit has an applied potential of 120 V and three resistors are connected in series, each rated at 5 Ω, 10 Ω, and 15 Ω respectively.

Step 1. Find the total resistance in the circuit.

$$R_T = R_1 + R_2 + R_3$$

$$R_T = 5\ \Omega + 10\ \Omega + 15\ \Omega$$

$$R_T = 30\ \Omega$$

Step 2. Determine the circuit current.

$$I = \frac{E_T}{R_T}$$

$$I = \frac{120\,V}{30\ \Omega}$$

$$I = 4\ A$$

Step 3. Use the power equation to calculate the power for each resistor.

$$P_{1(2)(3)} = I^2 \times R_{1(2)(3)}$$

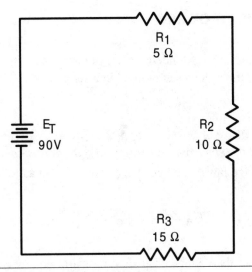

Figure 2-31: Solving for total power in a series circuit.

Step 4. Calculate the power for resistor R_1.

$$P_1 = (4 \text{ A})2 \times 5 \text{ } \Omega$$

$$P_1 = 80 \text{ W}$$

Step 5. Calculate the power for resistors R_2 and R_3 using the same steps as given in Step 4.

$$P_2 = 160 \text{ W}$$

$$P_3 = 240 \text{ W}$$

Step 6. Obtain the total power by adding all power values.

$$P_T = 80 \text{ W} + 160 \text{ W} + 240 \text{ W}$$

$$P_T = 480 \text{ W}$$

When the total source voltage and the total source amperage are known, the total wattage may be found by multiplying the volts times the amps (volt-amperes). Let's check the previous example with this method.

$$P_{Source} = E_{Source} \times I_{Source}$$

$$P_{Source} = 120 \text{ V} \times 4 \text{ A}$$

$$P_{Source} = 480 \text{ VA (W)}$$

KIRCHHOFF'S VOLTAGE LAW

In 1847, G. R. Kirchhoff extended the use of Ohm's law by developing a simple concept concerning the voltages contained in a series circuit loop. Kirchhoff's law states:

> *The algebraic sum of the voltage drops in any closed path in a circuit and the electromotive forces in that path is equal to zero.*

Kirchhoff's voltage law can be written as an equation as follows:

$$E_a + E_b + E_c + \ldots + E_n = 0$$

where E_a, E_b, etc. are the voltage drops or emg's around any closed circuit loop.

To set up the equation for an actual circuit, the following procedure is used:

Step 1. Assume a direction of current through the circuit.

Step 2. Using the assumed direction of current, assign polarities to all resistors through which the current flows.

Step 3. Place the correct polarities on any sources included in the circuit.

Step 4. Starting at any point in the circuit, trace around the circuit, writing down the amount and polarity of the voltage across each component in succession. The polarity used is the sign after the assumed current has passed through the component. Stop when the point at which the trace was started is reached.

Step 5. Place these voltages, with their polarities, into the equation and solve for the desired quantity.

To place the above procedures in use, assume that three resistors are connected in series with a 50-volt source. What is the voltage across the third resistor if the voltage drops across the first two resistors are 25 V and 15 V respectively?

Step 1. Draw a diagram such as the one shown in Figure 2-32.

Step 2. Draw an arrow indicating the assumed direction of current flow. Again, see Figure 2-32.

Step 3. Using the current direction arrow as made in Step 2, mark the polarity (– or +) at each end of each resistor and also on the terminals of the source. These markings are also shown in Figure 2-32.

Step 4. Starting at point A, trace around the circuit in the direction of current flow, recording the voltage and polarity of each component.

Step 5. Starting at point A and using the components from the circuit, we have:

$$(+E_x) + (+E_2) + (+E_1) + (-E_a) = 0$$

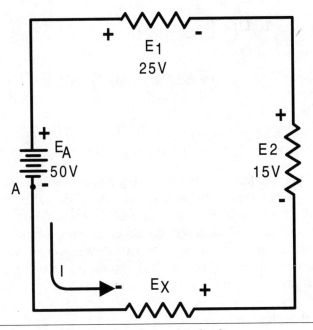

Figure 2-32: Determining unknown voltage in a series circuit.

Step 6. Substitute known values in the equation from the circuit.

$$E_X + 15 \text{ V} + 25 \text{ V} - 50 \text{ V} = 0$$
$$E_X - 10 \text{ V} = 0$$
$$E_X = 10 \text{ V}$$

The unknown voltage (E_X) is found to be 10 V.

Solving for Unknown Current

Using the same procedure as above, problems may be solved in which the current is the unknown quantity.

For example, let's assume that a series circuit has a source voltage of 60 V and contains three resistors of 5 Ω, 10 Ω, and 15 Ω. Find the circuit current.

Step 1. Draw and label the circuit as shown in Figure 2-33.

Step 2. Start at any point and write out the loop equation.

$$E_2 + E_1 + E_A + E_3 = 0$$

Step 3. Since E = IR, substitute known values in the equation.

$$(I \times R_2) + (I \times R_1) + E_A + (I \times R_3) = 0$$

65

$$(I \times 10\ \Omega) + (I \times 5\ \Omega) + (-60\ V) + (I \times 15\ \Omega) = 0$$

Step 4. Combine like terms.

$$(I \times 30\ \Omega) + (-60\ V) = 0$$

$$I = \frac{60\ V}{30\ \Omega}$$

$$I = 2\ A$$

Since the current obtained in the preceding calculation is a positive 2 A, the assumed direction of current was correct. However, if the calculation had been a negative value, the assumed direction of current flow would be incorrect. Even if the wrong current direction is assumed, the amount of current in the calculation will be the same. The polarity, however, is negative if the wrong current direction is chosen. In this case, all that is required is to reverse the direction of the assumed current flow. However, should it be necessary to use this negative current value in further calculations on the circuit using Kirchhoff's law, the negative polarity should be retained in the calculations.

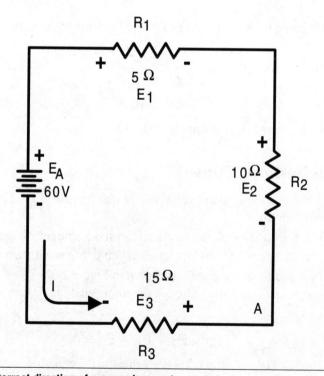

Figure 2-33: Correct direction of assumed current.

PARALLEL DC CIRCUITS

A *parallel circuit* is defined as one having more than one current path connected to a common voltage source. Parallel circuits, therefore, must contain two or more resistances which are not connected in series. An example of a basic parallel circuit is shown in Figure 2-34.

Start at the voltage source (ES) and trace counterclockwise around the circuit. Two complete and separate paths can be identified in which current can flow. One path is traced from the source, through resistance R_1, and back to the source. The other path is from the source, through resistance R_2, and back to the source.

Voltage in a Parallel Circuit

The source voltage in a series circuit divides proportionately across each resistor in the circuit. However, in a parallel circuit, the same voltage is present in each branch. In Figure 2-34, this voltage is equal to the applied voltage (E_S) and can be expressed in the following equation:

$$E_S = E_{R1} = E_{R2}$$

Voltage measurements taken across the resistors of a parallel circuit, as illustrated in Figure 2-35 on the next page. Each voltmeter indicates the same amount of voltage. Also note that the voltage across each resistor in the circuit is the same as the applied voltage.

For example, assume that the current through a resistor of a parallel circuit is known to be 4.5 mA (4.5mA) and the value of the resistor is 30,000 Ω (30 kΩ). What is the source voltage?

The circuit in question is shown in Figure 2-36 on the nex page and the source voltage may be found by using the basic Ohm's law equation:

$$E = IR$$

Substituting the known values in the equation, we have the following:

$$E_{R2} = .0045 \text{ amp} \times 30,000 \ \Omega$$

$$E_{R2} = 135 \text{ V}$$

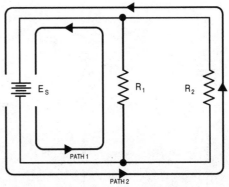

Figure 2-34: A basic parallel circuit.

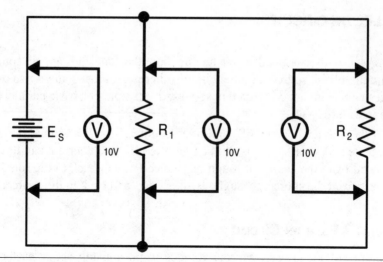

Figure 2-35: Voltage comparison in a parallel circuit.

Since the source voltage is equal to the voltage of a branch, 135 V is the source voltage and is also the voltage applied to each branch of this circuit.

Current in a Parallel Circuit

Ohm's law states that the current in a circuit is inversely proportional to the circuit resistance. This fact is true in both series and parallel circuits.

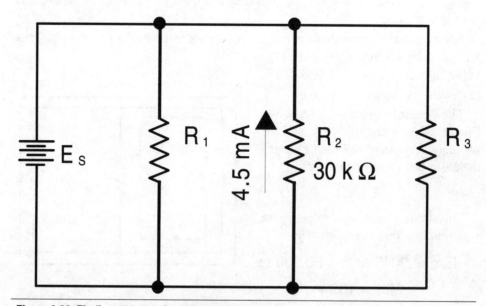

Figure 2-36: Finding source voltage in a parallel circuit.

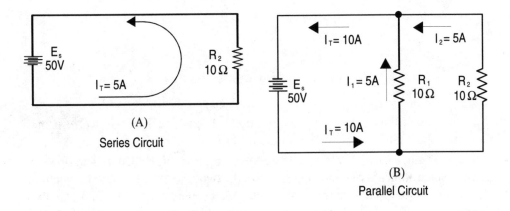

(A)
Series Circuit

(B)
Parallel Circuit

Figure 2-37: Analysis of current in a series and parallel circuit.

There is a single path for current in a series circuit. The amount of current is determined by the total resistance of the circuit and the applied voltage. In a parallel circuit, the source current divides among the available paths.

Part (A) of Figure 2-37 shows a basic series circuit. Here, the total current must pass through the single resistor (R_1). Note that the applied voltage equals 50 V and the resistance of R_1 is 10 Ω. The amount of current can be determined by using Ohm's law and is calculated as follows:

$$I = \frac{E}{R}$$

$$I_T = \frac{50\ V}{10\ \Omega}$$

$$I_T = 5\ A$$

Part (B) of Figure 2-37 shows the same resistor (R_1) with a second resistor (R_2) of equal value connected in parallel across the voltage source. When Ohm's law is applied, the current flow through each resistor is found to be the same as the current through the single resistor in part (A).

$$I = \frac{E}{R}$$

$$ES = ER1 = ER2$$

$$I_{R1} = \frac{50\ V}{10\ \Omega}$$

$$I_{R1} = 5 \text{ A}$$

$$I_{R2} = \frac{50 \text{ V}}{10 \text{ }\Omega}$$

$$I_{R2} = 5 \text{ A}$$

It is apparent that if there are 5 A of current through each of the two resistors, there must be a total current of 10 A drawn from the source.

The total current of 10 A leaves the negative terminal of the battery and flows to point a. Since point a is a connecting point for the two resistors, it is called a junction. At junction a, the total current divides into two currents of 5 A each. These two currents flow through their respective resistors and rejoin at junction b. The total current then flows from junction b back to the positive terminal of the source. The source supplies a total current of 10 A and each of the two equal resistors carries one-half of the total current.

Each individual current path in the circuit in Figure 2-37(B) is referred to as a *branch*. Each branch carries a current that is a portion of the total current. Two or more branches form a *network*.

From the previous explanation, the characteristics of current in a parallel circuit can be expressed in terms of the following general equation:

$$I_T = I_1 + I_2 + \ldots + I_n$$

Kirchhoff's Current Law

The division of current in a parallel network follows a definite pattern. This pattern is described by *Kirchhoff's current law* which states:

> *The algebraic sum of the currents entering and leaving any junction of conductors is equal to zero.*

This law can be stated mathematically as:

$$I_a + I_b + \ldots + I_n = 0$$

where: I_a, I_b, etc. are the currents entering and leaving the junction. Currents entering the junction are considereed to be positive and currents leaving the junction are considered to be negative. When solving a problem using Kirchhoff's current law, the currents must be placed into the equation with the proper polarity signs attached.

Now let's use Kirchhoff's current law to solve for the value of I_3 in Figure 2-38. The known values are first substitued in Kirchhoff's current law equation.

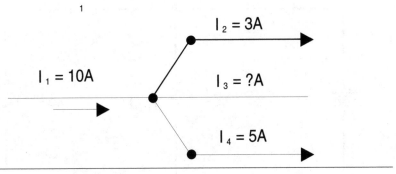

Figure 2-38: Circuit with four current values.

$$I_1 + I_2 + I_3 + I_4 = 0$$

$$10 \text{ amps} + (-3\text{ A}) + I_3 + (-5\text{ A}) = 0$$

$$I_3 + 2\text{ A} = 0$$

$$I_3 = -2\text{ A}$$

Current I_3 has a value of 2 A, and the negative sign shows it to be a current leaving the junction.

Resistance In Parallel Circuits

Figure 2-39 on the next page shows two resistors connected in parallel across a 5-volt battery. Each has a resistance value of 10 Ω. A complete circuit consisting of two parallel paths is formed and current flows as shown.

Computing the individual currents show 0.5 A flows through each resistor. The total current flowing from the battery to the junction of the resistors, and returning from the resistors to the battery, is equal to 1 A.

The total resistance of the circuit can be calculated by using the values of total voltage (E_T) and total current (I_T).

$$R = \frac{E}{I}$$

$$RT = \frac{5\text{ V}}{1\text{ A}}$$

$$RT = 5\text{ }\Omega$$

This computation shows the total resistance to be 5 Ω; one-half the value of either of the two resistors.

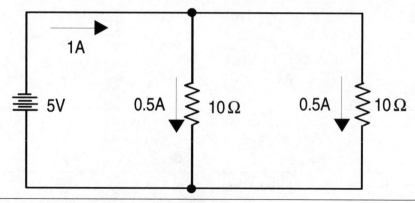

Figure 2-39: Two equal resistors connected in parallel.

> *The total resistance of a parallel circuit is smaller than any of the individual resistors.*

In other words, the total resistance in a parallel circuit is not the sum of the individual resistor values as was the case in a series circuit.

There are several methods used to determine the total or equivalent resistance of parallel circuits. The best method for a given circuit depends on the number and value of the resistors. Where all resistors in the circuit are of the same value, the following simple equation may be used:

$$R_T = \frac{R}{N}$$

where: R_T = total parallel resistance

R = ohmic value of one resistor

N = number of resistors

N = number of resistors

The equation is valid for any number of parallel resistors of equal value.

The total resistance of parallel circuits can be found if the individual resistance values are known along with the source voltage. The following equation is the most common:

$$\frac{1}{R_T} = \frac{1}{R_1} + \frac{1}{R_2} + \frac{1}{R_3} + \cdots \frac{1}{R_n}$$

When using the preceding equation to determine the resistance in a parallel circuit, convert the fractions to a common denominator. For example, let's find the total resistance in a parallel circuit with two resistors rated at 3 Ω and 6 Ω respectively.

$$\frac{1}{R_T} = \frac{1}{3\,\Omega} + \frac{1}{6\Omega}$$

$$\frac{1}{R_T} = \frac{2}{6\,\Omega} + \frac{1}{6\Omega}$$

$$\frac{1}{R_T} = \frac{3}{6\,\Omega}$$

$$\frac{1}{R_T} = \frac{1}{2\,\Omega}$$

Since both sides are reciprocals, (divided into one) disregard the reciprocal function.

$$R_T = 2\Omega$$

When only two resistors, each of either the same or different values, are in a parallel circuit, the following equation may be used to find the total resistance in the circuit.

$$R_T = \frac{R_1 \times R_2}{R_1 + R_2}$$

Using the above equation, what is the total resistance in the circuit shown in Figure 2-40?

$$R_T = \frac{20\,\Omega \times 30\,\Omega}{20\,\Omega + 30\,\Omega}$$

$$R_T = \frac{600}{50}\,\Omega$$

$$R_T = 12\Omega$$

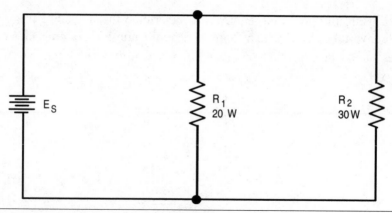

Figure 2-40: Parallel circuit with two unequal resistors.

Equivalent Circuits

In dealing with electrical circuits, it is sometimes necessary to reduce a complex circuit into a simpler form. Any complex circuit consisting of resistances can be redrawn (reduced) to a basic equivalent circuit containing the voltage source and a single resistor representing total resistance. This process is called reduction to an *equivalent circuit*.

Figure 2-41 shows a parallel circuit with three resistors of equal value and the redrawn equivalent circuit. The parallel circuit shown in part A shows the original circuit. To create the equivalent circuit, first calculate the total resistance in the circuit.

$$R_T = \frac{R}{N}$$

$$R_T = \frac{45\ \Omega}{3}$$

$$R_T = 15\ \Omega$$

Once the equivalent resistance is known, a new circuit is drawn consisting of a single resistor (to represent the equivalent resistance) and the voltage source, as shown in part B.

SERIES-PARALLEL DC CIRCUITS

In the preceding sections, series and parallel dc circuits have been considered separately. Electricians often encounter circuits consisting of both series and parallel elements. A circuit of this type is referred to as a *combination circuit*. Solving for the

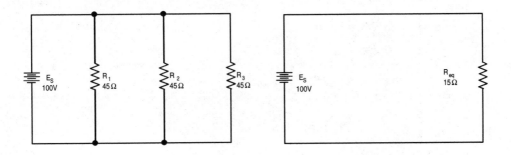

Figure 2-41: Parallel circuit (A) with equivalent circuit (B).

quantities and elements in a combination circuit is simply a matter of applying the laws and rules discussed up to this point.

The basic technique used for solving dc combination-circuit problems is the use of equivalent circuits. To simplify a complex circuit to a simple circuit containing only one load, equivalent circuits are substituted (on paper) for the complex circuit they represent — the technique briefly discussed in the preceding section of this chapter.

To demonstrate the method used to solve combination circuit problems, refer to the circuit in Figure 2-42A. Examination of this circuit shows that the only quantity that can be computed with the given information is the equivalent resistance of R_2 and R_3. Since only two resistors are contained in this part of the circuit, and since these resistors are connected in parallel, the product over the sum equation may be used to obtain the total resistance for this portion of the circuit.

$$R_T = \frac{R_2 \times R_3}{R_2 + R_3}$$

$$R_T = \frac{20\ \Omega \times 30\ \Omega}{20\ \Omega + 30\ \Omega}$$

$$R_T = \frac{600}{50}\ \Omega$$

$$R_T = 12\ \Omega$$

Now that the equivalent resistance for R_2 and R_3 has been calculated, the circuit can be redrawn as a series circuit as shown in Figure 2-42(B). The total resistance for the entire circuit may now be calculated as follows:

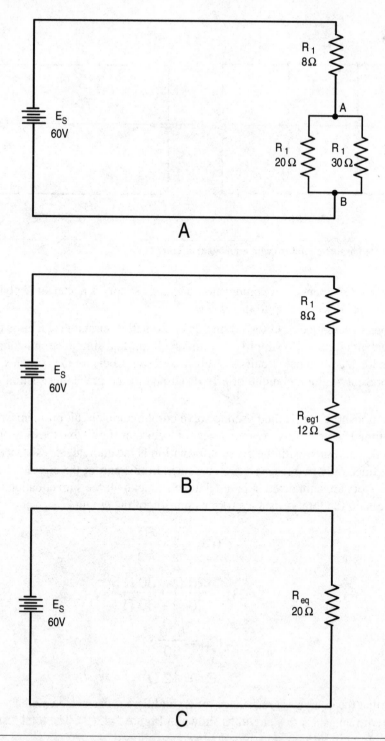

Figure 2-42: Steps in reducing a combination circuit to its simplest form.

$$R_T = 8\ \Omega + 12\ \Omega$$

$$R_T = 20\ \Omega$$

The original circuit can be redrawn with a single resistor that represents the equivalent resistance of the entire circuit as shown in Figure 2-42C. After doing this, the total current in the circuit may be found.

$$I_T = \frac{60\ V}{20\ \Omega}$$

$$I_T = 3\ A$$

Summary

- A basic electric circuit consists of a source of electrical energy connected to a load. The load uses the energy and changes it to a useful form.

- A schematic diagram is a "picture" of a circuit that uses symbols to represent components. The space required to depict an electrical or electronic circuit is greatly reduced by the use of a schematic diagram.

- Ohm's law can be transposed to find one of the values in a circuit if the other two values are known.

- The same current flows through each part of a series circuit.

- The total resistance of a series circuit is equal to the sum of the individual resistances.

- The total voltage across a series circuit is equal to the sum of the individual voltage drops.

- The voltage drop across a resistor in a series circuit is proportional to the ohmic value of the resistor.

- The total power in a series circuit is equal to the sum of the individual power used by each circuit component.

Chapter 3

Security Systems and the NEC®

The design and installation of security/fire-alarm systems employ a wide variety of techniques, often involving special types of equipment and materials designed for specific applications. Many security systems operate on low-voltage circuits, but are installed similarly as conventional electrical circuits for light and power. All installations, when used in buildings, must conform to applicable National Electrical Code® (NEC) requirements, local ordinances, and instructions provided by equipment and component manufacturers. This chapter explains the key terms and basic layout of the NEC. A brief review of the individual NEC sections that apply to security systems is also covered.

INTRODUCTION TO THE NEC

Since the first central-station electric generating plant was developed in New York City in 1882 by Thomas A. Edison, the electrical construction industry has grown at an astonishing rate to become one of the largest industries in the United States. The first generating plant created public demand for the use of electric lighting and power in existing buildings, as well as for new construction.

These first electrical wiring installations were usually laid out by workers employed and trained by the power companies, and the majority of these installations were "designed" by the mechanics on the job, often as the work progressed. Building contractors then began hiring mechanics of their own to install electrical wiring systems, but because of the special skills and knowledge required, these same builders soon began leaving the wiring installations to mechanics who began to specialize in this work as electrical contractors.

As the electrical construction continued to become a more important part of the general building construction, architects began to prepare layouts of the desired electrical systems on their architectural drawings. This layout usually indicated the lighting outlets, base "plugs," and light switches by means of certain symbols. A line was sometimes drawn from a lighting outlet to a wall switch to indicate how the various lamps were to be controlled, but this was usually the extent of the electrical design. The details of wiring, number of circuits, and the like, were still left to the mechanics (electricians) installing the system. As electrical systems became more extensive and complex, electrical contractors began hiring drafters to prepare working drawings to supplement the sketchy outlet layout on the architectural drawings, to provide a basis for preparing estimates, and to give instructions to electricians in the field.

From that point on, electrical construction continued to become a more important part of general building construction, and soon the architects began to prepare more extensive layouts of the electrical systems, until finally separate drawings were included along with the architectural drawings. As the volume of such layout work increased and electrical systems became still more extensive and complex, a greater engineering knowledge of power and illumination requirements became necessary. Persons with the proper knowledge and training began to devote their time exclusively to designing and laying out electrical installations as consulting engineers. These consulting engineers conveyed their designs by means of working drawings that used symbols, lines, notations, and written specifications. Thus, the electrical designer became a very important cog in the wheel of electrical construction. Yet, the best electrical designs, specifying the best materials and equipment, are useless without trained workers to properly install the systems. Consequently, the trained electrical technician is indispensable in the building construction industry . . . and a thorough knowledge of the NEC is one of the first requirements in becoming a trained electrical technician. In fact, the NEC is probably the most widely used and generally accepted code in the world. It is used as an electrical installation, safety, and reference guide in the United States, and in many other parts of the world as well.

Purpose and History of the NEC

Owing to the potential fire and explosion hazards caused by the improper handling and installation of electrical wiring, certain rules in the selection of materials, quality of workmanship, and precautions for safety must be followed. To standardize and simplify these rules and provide a reliable guide for electrical construction, the National Electrical Code (NEC) was developed. The NEC (Figure 3-1), originally prepared in 1897, is frequently revised to meet changing conditions, improved equipment and materials, and new fire hazards. It is a result of the best efforts of electrical engineers, manufacturers of electrical equipment, insurance underwriters, fire fighters, and other concerned experts throughout the country.

The NEC is now published by the National Fire Protection Association (NFPA), Batterymarch Park, Quincy, Massachusetts 02269. It contains specific rules and regulations intended to help in the practical safeguarding of persons and property from hazards arising from the use of electricity.

Although the NEC itself states, "This Code is not intended as a design specification nor an instruction manual for untrained persons," it does provide a sound basis for the

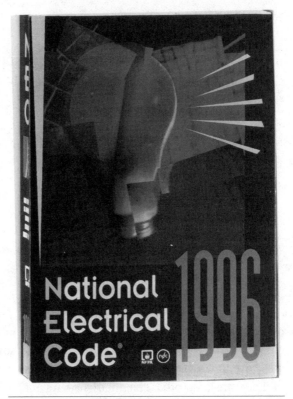

Figure 3-1: The NEC has become the bible of the electrical construction industry.

study of electrical installation procedures — under the proper guidance. The probable reason for the NEC's self-analysis is that the code also states, "This Code contains provisions considered necessary for safety. Compliance therewith and proper maintenance will result in an installation essentially free from hazard, but not necessarily efficient, convenient, or adequate for good service or future expansion of electrical use."

The NEC, however, has become the bible of the electrical construction industry, and anyone involved in electrical work, in any capacity, should obtain an up-to-date copy, keep it handy at all times, and refer to it frequently.

Whether you are installing a new security system or repairing an existing one, all electrical work must comply with the current National Electrical Code (NEC) and all local ordinances. Like most laws, the NEC is easier to work with once you understand the language and know where to look for the information you need.

This chapter is not a substitute for the NEC. You need a copy of the most recent edition and it should be kept handy at all times. The more you know about the Code, the more you are likely to refer to it.

NEC TERMINOLOGY

There are two basic types of rules in the NEC: mandatory rules and advisory rules. Here is how to recognize the two types of rules and how they relate to all types of electrical systems.

- Mandatory rules—All mandatory rules have the word shall in them. The word "shall" means must. If a rule is mandatory, you must comply with it.

- Advisory rules—All advisory rules have the word should in them. The word "should" in this case means recommended but not necessarily required. If a rule is advisory, compliance is discretionary. If you want to comply with it, do so. But they are not mandatory.

Be alert to local amendments to the NEC. Local ordinances may amend the language of the NEC, changing it from should to shall. This means that you must do in that county or city what may only be recommended in some other area. The office that issues building permits will either sell you a copy of the code that's enforced in that area or tell you where the code is sold. In rare instances, the electrical inspector having jurisdiction over the area, may issue these regulations verbally.

There are a few other "landmarks" that you will encounter while looking through the NEC. These are summarized in Figure 3-2, and a brief explanation of each follows:

Explanatory material: Explanatory material in the form of Fine Print Notes is designated (FPN). Where these appear, the FPNs normally apply to the NEC Section or paragraph immediately preceding the FPN.

Change bar: A change bar in the margins indicates that a change in the NEC has been made since the last edition. When becoming familiar with each new edition of the NEC, always review these changes. There are also several illustrated publications on the market that point out changes in the NEC with detailed explanations of each. Such publications make excellent reference material.

Bullets: A filled-in circle called a "bullet" indicates that something has been deleted from the last edition of the NEC. Although not absolutely necessary, many electricians like to compare the previous NEC edition to the most recent one when these bullets are encountered, just to see what has been omitted from the latest edition. The most probable reasons for the deletions are errors in the previous edition, or obsolete items.

Extracted text: Material identified by the superscript letter x includes text extracted from other NFPA documents as identified in Appendix A of the NEC.

As you open the NEC book, you will notice several different types of text used. Here is an explanation of each.

Mandatory rules are characterized by
the use of the word:

SHALL

A recommendation or that which is
advised but not required is
characterized by the use of the word:

SHOULD

Explanatory material in the form of
Fine Print Notes is designated:

(FPN)

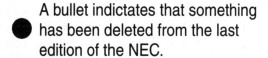

A change bar in the margins
indicates that a change in the
NEC has been made since the
last edition.

A bullet indictates that something
has been deleted from the last
edition of the NEC.

Figure 3-2: NEC terminology.

1. *Black Letters:* Basic definitions and explanations of the NEC.

2. *Bold Black Letters:* Headings for each NEC application.

3. *Exceptions:* These explain the situations when a specific rule does not apply. Exceptions are written in italics under the Section or paragraph to which they apply.

4. *Tables:* Tables are often included when there is more than one possible application of a requirement. See Figure 3-3.

5. *Diagrams:* A few diagrams are scattered throughout the NEC to illustrate certain NEC applications. See Figure 3-4.

Size of Largest Service-Entrance Conductor or Equivalent Area for Parallel Conductors		Size of Grounding Electrode Conductor	
Copper	Aluminum or Copper-Clad Aluminum	Copper	Aluminum or Copper-Clad Aluminum
2 or smaller	1/0 or smaller	8	6
1 or 2	2/0 or 3/0	6	4
2/0 or 3/0	4/0 or 250 kcmil	4	2
Over 3/0 through 350 kcmil	Over 250 kcmil through 500 kcmil	2	1/0
Over 350 kcmil through 600 kcmil	Over 500 kcmil through 900 kcmil	1/0	3/0
Over 600 kcmil through 1100 kcmil	Over 900 kcmil through 1750 kcmil	2/0	4/0
Over 1100 kcmil	Over 1750 kcmil	3/0	250 kcmil

Figure 3-3: Typical NEC table.

LEARNING THE NEC LAYOUT

The NEC is divided into the Introduction (Article 90) and nine chapters. Chapters 1, 2, 3, and 4 apply generally; Chapters 5, 6, and 7 apply to special occupancies, special equipment, or other special conditions. These latter chapters supplement or modify the general rules. Chapters 1 through 4 apply except as amended by Chapters 5, 6, and 7 for the particular conditions.

While looking through these NEC chapters, if you should encounter a word or term that is unfamiliar, look in Chapter 1, Article 100 — Definitions. Chances are, the term will be found here. If not, look in the Index for the word and the NEC page number. Many terms are included in Article 100, but others are scattered throughout the book.

For definitions of terms not found in the NEC, obtain a copy of *Illustrated Dictionary for Electrical Workers*, available from Delmar Publishers, Inc., Albany, New York.

Chapter 8 of the NEC covers communications systems and is independent of the other chapters except where they are specifically referenced therein.

Chapter 9 consists of tables and examples.

There is also the NEC Contents at the beginning of the book and a comprehensive index at the back of the book. You will find frequent use for both of these helpful "tools" when searching for various installation requirements.

Each chapter is divided into one or more Articles. For example Chapter 1 contains Articles 100 and 110. These Articles are subdivided into Sections. For example, Article 110 of Chapter 1 begins with Section 110-2. Approval. A bullet in the margin

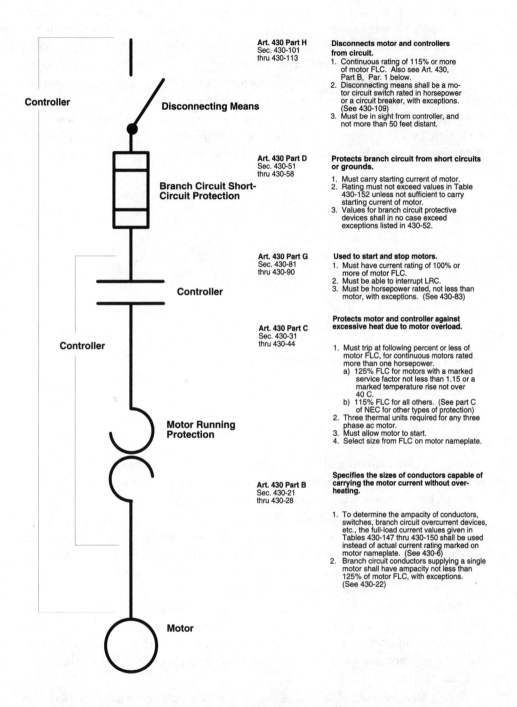

Controller

Disconnecting Means

Art. 430 Part H
Sec. 430-101
thru 430-113

Disconnects motor and controllers from circuit.
1. Continuous rating of 115% or more of motor FLC. Also see Art. 430, Part B, Par. 1 below.
2. Disconnecting means shall be a motor circuit switch rated in horsepower or a circuit breaker, with exceptions. (See 430-109)
3. Must be in sight from controller, and not more than 50 feet distant.

Branch Circuit Short-Circuit Protection

Art. 430 Part D
Sec. 430-51
thru 430-58

Protects branch circuit from short circuits or grounds.
1. Must carry starting current of motor.
2. Rating must not exceed values in Table 430-152 unless not sufficient to carry starting current of motor.
3. Values for branch circuit protective devices shall in no case exceed exceptions listed in 430-52.

Controller

Art. 430 Part G
Sec. 430-81
thru 430-90

Used to start and stop motors.
1. Must have current rating of 100% or more of motor FLC.
2. Must be able to interrupt LRC.
3. Must be horsepower rated, not less than motor, with exceptions. (See 430-83)

Controller

Motor Running Protection

Art. 430 Part C
Sec. 430-31
thru 430-44

Protects motor and controller against excessive heat due to motor overload.

1. Must trip at following percent or less of motor FLC, for continuous motors rated more than one horsepower.
   a) 125% FLC for motors with a marked service factor not less than 1.15 or a marked temperature rise not over 40 C.
   b) 115% FLC for all others. (See part C of NEC for other types of protection)
2. Three thermal units required for any three phase ac motor.
3. Must allow motor to start.
4. Select size from FLC on motor nameplate.

Art. 430 Part B
Sec. 430-21
thru 430-28

Specifies the sizes of conductors capable of carrying the motor current without overheating.

1. To determine the ampacity of conductors, switches, branch circuit overcurrent devices, etc., the full-load current values given in Tables 430-147 thru 430-150 shall be used instead of actual current rating marked on motor nameplate. (See 430-6)
2. Branch circuit conductors supplying a single motor shall have ampacity not less than 125% of motor FLC, with exceptions. (See 430-22)

Motor

Figure 3-4: Typical NEC diagram; several are scattered throughout the NEC for clarity.

indicates that Section 110-1 has been deleted from the last NEC edition. Some sections may contain only one sentence or a paragraph, while others may be further subdivided into lettered or numbered paragraphs such as (a), (1), (2), and so on.

Begin your study of the NEC with Articles 90, 100 and 110. These three articles have the basic information that will make the rest of the NEC easier to understand. Article 100 defines terms you will need to understand the code. Article 110 gives the general requirements for electrical installations. Read these three articles over several times until you are thoroughly familiar with all the information they contain. It's time well spent. For example, Article 90 contains the following sections:

- Purpose (90-1)

- Scope (90-2)

- Code Arrangement (90-3)

- Enforcement (90-4)

- Mandatory Rules and Explanatory Material (90-5)

- Formal Interpretations (90-6)

- Examination of Equipment for Safety (90-7)

- Wiring Planning (90-8)

Once you are familiar with Articles 90, 100, and 110 you can move on to the rest of the NEC. There are several key sections you will use often in servicing electrical systems. Let's discuss each of these important sections.

Wiring Design and Protection: Chapter 2 of the NEC discusses wiring design and protection, the information electrical technicians need most often. It covers the use and identification of grounded conductors, branch circuits, feeders, calculations, services, overcurrent protection and grounding. This is essential information for any type of electrical system, regardless of the type.

Chapter 2 is also a "how-to" chapter. It explains how to provide proper spacing for conductor supports, how to provide temporary wiring and how to size the proper grounding conductor or electrode. If you run into a problem related to the design/installation of a conventional electrical system, you can probably find a solution for it in this chapter.

Wiring Methods and Materials: Chapter 3 has the rules on wiring methods and materials. The materials and procedures to use on a particular system depend on the type of building construction, the type of occupancy, the location of the wiring in

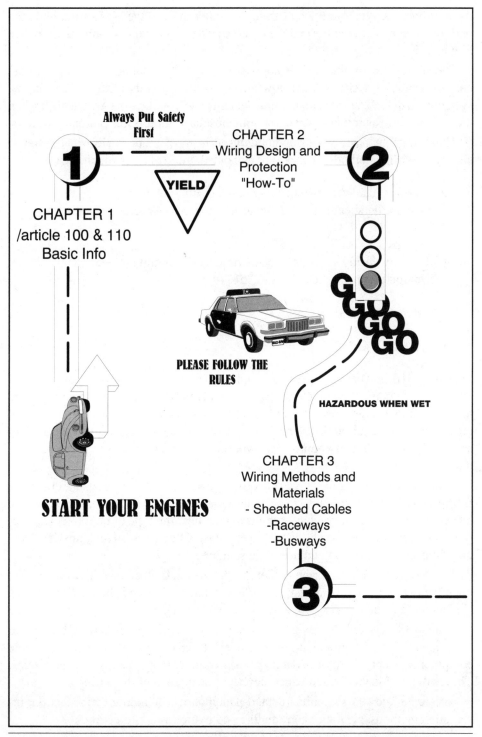

Figure 3-5: Become thoroughly familiar with Articles 90, 100, and 110 before continuing.

the building, the type of atmosphere in the building or in the area surrounding the building, mechanical factors and the relative costs of different wiring methods. See Figure 3-5.

The provisions of this article apply to all wiring installations except remote control switching (Article 725), low-energy power circuits (Article 725), signal systems (Article 725), communication systems and conductors (Article 800) when these items form an integral part of equipment such as motors and motor controllers.

There are four basic wiring methods used in most modern electrical systems. Nearly all wiring methods are a variation of one or more of these four basic methods:

- Sheathed cables of two or more conductors, such as nonmetallic-sheathed cable and armored cable (Articles 330 through 339)

- Raceway wiring systems, such as rigid steel conduit and electrical metallic tubing (Articles 342 to 358)

- Busways (Article 364)

- Cabletray (Article 318)

Article 310 in Chapter 3 gives a complete description of all types of electrical conductors. Electrical conductors come in a wide range of sizes and forms. Be sure to check the working drawings and specifications to see what sizes and types of conductors are required for a specific job. If conductor type and size are not specified, choose the most appropriate type and size meeting standard NEC requirements.

Articles 318 through 384 give rules for raceways, boxes, cabinets and raceway fittings. Outlet boxes vary in size and shape, depending on their use, the size of the raceway, the number of conductors entering the box, the type of building construction and atmospheric conditions of the areas. Chapter 3 should answer most questions on the selection and use of these items.

The NEC does not describe in detail all types and sizes of outlet boxes. But manufacturers of outlet boxes have excellent catalogs showing all of their products. Collect these catalogs. They are essential to your work.

Article 380 covers the switches, push buttons, pilot lamps, receptacles and convenience outlets you will use to control electrical circuits or to connect portable equipment to electric circuits. Again, get the manufacturers' catalogs on these items. They will provide you with detailed descriptions of each of the wiring devices.

Article 384 covers switchboards and panelboards, including their location, installation methods, clearances, grounding and overcurrent protection.

Equipment For General Use

Chapter 4 of the NEC begins with the use and installation of flexible cords and cables, including the trade name, type letter, wire size, number of conductors, conductor insulation, outer covering and use of each. The chapter also includes fixture wires, again giving the trade name, type letter and other important details.

Article 410 on lighting fixtures is especially important. It gives installation procedures for fixtures in specific locations. For example, it covers fixtures near combustible material and fixtures in closets. The NEC does not describe how many fixtures will be needed in a given area to provide a certain amount of illumination.

Article 430 covers electric motors, including mounting the motor and making electrical connections to it. Motor controls and overload protection are also covered.

Articles 440 through 460 cover air conditioning and heating equipment, transformers and capacitors.

Article 480 gives most requirements related to battery-operated electrical systems. Storage batteries are seldom thought of as part of a conventional electrical system, but they often provide standby emergency lighting service. They may also supply power to security systems that are separate from the main ac electrical system. See Figure 3-6.

Special Occupancies

Chapter 5 of the NEC covers special occupancy areas. These are areas where the sparks generated by electrical equipment may cause an explosion or fire. The hazard may be due to the atmosphere of the area or just the presence of a volatile material in the area. Commercial garages, aircraft hangers and service stations are typical special occupancy locations.

Articles 500 – 501 cover the different types of special occupancy atmospheres where an explosion is possible. The atmospheric groups were established to make it easy to test and approve equipment for various types of uses.

Articles 501-4, 502-4, and 503-3 cover the installation of explosion-proof wiring. An explosion-proof system is designed to prevent the ignition of a surrounding explosive atmosphere when arcing occurs within the electrical system.

There are three main classes of special occupancy location

- Class I (Article 501): Areas containing flammable gases or vapors in the air. Class I areas include paint spray booths, dyeing plants where hazardous liquids are used and gas generator rooms.

- Class II (Article 502): Areas where combustible dust is present, such as grain handling and storage plants, dust and stock collector areas and sugar pulverizing plants. These are areas where, under normal

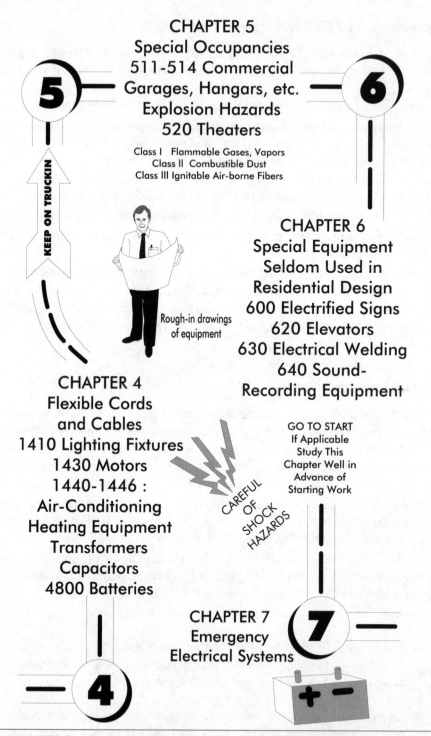

CHAPTER 5
Special Occupancies
511-514 Commercial
Garages, Hangars, etc.
Explosion Hazards
520 Theaters

Class I Flammable Gases, Vapors
Class II Combustible Dust
Class III Ignitable Air-borne Fibers

KEEP ON TRUCKIN

Rough-in drawings
of equipment

CHAPTER 6
Special Equipment
Seldom Used in
Residential Design
600 Electrified Signs
620 Elevators
630 Electrical Welding
640 Sound-
Recording Equipment

CHAPTER 4
Flexible Cords
and Cables
1410 Lighting Fixtures
1430 Motors
1440-1446 :
Air-Conditioning
Heating Equipment
Transformers
Capacitors
4800 Batteries

GO TO START
If Applicable
Study This
Chapter Well in
Advance of
Starting Work

CAREFUL OF SHOCK HAZARDS

CHAPTER 7
Emergency
Electrical Systems

Figure 3-6: NEC Chapters 1 through 4 apply except as amended by Chapters 5, 6, and 7 for some conditions.

operating conditions, there may be enough combustible dust in the air to produce explosive or ignitable mixtures.

- Class III (Article 503): Areas that are hazardous because of the presence of easily ignitable fibers or flyings in the air, although not in large enough quantity to produce ignitable mixtures. Class III locations include cotton mills, rayon mills, and clothing manufacturing plants.

Article 511 and 514 regulate garages and similar locations where volatile or flammable liquids are used. While these areas are not always considered critically hazardous locations, there may be enough danger to require special precautions in the electrical installation. In these areas, the NEC requires that volatile gases be confined to an area not more than 4 ft above the floor. So in most cases, conventional raceway systems are permitted above this level. If the area is judged critically hazardous, explosionproof wiring (including seal-offs) may be required. See Figure 3-7.

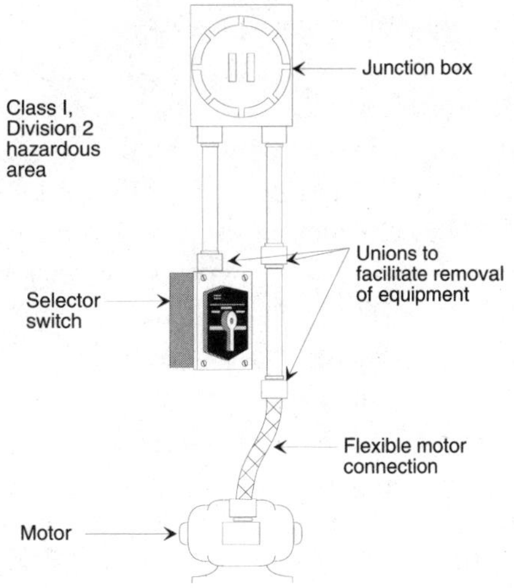

Article 520 regulates theaters and similar occupancies where fire and panic can cause hazards to life and property. Drive-in theaters do not present the same hazards as enclosed auditoriums. But the projection rooms and adjacent areas must be properly ventilated and wired for the protection of operating personnel and others using the area.

Chapter 5 also covers residential storage garages, aircraft hangars, service stations, bulk storage plants, health care facilities, mobile homes and parks, and recreation vehicles and parks.

When security technicians are installing systems in hazardous locations, extreme caution must be used. You may be working with only 12 or 24 V, but a spark caused by, say, an improper connection can set off a violent explosion. You may have already witnessed a low-voltage explosion in the common automotive battery. Although only 12 V dc are present, if a spark occurs near the battery and battery gases are leaking through the battery housing, chances are the battery will explode with a report similar to a shotgun firing.

Figure 3-7: Explosionproof fittings must be used for electrical wiring in most hazardous areas.

When installing security systems in Class I, Division 1 locations, explosionproof fittings are required and most electrical wiring must be enclosed in rigid steel conduit (pipe).

Special Equipment

Residential electrical workers will seldom need to refer to the Articles in Chapter 6 of the NEC, but the items in Chapter 6 are frequently encountered by commercial and industrial electrical workers.

Article 600 covers electric signs and outline lighting. Article 610 applies to cranes and hoists. Article 620 covers the majority of the electrical work involved in the installation and operation of elevators, dumbwaiters, escalators and moving walks. The manufacturer is responsible for most of this work. The electrician usually just furnishes a feeder terminating in a disconnect means in the bottom of the elevator shaft. The electrician may also be responsible for a lighting circuit to a junction box midway in the elevator shaft for connecting the elevator cage lighting cable and exhaust fans. Articles in Chapter 6 of the NEC give most of the requirements for these installations.

Article 630 regulates electric welding equipment. It is normally treated as a piece of industrial power equipment requiring a special power outlet. But there are special conditions that apply to the circuits supplying welding equipment. These are outlined in detail in Chapter 6 of the NEC.

Article 640 covers wiring for sound-recording and similar equipment. This type of equipment normally requires low-voltage wiring. Special outlet boxes or cabinets are usually provided with the equipment. But some items may be mounted in or on standard outlet boxes. Some sound-recording electrical systems require direct current, supplied from rectifying equipment, batteries or motor generators. Low-voltage alternating current comes from relatively small transformers connected on the primary side to a 120-V circuit within the building.

Other items covered in Chapter 6 of the NEC include: X-ray equipment (Article 660), induction and dielectric heat-generating equipment (Article 665) and machine tools (Article 670).

If you ever have work that involves Chapter 6, study the chapter before work begins. That can save a lot of installation time. Here is another way to cut down on labor hours and prevent installation errors. Get a set of rough-in drawings of the equipment being installed. It is easy to install the wrong outlet box or to install the right box in the wrong place. Having a set of rough-in drawings can prevent those simple but costly errors.

SPECIAL CONDITIONS

In most commercial buildings, the NEC and local ordinances require a means of lighting public rooms, halls, stairways and entrances. There must be enough light to allow the occupants to exit from the building if the general building lighting is interrupted. Exit doors must be clearly indicated by illuminated exit signs.

Chapter 7 of the NEC covers the installation of emergency lighting systems. These circuits should be arranged so that they can automatically transfer to an alternate source of current, usually storage batteries or gasoline-driven generators. As an alternative in some types of occupancies, you can connect them to the supply side of the main service so disconnecting the main service switch would not disconnect the emergency circuits. See Article 700. NEC Chapter 7 also covers a variety of other equipment, systems and conditions that are not easily categorized elsewhere in the NEC.

Chapter 8 is a special category for wiring associated with electronic communications systems including telephone and telegraph, radio and TV, fire and burglar alarms, and community antenna systems. This is one NEC Chapter that the security technician must understand thoroughly. See Figure 3-8 on the next page.

USING THE NEC

Once you become familiar with the NEC through repeated usage, you will generally know where to look for a particular topic. While this chapter provides you with an initial familiarization of the NEC layout, much additional usage experience will be needed for you to feel comfortable with the NEC's content. Here's how to locate information on a specific subject.

Step 1. Look through the Contents. You may spot the topic in a heading or subheading. If not, look for a broader, more general subject heading under which the specific topic may appear. Also look for related or similar topics. The Contents will refer you to a specific page number.

Step 2. If you do not find what you're looking for in the Contents, go to the index at the back of the book. This alphabetic listing is finely divided into different topics. You should locate the subject here. The index, however, will refer to you either an Article or Section number (not a page number) where the topic is listed.

Step 3. If you cannot find the required subject in the Index, try to think of alternate names. For example, instead of wire, look under conductors; instead of outlet box, look under boxes, outlet, and so on.

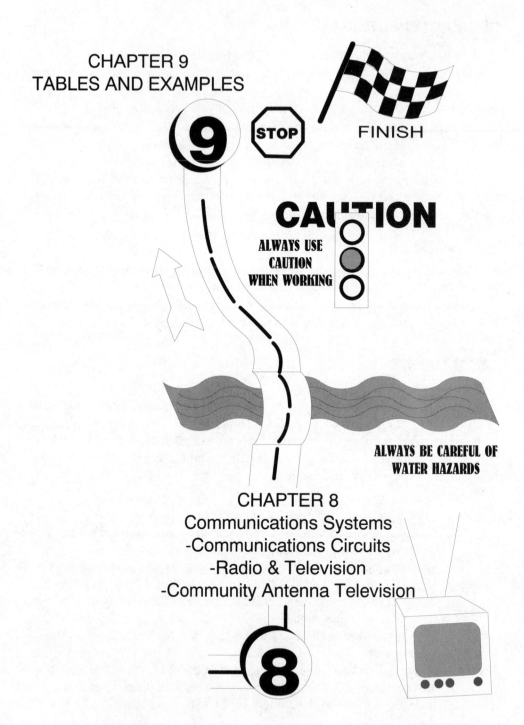

Figure 3-8: The main text of the NEC ends with Chapter 9 — Tables and Examples.

The NEC is not an easy book to read and understand at first. In fact, seasoned electrical workers and technicians sometimes find it confusing. Basically, it is a reference book written in a legal, contract-type language and its content does assume prior knowledge of most subjects listed. Consequently, you will sometimes find the NEC frustrating to use because terms aren't always defined, or some unknown prerequisite knowledge is required. To minimize this problem, it is recommended that you obtain one of the several NEC supplemental guides that are designed to explain and supplement the NEC. One of the best is *The National Electrical Code Handbook*, available from the NFPA, Batterymarch Park, Quincy, MA 02269 or from your local book store.

Practical Application

Let's assume that you are installing a 120-V outlet box to provide the power supply for a surveillance camera in a commercial office. The owner wants the outlet box surface-mounted and located behind a curtain of their sliding glass patio doors. To determine if this is a NEC violation or not, follow these steps:

Step 1. Turn to the Contents of the NEC book, which begins on page 70-V.

Step 2. Find the chapter that would contain information about the general application you are working on. For this example, Chapter 4—Equipment for General Use should cover track lighting.

Step 3. Now look for the article that fits the specific category you are working on. In this case, Article 410 covers lighting fixtures, lampholders, lamps, and receptacles.

Step 4. Next locate the NEC Section within the NEC Article 410 that deals with the specific application. For this example, refer to Part R—Lighting Track.

Step 5. Turn to the page listed. The 1993 NEC gives page 350.

Step 6. Read NEC Section 410-100, Definition to become familiar with track lighting. Continue down the page with NEC Section 410-101 and read the information contained therein. Note that paragraph (c) under NEC Section 410-101 states the following:

> *(c) Locations Not Permitted. Lighting track shall not be installed (1) where subject to physical damage; (2) in wet or damp locations; (3) where subject to corrosive vapors; (4) in storage battery rooms; (5) in hazardous (classified) locations; (6) where concealed; (7) where extended through walls or partitions; (8) less than 5 feet above the finished floor except where protected from*

physical damage or track operating at less than 30 volts RMS open-circuit voltage.

Step 7. Read NEC Section 410-101, paragraph (c) carefully. Do you see any conditions that would violate any NEC requirements if the track lighting is installed in the area specified? In checking these items, you will probably note condition (6), "where concealed." Since the track lighting is to be installed behind a curtain, this sounds like an NEC violation. But let's check further.

Step 8. Let's get an interpretation of the NEC's definition of "concealed." Therefore, turn to Article 100 — definitions and find the main term "concealed." It reads as follows:

Concealed: Rendered inaccessible by the structure or finish of the building....

Step 9. After reading the NEC's definition of "concealed," although the track lighting may be out of sight (if the curtain is drawn), it will still be readily accessible for maintenance. Consequently, the track lighting is really not concealed according to the NEC definition.

When using the NEC to determine correct electrical-installation requirements, please keep in mind that you will nearly always have to refer to more than one Section. Sometimes the NEC itself refers the reader to other Articles and Sections. In some cases, the user will have to be familiar enough with the NEC to know what other NEC Sections pertain to the installation at hand. It's a confusing situation to say the least, but time and experience in using the NEC frequently will make using it much easier.

Now let's take another example to further acquaint you with navigating the NEC.

Suppose you are installing Type SE (service-entrance) cable on the side of a home. You know that this cable must be secured, but you aren't sure of the spacing between cable clamps. To find out this information, use the following procedure:

Step 1: Look in the NEC Table of Contents and follow down the list until you find an appropriate category.

Step 2: Article 230 under Chapter 3 will probably catch your eye first, so turn to the page where Article 230 begins in the NEC.

Step 3: Glance down the section numbers, 230-1, Scope, 230-2, Number of Services, etc. until you come to Section 230-51, Mounting Supports. Upon reading this section, you will find in paragraph (a) — Service - Entrance Cables — that "Service-entrance cable shall be supported by straps or other approved means within 12 inches (305 mm) of every service head, gooseneck, or connection to a raceway or enclosure and at intervals not exceeding 30 inches (762 mm)."

After reading this section, you will know that a cable strap is required within 12 inches of the service head and within 12 inches of the meter base. Furthermore, the cable must be secured in between these two termination points at intervals not exceeding 30 in.

DEFINITIONS

Many definitions of terms dealing with the NEC may be found in NEC Article 100. However, other definitions are scattered throughout the NEC under their appropriate category. For example the term lighting track, as discussed previously, is not listed in Article 100. The term is listed under NEC Section 410-100 and reads as follows:

> *Lighting track is a manufactured assembly designed to support and energize lighting fixtures that are capable of being readily repositioned on the track. Its length may be altered by the addition or subtraction of sections of track.*

Regardless of where the definition may be located — in Article 100 or under the appropriate NEC Section elsewhere in the book — the best way to learn and remember these definitions is to form a mental picture of each item or device as you read the definition. For example, turn to page 70-5 of the 1993 NEC and under Article 100 — Definitions, scan down the page until you come to the term "Attachment Plug (Plug Cap) (Cap)." After reading the definition, you will probably have already formed a mental picture of attachment plugs. See Figure 3-9 for some of the more common attachment plugs.

Once again, scan through the definitions until the term "Appliance" is found. Read the definition and then try to form a mental picture of what appliances look like. Some of the more common appliances appear in Figure 3-10. They should be familiar to everyone.

Each and every term listed in the NEC should be understood. Know what the item looks like and how it is used on the job. If a term is unfamiliar, try other reference books such as manufacturers' catalogs for an illustration of the item. Then research the item further to determine its purpose in electrical systems. Once you are familiar with all the common terms and definitions found in the NEC, navigating through the NEC (and understanding what you read) will be much easier.

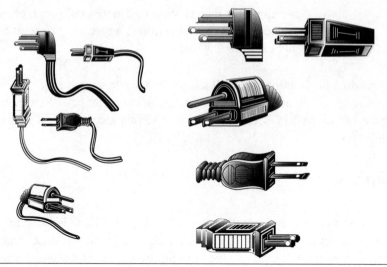

Figure 3-9: Attachment plugs in common use.

TESTING LABORATORIES

There are many definitions included in Article 100. You should become familiar with the definitions. Since a copy of the latest NEC is compulsory for any type of electrical wiring, there is no need to duplicate them here. However, here are two definitions that you should become especially familiar with:

- Labeled — Equipment or materials to which has been attached a label, symbol or other identifying mark of an organization acceptable to the authority having jurisdiction and concerned with product evaluation, that maintains periodic inspection of production of labeled equipment or materials, and by whose labeling the manufacturer indicates compliance with appropriate standards or performance in a specified manner.

- Listed — Equipment or materials included in a list published by an organization acceptable to the authority having jurisdiction and concerned with product evaluation, that maintains periodic inspection of production of listed equipment or materials, and whose listing states either that the equipment or material meets appropriate designated standards or has been tested and found suitable for use in a specified manner. Besides installation rules, you will also have to be concerned with the type and quality of materials that are used in electrical wiring systems. Nationally recognized testing laboratories (Underwriters' Laboratories, Inc. is one) are product safety certification laboratories.

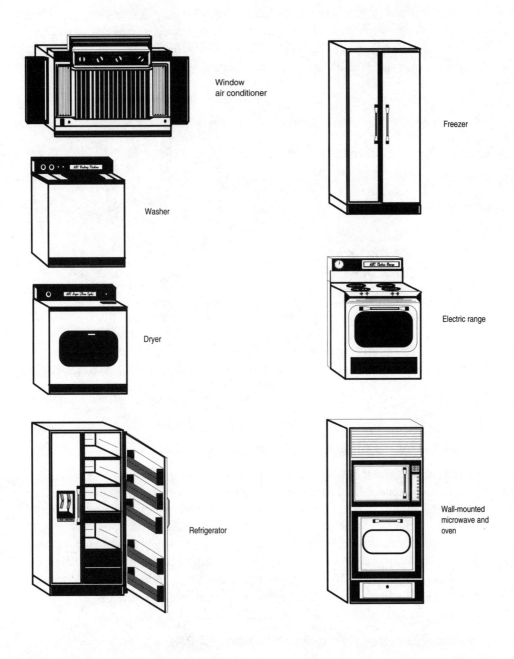

Window
air conditioner

Freezer

Washer

Electric range

Dryer

Refrigerator

Wall-mounted
microwave and
oven

Figure 3-10: Typical appliances.

They establish and operate product safety certification programs to make sure that items produced under the service are safeguarded against reasonable foreseeable risks. Some of these organizations maintain a worldwide network of field representatives who make unannounced visits to manufacturing facilities to countercheck products bearing their "seal of approval." See Figure 3-11.

However, proper selection, overall functional performance and reliability of a product are factors that are not within the basic scope of UL activities.

To fully understand the NEC, it is important to understand the organizations that govern it.

Figure 3-11: UL label.

Nationally Recognized Testing Laboratory (NRTL)

Nationally Recognized Testing Laboratories are product safety certification laboratories. They establish and operate product safety certification programs to make sure that items produced under the service are safeguarded against reasonable foreseeable risks. NRTL maintains a worldwide network of field representatives who make unannounced visits to factories to countercheck products bearing the safety mark.

National Electrical Manufacturers Association (NEMA)

The National Electrical Manufacturers Association was founded in 1926. It is made up of companies that manufacture equipment used for generation, transmission, distribution, control, and utilization of electric power. The objectives of NEMA are to maintain and improve the quality and reliability of products; to ensure safety standards in the manufacture and use of products; to develop product standards covering such matters as naming, ratings, performance, testing, and dimensions. NEMA participates in developing the NEC and the National Electrical Safety Code and advocates their acceptance by state and local authorities.

National Fire Protection Association (NFPA)

The NFPA was founded in 1896. Its membership is drawn from the fire service, business and industry, health care, educational and other institutions, and individuals in the fields of insurance, government, architecture, and engineering. The duties of the NFPA include:

- Developing, publishing, and distributing standards prepared by approximately 175 technical committees. These standards are intended to minimize the possibility and effects of fire and explosion.

- Conducting fire safety education programs for the general public.

- Providing information on fire protection, prevention, and suppression.

- Compiling annual statistics on causes and occupancies of fires, large-loss fires (over 1 million dollars), fire deaths, and firefighter casualties.

- Providing field service by specialists on electricity, flammable liquids and gases, and marine fire problems.

- Conducting research projects that apply statistical methods and operations research to develop computer modes and data management systems.

The Role of Testing Laboratories

Testing laboratories are an integral part of the development of the code. The NFPA, NEMA, and NRTL all provide testing laboratories to conduct research into electrical equipment and its safety. These laboratories perform extensive testing of new products to make sure they are built to code standards for electrical and fire safety. These organizations receive statistics and reports from agencies all over the United States concerning electrical shocks and fires and their causes. Upon seeing trends developing concerning association of certain equipment and dangerous situations or circumstances, this equipment will be specifically targeted for research.

CODES AND ORDINANCES AFFECTING SECURITY SYSTEMS

Electrical systems falling under the heading of "signaling" include such categories as security, fire alarm, and similar systems — employing a wide variety of techniques, often involving special types of equipment and materials designed for specific applications. Many of these systems operate on low-voltage circuits but are installed similarly to conventional electrical circuits for light and power. In all cases, however, when designing or installing systems for use in buildings, the installations must conform to applicable NEC requirements.

Several NEC Sections will apply directly to signaling circuits. Some of these sections follow:

- Alarm systems for health care facilities, NEC Section 517-32(c) and 518-42(c).

- Burglar alarms, NEC Sections 230-82 Exception 5, and 230-94, Exception 4.

- Fire alarms, NEC Sections 230-82, Exception 5, and 230-94, Exception 4.

- Fire protection, NEC Article 760.

- Remote control signaling, NEC Article 725.

While reviewing these NEC sections, remember that all security systems have three functions in common:

- Detection

- Control

- Annunciation (or alarm) signaling

Many systems incorporate switches or relays that operate because of entry, movement, pressure, infrared-beam interruption, and the like. The control senses operation of the detector with a relay and produces an output that may operate a bell, siren, silent alarm — such as a telephone dialer to law enforcement agencies — and similar devices. The controls frequently contain ON-OFF switches, test meters, time delays, power supplies, standby batteries, and terminals for connecting the system together. The control output usually provides power to operate signaling devices or switch contacts for silent alarms.

One of the simplest and most common electric signal systems is the residential door-chime system. Such a system contains a low-voltage power source, one or more pushbuttons, wire, and a set of chimes.

The wiring diagram in Figure 3-12 shows a typical two-note chime controlled at two locations. One button, at the main entrance, will sound the two notes when pushed, while the other button, at the rear door, will sound only one note when pushed.

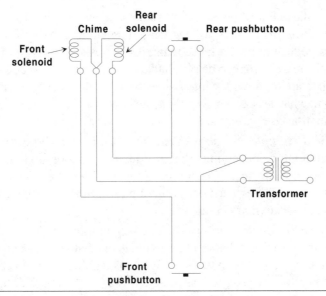

Figure 3-12: Typical two-note chime signaling circuit.

Signal Circuit Components

Wire sizes for the majority of low-voltage systems range from No. 22 to No. 18 AWG. However, where larger-than-normal currents are required or when the distance between the outlets is long, it may be necessary to use wire sizes larger than specified to prevent excessive voltage drop.

At least some parts of almost all security systems require line-voltage (120/240 V) connections. The control panel, for example, is almost always supplied with line voltage. These circuits are installed exactly like conventional electrical circuits for light and power, and all NEC regulations must be followed.

There are also many security components besides the main control panel that require 120-V ac power. A few are listed below.

Direct-Wired, Single-Station Smoke Detectors: These units are 120-volt ac powered with two wires for connection to the electrical system. They usually include a power indicator lamp with a push-to-test button but normally do not have other extra features. They are designed to be used where only one detector is desired or where units are not to be interconnected.

Direct-Wired Multiple Stations: These devices are 120-V ac powered and designed to be interconnected so that when one unit senses a fire and alarms, all units will alarm. Two types of interconnect methods are used. One method utilizes a three-wire (hot, neutral, and interconnect) interconnection at 120 V ac. This system must meet NEC requirements for 120-V ac wiring and all units in this system must be installed on the same 120-V ac circuit. The second method incorporates a transformer in the unit to allow interconnection at a low voltage. This will allow the interconnect wiring to be low-voltage cable (signaling cable). NEC Article 725 specifies this voltage to be not more than 30 volts. Also, this type of interconnect allows the units in the system to be installed on different 120-V ac circuits if desired. Only two wires are required for interconnection. While the 120-V ac interconnect units are somewhat less expensive than the low-voltage interconnect units, the overall installation costs with the low-voltage units will be less.

Direct-Wired Multiple Station with Auxiliary Contacts: These models are 120-volt ac powered interconnect units that also include a set of auxiliary contacts for connection to remote devices. The auxiliary contacts can be used to operate remote horns, lights, or shut off exhaust or ventilating fans. Such units have an additional pair of leads for the auxiliary contacts.

Battery Powered Single Station: Most battery powered units are single station devices powered by a 9-volt battery. UL requires that batteries last at least one year under normal use and that such units produce an audible signal indication of a low battery condition for seven days. Use of batteries other than ones designated by the manufacturer can cause the device to fail to operate, or operate improperly. This is due to the circuitry of the unit being designed to match the performance of specified batteries.

UL Listings: Smoke and fire detectors are usually tested for compliance with UL Standard No. 217. However, periodic changes are made in this standard and manufacturers are required to re submit their units in order to maintain their listing.

Installation: A specific mounting position for smoke and fire detectors is necessary to permit the proper entrance of aerosols to activate the detector. Most units are designed for wall or ceiling mounting and recommended positions are indicated in the instruction manual or sheet supplied with the unit. Mounting in a position not specified may make the unit less sensitive or the response unpredictable.

The locations and quantity of units required in an installation can vary, depending on the authority involved in the installation. However, almost all require one detector outside sleeping areas and many authorities are requiring interconnect units in mulatto-floor dwellings.

It is further recommended, if not required, that ionization type units not be located in the kitchen or in any area where they will be affected by products of combustion.

The following are some of the authorities that regulate the number of placement of smoke and fire detectors:

- Building Officials and Code Administrators (BOCA)

- Uniform Building Code (UBC)

- Federal Housing Administration (FHA – HUD)

● National Fire Protection Association (NFPA)

In addition, many state and local ordinances now also have requirements for smoke and fire detectors.

According to a study by the NFPA, residential fires kill more than half of all the people who die in fires. It has also been established that fatal fires usually occur when the family is asleep. Studies have also shown that 85 percent of all cases of death could have been prevented if smoke and fire detectors had been installed in accordance with recommended standards.

The following illustrations, beginning with Figure 3-13, summarize the NEC requirements for NEC Article 725. Please consult the actual code book for details.

Summary

The National Electrical Code specifies the minimum provisions necessary for protecting people and property from hazards arising from the use of electricity and electrical equipment. Anyone involved in any phase of the electrical industry must

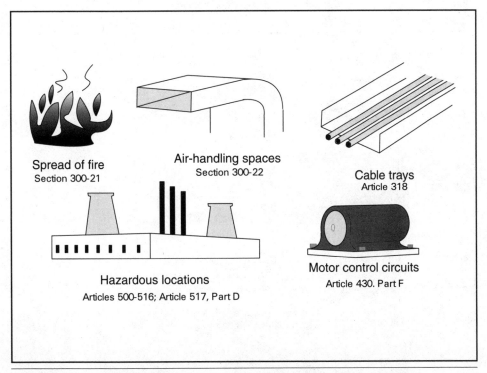

Figure 3-13: Applicable locations and other NEC Articles that should be consulted.

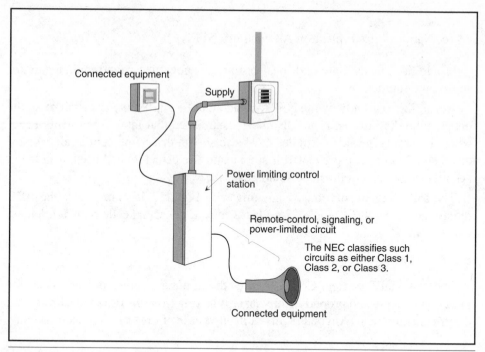

Figure 3-14: Summary of NEC Section 725-3 — Classifications.

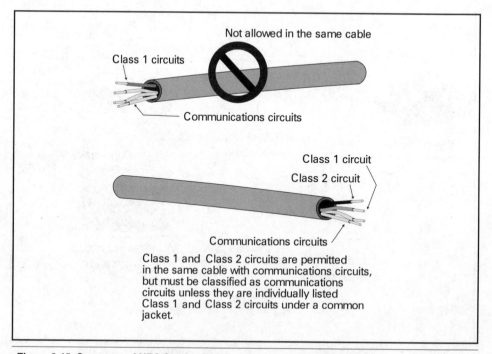

Figure 3-15: Summary of NEC Section 725-5 — Communications Cables.

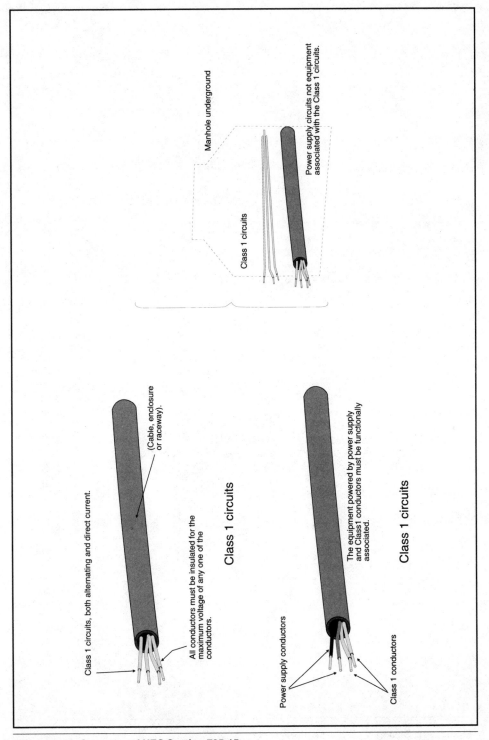

Figure 3-16: Summary of NEC Section 725-15.

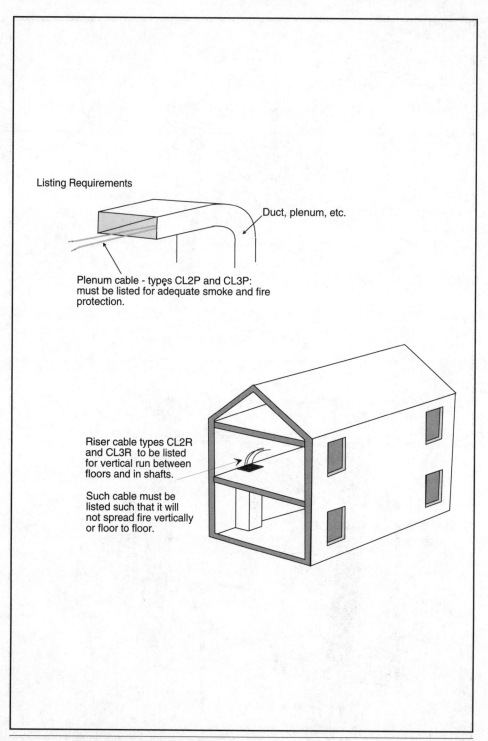

Listing Requirements

Duct, plenum, etc.

Plenum cable - types CL2P and CL3P:
must be listed for adequate smoke and fire
protection.

Riser cable types CL2R
and CL3R to be listed
for vertical run between
floors and in shafts.

Such cable must be
listed such that it will
not spread fire vertically
or floor to floor.

Figure 3-17: Summary of NEC Section 725-51.

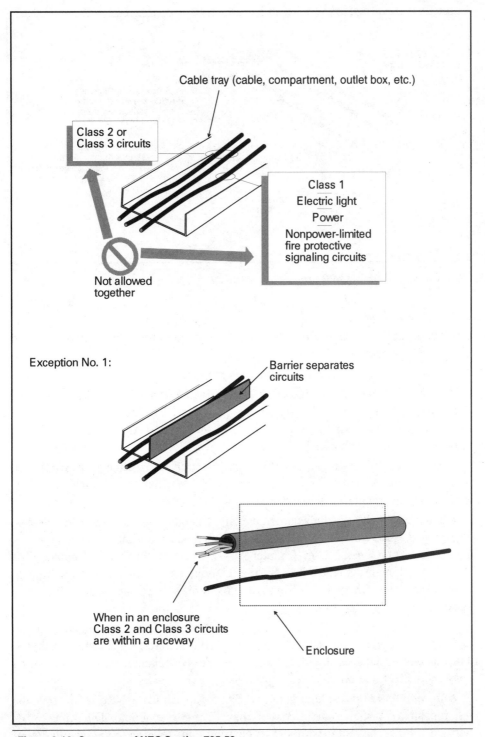

Cable tray (cable, compartment, outlet box, etc.)

Class 2 or
Class 3 circuits

Class 1

Electric light

Power

Nonpower-limited
fire protective
signaling circuits

Not allowed
together

Exception No. 1:

Barrier separates
circuits

When in an enclosure
Class 2 and Class 3 circuits
are within a raceway

Enclosure

Figure 3-18: Summary of NEC Section 725-52.

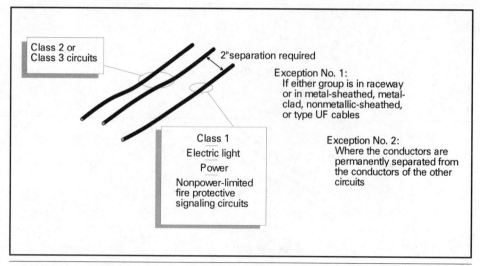

Class 2 or
Class 3 circuits

2"separation required

Exception No. 1:
If either group is in raceway
or in metal-sheathed, metal-
clad, nonmetallic-sheathed,
or type UF cables

Class 1

Electric light

Power

Nonpower-limited
fire protective
signaling circuits

Exception No. 2:
Where the conductors are
permanently separated from
the conductors of the other
circuits

Figure 3-19: Summary of NEC Section 725-52 (*Cont.*).

be aware of how to use and apply the code on the job. Using the NEC will help you to safely install and maintain the electrical security equipment and systems that you come into contact with.

The NEC is composed of the following components:

Appendix: Appendix A includes material extracted from other NFPA documents. Appendix B is not part of the requirements of the NEC and contains additional material for informational purposes only. Appendix A and Appendix B are located at the end of the code book.

Article: Beginning with Article 90 — Introduction, and ending with Article 820 — Community Antenna Television and Radio Distribution Systems, the NEC Articles are the main topics in the code book.

Chapter: The NEC includes nine chapters. Chapter 1 — General, Chapter 2 — Wiring and Protection, Chapter 3 — Wiring Methods and Materials, Chapter 4 — Equipment for General Use, Chapter 5 — Special Occupancies, Chapter 6 — Special Equipment, Chapter 7 — Special Conditions, Chapter 8 — Communications Systems and Chapter 9 — Tables and Examples. The Chapters form the broad structure of the NEC.

Contents: Located among the first pages of the code book, the contents section provides a complete outline of the Chapters, Articles, Parts, Tables, and Examples. The contents section, used with the index, provides excellent direction for locating answers to electrical problems and questions.

Diagrams and Figures: Diagrams and Figures appear in the NEC to illustrate the relationship of Articles and Parts of the NEC. For example, Diagram 230-1, Services, shows the relationship of Articles and Parts relating to the installation of electric services.

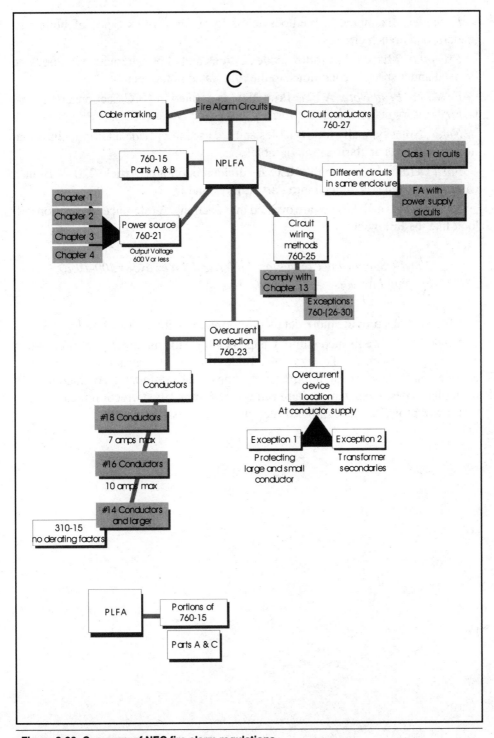

Figure 3-20: Summary of NEC fire-alarm regulations.

Examples: Examples in methods to perform for various types of buildings, feeders, and branch circuits.

Exceptions: Exceptions follow code sections and allow alternative methods, to be used under specific conditions, to the rule stated in the section.

FPN Fine Print Note: A Fine Print Note is defined in NEC Section 110-1; that is, explanatory material is in the form of Fine Print Notes (FPN).

Notes: Notes typically follow tables and are used to provide additional information to the tables or clarification of tables.

Part: Certain Articles in the NEC are divided into Parts. Article 220 — Branch Circuit and Feeder is divided into Part A, B, C, and D.

Section: Parts and Articles are divided into Sections. A reference to a section will look like the following:

> *300-19, Supporting Conductors in Vertical Raceways or 300-19(a) Spacing Intervals — Maximum.*

NEC Sections provide more detailed information within NEC Articles.

Table: Tables are located within Chapters to provide more detailed information explaining code content. For example, Table 310-16 lists ampacities for insulated conductors for copper, aluminum, and copper-clad aluminum conductors with insulation types, sizes, temperature ratings, and ampacity correction factors. Such tables will prove invaluable for all security-system installations.

Chapter 4
Basic Installation Techniques

Before the installation of a security system is started, a sketch of the building or area should be prepared or the original working drawings (prints) should be obtained. This sketch should be drawn to scale and should show the location of all windows and doors, chases, closets, etc. A simple riser diagram showing the various components such as smoke and heat sensors, control panels, and alarm signaling devices should also appear on the sketch. When this is completed, the security technician can begin the installation of the security system.

INSTALLATION BASICS

The installation of a protective security/fire-alarm circuit should always start at the circuit's energy source, as if it were an end-of-the-line battery — a battery remote from the control panel — even though it may actually be a power supply installed in the control panel. A pair of wires are run from this power source to the first contact location, but just the positive wire is cut and connected to the two contact terminals as shown in Figure 4-1. The neutral or common wire is not cut, but continues on in parallel with the positive wire. The pair is then run on to the next contact — be it door, window, or sensor — and again only the hot or positive wire

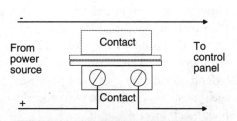

Figure 4-1: Contacts are connected only to the positive wire. The neutral or common remains unbroken.

113

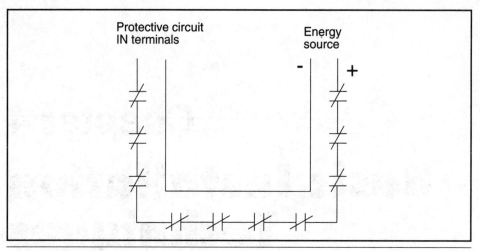

Figure 4-2: Both the negative and positive conductors are run to all contacts even though the system should operate with just a single-wire, positive-leg wire run from contact to contact.

is connected to the contacts. This procedure is repeated until all contacts are wired in series, and then the pair of wires is run from the last contact device on the system to the protective-circuit terminals in the main control panel. Although the markings will vary from manufacturer to manufacturer, the terminals for the starting connections will read something like LOOP POWER OUT, while the terminating terminals will read IN or a similar term.

A simple circuit of the wiring connections just described is shown in Figure 4-2. Obviously, the system would operate with just a single-wire, positive-leg circuit run from contact to contact, with the negative or common power-supply terminal connected directly to the negative protective-circuit terminal within the control panel or cabinet. However, manufacturers of security equipment discourage this practice, since troubleshooting a single-wire circuit can be extremely time-consuming and the single wire is more vulnerable to defeat by an intruder with no trouble symptoms occurring to warn the user of the loss of protection.

An exit/entry delay relay is sometimes used on security systems so that authorized personnel may exit and enter (using their door keys) without activating the alarm. However, a shunt switch is more often preferred (see Figure 4-3). The purpose of the shunt lock is to enable an authorized person with a key to shunt out the contacts on the door used for entry/exit, allowing him or her to enter or leave the premises without causing an alarm when the alarm system is turned on. The shunt lock does extend outside the protected premises, however, and it is a potential weak link in the system. Following the two procedures suggested below makes defeat of the shunt lock much more difficult.

- Install the shunt lock at the door that is most brightly illuminated and most readily visible to passersby.

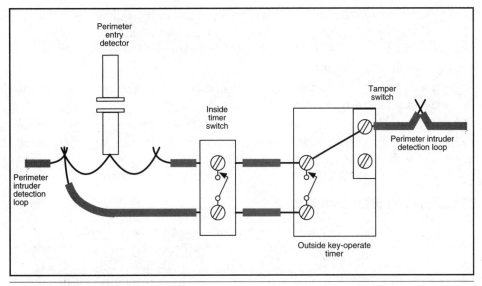

Figure 4-3: Typical shunt switch circuit.

● Wire the shunt lock switch to the magnetic contact terminals as shown in Figure 4-4. This arrangement traps the lock, so that any attempt to pull it out to gain access to its terminals will break the positive side of the protective circuit and cause an alarm to sound.

Contacts used to signal the opening of door, windows, gates, drawers, etc., are usually mounted on the frame of the door or window, while the magnet unit is mounted on the door or window (moving part) itself. The two units should be positioned so that the magnet is close to and parallel with the switch when the door or window is closed. This keeps the shunt lock actuated, but opening the door or window moves the magnet away and releases the switch mechanism.

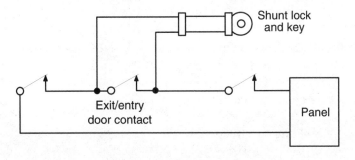

Figure 4-4: Wire the shunt lock switch to the magnetic contacts as shown.

As long as the faces of the switch and magnet are parallel and in close proximity when the door or window is closed, they may be oriented side-to-side, top-to-top, or top-to-side. Mounting spacers may be used under the units if necessary to improve their alignment and proximity.

Terminal covers are available for most makes of door contacts to protect the terminal connections against tapering.

The wiring of any alarm system is installed like any other type of low-voltage signal system; that is, one must locate the outlets, furnish a power supply, and finally interconnect the components with the proper size and wire type.

Quality of Workmanship

Since most security/fire-alarm systems are operated on low-voltage circuits, many installers might not pay as strict attention to the quality of the workmanship and materials as they would when installing conventional electrical wiring for lighting and power. Security/fire-alarm systems are worthy of the best materials and the best workmanship and strict attention to quality work should always be given.

Care must be taken to ensure that all visible components are installed adjacent to and parallel to building lines to give a neat appearance. All wiring should be concealed where possible, and the wiring that must be exposed should have square corners and should be installed so that it is as inconspicuous as possible.

Only new material of the highest quality should be used and this material should be approved by UL or a similar testing agency. Remember that the protection of the owner's building and its contents are dependent — to a great extent — on the quality of the security system installed.

WIRING METHODS

Several types of wiring methods are used for security-system installations. The methods used on a given project are determined by several factors:

- The installation requirements set forth in the NEC and/or by the manufacturer of the security equipment

- Local codes and ordinances

- Type of building construction

- Location of the wiring in the building

- Importance of the wiring system's appearance

- Costs and budget

In general, two types of basic wiring methods are used in the majority of electrical systems:

- Open wiring

- Concealed wiring

In open-wiring systems, the outlets, security devices and cable or raceway systems are installed on the surfaces of the walls, ceilings, columns, and the like where they are in view and readily accessible. Such wiring is often used in areas where appearance is not important and where it may be desirable to make changes in the security system at a later date. You will frequently find open-wiring systems in mechanical rooms and in interior parking areas of commercial buildings and in almost every manufacturing area of industrial establishments.

Concealed wiring systems have all cable and raceway runs concealed inside of walls, partitions, ceilings, columns, and behind baseboards or molding where they are out of view and not readily accessible. This type of wiring system is generally used in all new construction with finished interior walls, ceilings, floors and is the preferred type where good appearance is important.

While most security/fire-alarm systems use low-voltage wiring for perimeter wiring to the various protective devices, the main control panel is nearly always powered with line-voltage; that is, 120 – 240 V. Many fire detection devices also utilize line-voltage circuits in order to cut down on the voltage drop over long circuit runs. Therefore, wiring methods suitable for these voltages are required and all such installations must comply with the latest edition of the NEC, along with all local ordinances.

The following wiring methods will cover the majority of all systems that will be encountered by the security technician.

RACEWAY SYSTEMS

A raceway is any channel used for holding wires, cables, or busbars, which is designed and used solely for this purpose. Types of raceways include rigid metal conduit, intermediate metal conduit (IMC), rigid nonmetallic conduit, flexible metal conduit, liquid-tight flexible metal conduit, electrical metallic tubing (EMT), underfloor raceways, cellular metal floor raceways, cellular concrete floor raceways, surface metal raceways, wireways, and auxiliary gutters. Raceways are constructed of either metal or insulating material.

Raceways provide mechanical protection for the conductors that run in them and also prevent accidental damage to insulation and the conducting metal. They also protect conductors from the harmful chemical attack of corrosive atmospheres and prevent fire hazards to life and property by confining arcs and flame due to faults in the wiring system.

One of the most important functions of metal raceways is to provide a path for the flow of fault current to ground, thereby preventing voltage build-up on conductor and equipment enclosures. This feature, of course, helps to minimize shock hazards to personnel and damage to electrical equipment. To maintain this feature, it is extremely important that all metal raceway systems be securely bonded together into a continuous conductive path and properly connected to the system ground, which in turn is connected to a grounding electrode such as a water pipe or a ground rod.

Rigid Metal Conduit

Rigid steel conduit is used for both exposed and concealed work. Where corrosion is likely to occur, corrosion-resistant rigid metal conduit and fittings must be used. Corrosion-resistant materials include aluminum, silicon bronze alloy, and plastic-coated steel. All conduit installed in wet locations should be mounted with at least ¼ in of air space between the conduit and the wall or other mounting surface.

Rigid metal conduit is available in 10-ft lengths (when the coupling is included in the measurement) with a threaded coupling on one end. The actual length of the conduit section alone is approximately 9 ft 10 in.

Most technicians prefer to use a hacksaw with a blade having 18 – 32 teeth per inch for cutting conduit. See Figure 4-5. For cutting larger sizes of conduit ($1\frac{1}{2}$ in and above), a special conduit cutter should be used to save time. While quicker to use, the conduit cutter almost always leaves an undesirable hump inside the conduit. If a power band saw is available on the job, it is preferred for cutting the larger sizes of conduit. Abrasive cutters are also popular for the larger sizes of conduit.

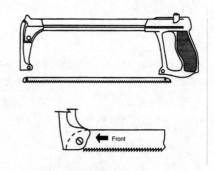

Figure 4-5: Most technicians prefer to use a hacksaw with a blade having 18 teeth per inch for cutting rigid steel conduit and 32 teeth per inch for cutting thinner-walled conduit.

Conduit cuts should be made square and the inside edge of the cut must be reamed to remove any burr or sharp edge that might damage wire insulation when the conductors are pulled inside the conduit. After reaming, most experienced electricians feel the inside of the cut with their finger to be sure that no burrs or sharp edges are present.

Lengths of conduit to be cut should be accurately measured for the size needed and an additional $\frac{3}{8}$ in should be allowed on the smaller sizes of conduit for terminations; the larger sizes of conduit will require approximately $\frac{1}{2}$ in for locknuts, bushings, and the like at terminations.

A good lubricant (cutting oil) is then used liberally during the thread-cutting process. If sufficient lubricant is used, cuts may be made cleaner and sharper, and the cutting dies will last much longer.

Full threads must be cut to allow the conduit ends to come close together in the coupling or to firmly seat in the shoulders of threaded hubs of conduit bodies. To obtain a full thread, run the die up on the conduit until the conduit barely comes through the die. This will give a good thread length adequate for all purposes. Anything longer will not fit into the coupling and will later corrode because threading removes the zinc or other protective coating from the conduit.

Clean, sharply cut threads also make a better continuous ground and save much trouble once the system is in operation.

Plastic-Coated Rigid Steel Conduit

Plastic-coated rigid conduit has a thin coating of polyvinyl chloride (PVC) over the metal conduit. This conduit is used when an environment calls for the ruggedness of rigid steel conduit and the corrosion resistance of PVC. The following establishments frequently use plastic-coated rigid steel conduit in their electrical wiring installations:

- Chemical plants

- Refineries

- Fertilizer plants

- Paper mills

- Waste-water treatment plants

This type of wiring method should be used even for low-voltage security-system wiring when the systems are installed in the establishments mentioned above.

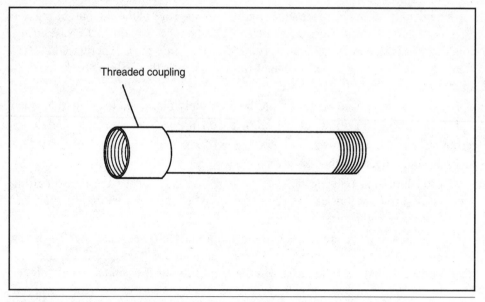

Figure 4-6: Aluminum conduit and threaded coupling.

Aluminum Conduit

Aluminum conduit (Figure 4-6) is typically used when chemical resistance to wet environments and some chemical environments is necessary. Aluminum conduit generally requires less maintenance in installations such as sewage plants and installations around salt water because of its special characteristics.

Aluminum conduit, being made of a nonmagnetic metal, can reduce voltage drop in conductors. Where ac current is involved, voltage drop in conductors placed in aluminum conduit may be as much as 20 percent less than that of conductors in steel conduit.

Aluminum conduit is much lighter than steel conduit. A ten-foot section of 3 in aluminum conduit weighs about 23 lb, compared to the 68-lb weight of its steel counterpart. This difference in weight provides some installation advantages. Prices of steel and aluminum vary regularly. However, in general, the price of aluminum conduit is about a third more than that of rigid steel conduit. Because aluminum conduit can be installed easily, the labor costs on some conduit installations will be lowered. Therefore, using aluminum conduit may actually cost less than using steel conduit.

NOTE

An anti-seize compound should be used on aluminum threaded fittings.

Intermediate Metal Conduit

Intermediate metal conduit (IMC) was developed to reduce the cost but retain the high strength of a rigid steel conduit system. IMC has a slightly larger internal diameter than galvanized rigid conduit (GRC). That is, the wall thickness of IMC is less than that of GRC. And size for size, IMC weighs approximately two-thirds less than GRC. The external diameter of a given size of IMC is the same as that of the same size GRC. Therefore, GRC fittings may be used with IMC. Because the threads on IMC and GRC are the same, no special threading tools are needed. Although the internal diameter of a given size of IMC is larger than that of the same size GRC, the conductor fill for both IMC and GRC is the same.

Pulling wire in IMC is often easier than pulling the same size and quantity of wire in GRC. That's because of the IMC's slightly larger internal diameter. Some contractors feel that threading IMC is more difficult than threading GRC because IMC is less ductile than GRC. Bending IMC is easier than bending GRC because of the reduced wall thickness. However, bending is sometimes complicated by "kinking" which may be caused by the increased hardness of IMC. Bending IMC is more difficult than bending EMT.

Rigid Nonmetallic Conduit

Rigid nonmetallic conduit is manufactured from a polyvinyl chloride base material (PVC). For this reason, rigid nonmetallic conduit is often referred to as "PVC." Because PVC conduit is noncorrosive, chemically inert, and non-aging, it is an excellent choice for installation in wet or corrosive environments. The corrosion problems which can occur with steel and aluminum rigid metal conduits do not occur with PVC.

PVC conduit is lighter than steel or aluminum rigid steel, IMC, and EMT. PVC is much easier to handle because it's lighter. And since the PVC joints are made with glue and require no threading, PVC conduit can usually be installed much faster than other types of conduit.

PVC conduit contains no ferrous or other metal. Because of this characteristic, the voltage drop of conductors carrying ac current in PVC will be less than that of identical conductors in metal conduit. Also, because of the absence of iron, no magnetic flux can be imposed into PVC by an ac current.

Electrical Metallic Tubing

Electrical metallic tubing (EMT) may be used for both exposed and concealed work except where it will be subjected to severe damage during use, in cinder concrete, or in fill where subjected to permanent moisture unless some means to protect it is provided; the tubing may be installed a minimum of 18 inches under the fill.

Threadless couplings and connectors are used for EMT installation and these should be installed so that the tubing will be made up tight. Where buried in masonry or installed in wet locations, couplings and connectors, as well as supports, bolts, straps, and screws, should be of a type approved for the conditions.

Bends in the tubing should be made with a tubing bender so that no injury will occur and so the internal diameter of the tubing will not be effectively reduced. The bends between outlets or termination points should contain no more than the equivalent of four quarter-bends (360° total), including those bends located immediately at the outlet or fitting (offsets).

All cuts in EMT are made with either a hacksaw, power hacksaw, tubing cutter, or other approved device. Once cut, the tubing ends should be reamed with a screwdriver handle or pipe reamer to remove all burrs and sharp edges that might damage conductor insulation.

EMT Couplings

EMT is joined by couplings. Two types are in common use:

- Set-screw couplings

- Compression couplings

Both types are shown in Figure 4-7 and a brief description of each follows.

As its name implies, the set-screw coupling relies on set screws to hold the EMT to the coupling. This type of coupling does not provide a seal and is not permitted to be used in wet locations. However, this type of coupling can be embedded in concrete.

Compression couplings provide a tight seal around the conduit, and may be used in some wet locations as stated in the NEC.

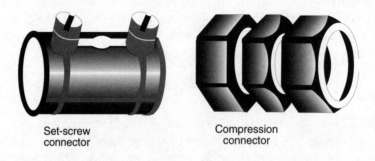

Set-screw
connector

Compression
connector

Figure 4-7: Two types of EMT couplings in common use.

Flexible Metal Conduit

Flexible metal conduit generally is manufactured in two types, a standard metal-clad type and a liquidtight type. The former type cannot be used in wet locations unless the conductors pulled in are of a type specially approved for such conditions. Neither type may be used where they will be subjected to physical damage or where any combination of ambient and/or conductor temperature will produce an operating temperature in excess of that for which the material is approved. Other uses are fully described in Articles 350 and 351 of the NEC.

When this type of conduit is installed, it should be secured by an approved means at intervals not exceeding $4\frac{1}{2}$ ft and within 12 in of every outlet box, fitting, or other termination points. In some cases, however, exceptions exist. For example, when flexible metal conduit must be finished in walls, ceilings, and the like, securing the conduit at these intervals would not be practical. Also, where more flexibility is required, lengths of not more than 3 ft may be utilized at termination points.

Flexible metal conduit may be used as a grounding means where both the conduit and the fittings are approved for the purpose. In lengths of more than 6 feet, it is best to install an extra grounding conductor within the conduit for added insurance.

Surface Metal Molding

When it is impractical to install the wiring in concealed areas, surface metal molding (Figures 4-8 through 4-11) is a good compromise, even though it is visible, the proper painting of it to match the color of the ceiling and walls makes it very inconspicuous. Surface metal molding is made from sheet metal strips drawn into shape and comes in various shapes and sizes with factory fittings to meet nearly every application found in finished areas of commercial buildings. A complete list of fittings can be obtained at your local electrical equipment supplier.

The running of straight lines of surface molding is simple. A length of molding with the coupling is slipped in the end, out enough so that the screw hole is exposed, and then the coupling is screwed to the surface to which the molding is to be attached. Then another length of molding is slipped on the coupling.

Factory fittings are used for corners and turns or the molding may be bent (to a certain extent) with a special bender. Matching outlet boxes for surface mounting are also available, and bushings are necessary at such boxes to prevent the sharp edges of the molding from injuring the insulation on the wire.

Clips are used to fasten the molding in place. The clip is secured by a screw and then the molding is slipped into the clip, wherever extra support of the molding is needed, and fastened by screws. When parallel runs of molding are installed, they may be secured in place by means of a multiple strap. The joints in runs of molding are covered by slipping a connection cover over the joints. Such runs of molding should be grounded the same as any other metal raceway, and this is done by use of

BRING FEED INTO 2000B BASE.
Back-feed connection shown.

INSTALL 2000B BASE ON SURFACE.
Starting with feed section, mount entire run off 2000B base with No. 8 flat head screw through screw piercings and knockouts. Cut base to length at corners and end of run, as required.

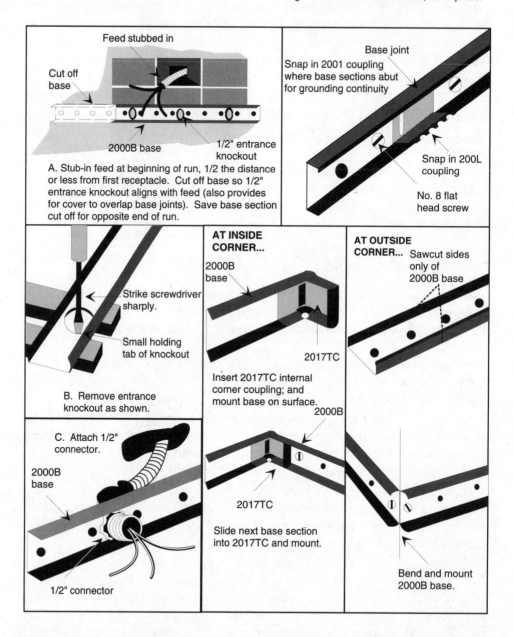

Feed stubbed in

Cut off base

2000B base

1/2" entrance knockout

A. Stub-in feed at beginning of run, 1/2 the distance or less from first receptacle. Cut off base so 1/2" entrance knockout aligns with feed (also provides for cover to overlap base joints). Save base section cut off for opposite end of run.

Base joint
Snap in 2001 coupling where base sections abut for grounding continuity

Snap in 200L coupling

No. 8 flat head screw

Strike screwdriver sharply.

Small holding tab of knockout

B. Remove entrance knockout as shown.

AT INSIDE CORNER...

2000B base

2017TC

Insert 2017TC internal corner coupling; and mount base on surface.

2000B

2017TC

Slide next base section into 2017TC and mount.

AT OUTSIDE CORNER... Sawcut sides only of 2000B base

Bend and mount 2000B base.

C. Attach 1/2" connector.

2000B base

1/2" connector

Figure 4-8: Installation methods of Wiremold 2000 Snapicoil.

CONNECT SNAPICOIL
TO FEED.

Lay out Snapicoil along entire run of base so that receptacles are not located over feed or in corners. Connect to feed wires with W30 pressure type wire connectors (for common connection of 2, 3, or 4 No. 12 or No. 14 solid conductors); NOT TO BE USED to connect equipment grounding conductors. Insert only conductors of same color in a connector.

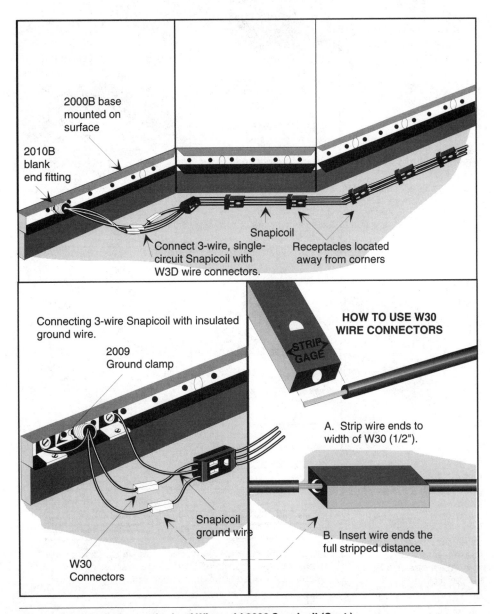

2000B base mounted on surface

2010B blank end fitting

Snapicoil

Connect 3-wire, single-circuit Snapicoil with W3D wire connectors.

Receptacles located away from corners

Connecting 3-wire Snapicoil with insulated ground wire.

2009 Ground clamp

Snapicoil ground wire

W30 Connectors

HOW TO USE W30 WIRE CONNECTORS

STRIP GAGE

A. Strip wire ends to width of W30 (1/2").

B. Insert wire ends the full stripped distance.

Figure 4-9: Installation methods of Wiremold 2000 Snapicoil (Cont.).

ASSEMBLE SNAPICOIL AND 2000C COVER IN 2000B BASE.

Cover sections should overlap base joints for rigidity and better ground continuity.

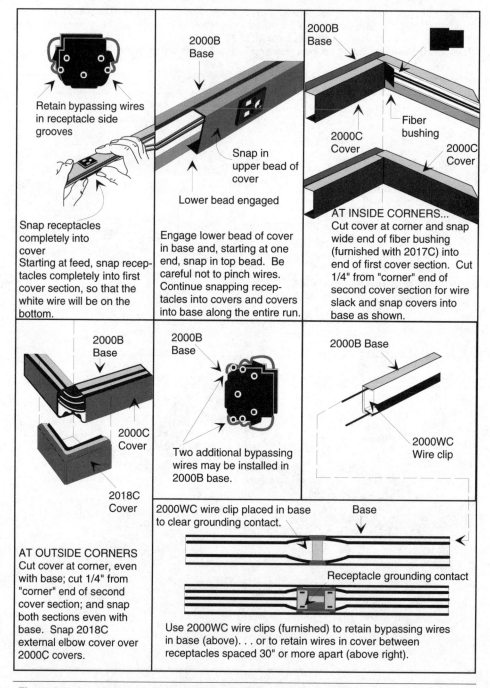

Retain bypassing wires in receptacle side grooves

Snap receptacles completely into cover
Starting at feed, snap receptacles completely into first cover section, so that the white wire will be on the bottom.

2000B Base

Snap in upper bead of cover

Lower bead engaged

Engage lower bead of cover in base and, starting at one end, snap in top bead. Be careful not to pinch wires. Continue snapping receptacles into covers and covers into base along the entire run.

2000B Base

Fiber bushing

2000C Cover

2000C Cover

AT INSIDE CORNERS...
Cut cover at corner and snap wide end of fiber bushing (furnished with 2017C) into end of first cover section. Cut 1/4" from "corner" end of second cover section for wire slack and snap covers into base as shown.

2000B Base

2000C Cover

2018C Cover

AT OUTSIDE CORNERS
Cut cover at corner, even with base; cut 1/4" from "corner" end of second cover section; and snap both sections even with base. Snap 2018C external elbow cover over 2000C covers.

2000B Base

Two additional bypassing wires may be installed in 2000B base.

2000B Base

2000WC Wire clip

2000WC wire clip placed in base to clear grounding contact.

Base

Receptacle grounding contact

Use 2000WC wire clips (furnished) to retain bypassing wires in base (above). . . or to retain wires in cover between receptacles spaced 30" or more apart (above right).

Figure 4-10: Installation methods of Wiremold 2000 Snapicoil (Cont.).

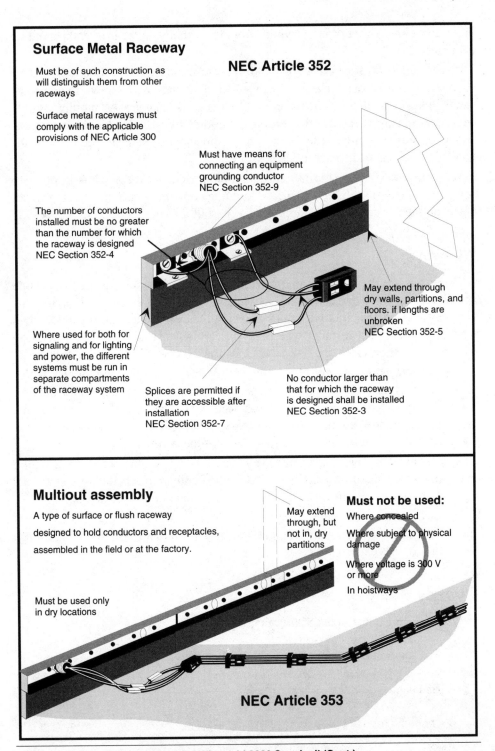

Surface Metal Raceway

NEC Article 352

Must be of such construction as will distinguish them from other raceways

Surface metal raceways must comply with the applicable provisions of NEC Article 300

Must have means for connecting an equipment grounding conductor
NEC Section 352-9

The number of conductors installed must be no greater than the number for which the raceway is designed
NEC Section 352-4

May extend through dry walls, partitions, and floors. if lengths are unbroken
NEC Section 352-5

Where used for both for signaling and for lighting and power, the different systems must be run in separate compartments of the raceway system

Splices are permitted if they are accessible after installation
NEC Section 352-7

No conductor larger than that for which the raceway is designed shall be installed
NEC Section 352-3

Multiout assembly

A type of surface or flush raceway

designed to hold conductors and receptacles,

assembled in the field or at the factory.

May extend through, but not in, dry partitions

Must not be used:

Where concealed

Where subject to physical damage

Where voltage is 300 V or more

In hoistways

Must be used only in dry locations

NEC Article 353

Figure 4-11: Installation methods of Wiremold 2000 Snapicoil (Cont.).

127

grounding clips. The current-carrying wires are normally pulled in after the molding is in place.

The installation of surface metal molding requires no special tools unless bending the molding is necessary. The molding is fastened in place with screws, toggle bolts, and the like, depending on the materials to which it is fastened. All molding should be run straight and parallel with the room or building lines, that is, baseboards, trims, and other room moldings. The decor of the room should be considered first and the molding made as inconspicuous as possible.

It is often desirable to install surface molding not used for wires in order to complete a pattern set by other surface molding containing current-carrying wires, or to continue a run to make it appear to be part of the room's decoration.

Wireways

Wireways are sheet-metal troughs with hinged or removable covers for housing and protecting wires and cables and in which conductors are held in place after the wireway has been installed as a complete system. They may be used only for exposed work and shouldn't be installed where they will be subject to severe physical damage or corrosive vapor nor in any hazardous location except NEC Class II, Division 2 .

The wireway structure must be designed to safely handle the sizes of conductors used in the system. Furthermore, the system should not contain more than 30 current-carrying conductors at any cross section. The sum of the cross-sectional areas of all contained conductors at any cross section of a wireway shall not exceed 20 percent of the interior cross-sectioned area of the wireway.

Splices and taps, made and insulated by approved methods, may be located within the wireway provided they are accessible. The conductors, including splices and taps, shall not fill the wireway to more than 75 percent of its area at that point.

Wireways must be securely supported at intervals not exceeding 5 ft, unless specially approved for supports at greater intervals, but in no case shall the distance between supports exceed 10 ft.

Wireway Fitting

Wireways are constructed of four major parts:

- The main housing or trough

- End cap

- U connector

- Trough cover

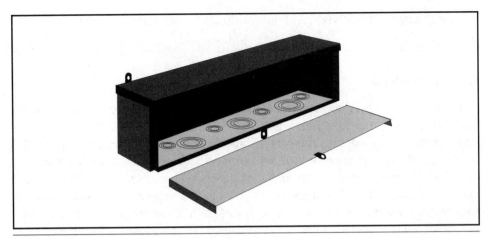

Figure 4-12: Raintight wireway.

There are also many different shapes of connectors to suit practically any application such as the trough cross, 90 degrees internal elbow, and T connector.

The wireway fittings are attached to the wireway duct with slip-on connectors. All attachments are made with nuts and bolts or screws. Usually, it is best to assemble sections of the wireway system on the floor and then raise the sections into position by hand. Both the fittings and the duct come with screw or hinged covers to permit conductors to be laid in or pulled through.

As you can see in Figure 4-12, this type of raceway is also manufactured in a raintight enclosure for outdoor use.

BUSWAYS

There are several types of busways or duct systems for electrical transmission and feeder purposes. Lighting duct, trolley duct, and distribution bus duct are just a few. All are designed for a specific purpose, and the security technician should become familiar with all types before an installation is laid out.

Lighting duct, for example, permits the installation of an unlimited amount of footage from a single working platform. As each section and the lighting fixtures are secured in place, the complete assembly is then simply transported to the area of installation and installed in one piece.

Trolley duct is widely used for industrial applications, and where the installation requires a continuous polarization to prevent accidental reversal, a polarizing bar is used. This system provides polarization for all trolley, permitting standard and detachable trolleys to be used on the same run.

Plug-in bus duct is also widely used for industrial applications, and the system consists of interconnected prefabricated sections of bus duct so formed that the complete assembly will be rigid in construction and neat and symmetrical in appearance.

CABLE TRAYS

Cable trays are used to support electrical conductors used mainly in industrial applications, but are sometimes used for communication and data processing conductors in large commercial establishments. The trays themselves are usually made up into a system of assembled, interconnected sections and associated fittings, all of which are made of metal or other noncombustible material. The finished system forms into a rigid structural run to contain and support single, multiconductor, or other wiring cables. Several styles of cable trays are available, including ladder, trough, channel, solid-bottom trays, and similar structures. See Figure 4-13.

A box or fitting must be installed at:

- Each conductor splice point

- Each outlet, switch point, or junction point

- Each pull point for the connection of conduit and other raceways

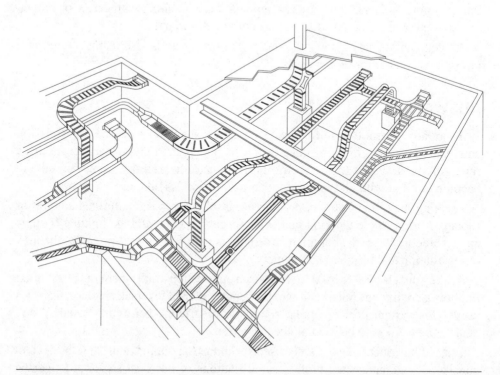

Figure 4-13: Typical cable tray system.

Furthermore, boxes or other fittings are required when a change is made from conduit to open wiring. Electrical workers also install pull boxes in raceway systems to facilitate the pulling of conductors.

In each case — raceways, outlet boxes, pull and junction boxes — the NEC specifies specific maximum fill requirements; that is, the area of conductors in relation to the box, fitting, or raceway system.

Cable Systems

Several types of cable systems are used to feed security equipment and also to provide perimeter protection circuits. We have already discussed some types of low-voltage cable in other chapters so a description of this type of cable will not be repeated here.

Instrumentation Control Wiring: This type of cable links the field-sensing, controlling, printout, and operating devices that form an electronic instrumentation control system for sophisticated security systems in large commercial buildings. The style and size of the control wiring must be matched to a specific job.

Control wiring usually has two or more insulated conductors as shown in Figure 4-14. An outer layer called the jacket protects the pairs of conductors inside. The number of pairs in a multiconductor cable depends on the size of the wire used. A multipair cable may consist of as many as 60 or more pairs of conductors.

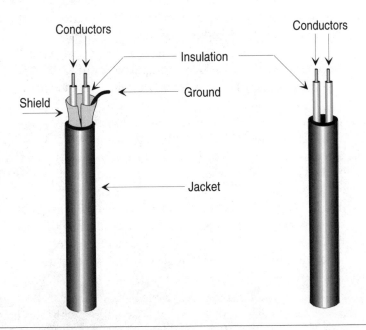

Figure 4-14: Two-conductor instrumentation control cable.

Shields are provided on control wiring to protect the electrical signals traveling through the conductors from electrical interference or noise. Shields are usually constructed of aluminum foil bonded to a plastic film. If the wiring is not properly shielded, electrical disturbances may cause erratic or erroneous control signals, false alarms, and improper operation of security devices.

A ground wire is a bare copper wire used to provide continuous contact with a specified grounding terminal. A ground wire allows connections of all the instruments within a loop to a common grounding system. In some electronic systems the grounding wire is called a drain wire.

In most cases, instruments connected to the system are not grounded at both ends of the circuit. This is to prevent unwanted ground loops in the system. If the ground is not to be connected at the end of the wire, do not remove the ground wire. Rather, fold it back and tape it to the cable. This is called floating the ground. This is done in case the ground at the opposite end of the conductors develops a problem.

Jackets: A synthetic plastic jacket covers and protects the components within the cable. Polyethylene and PVC jackets are the most commonly used. Some cable jackets have a nylon rip cord that allows the jacket to be peeled back without the use of a knife or cable cutter. This eliminates the possible nicking of the conductor insulation when preparing for terminations of the conductors.

Nonmetallic-Sheathed Cable (Type NM): This cable is manufactured in two- or three-wire assemblies, and with varying sizes of conductors. In both two- and three-wire cables, conductors are color-coded: one conductor is black while the other is white in two-wire cable; in three-wire cable, the additional conductor is red. Both types will also have a grounding conductor which is usually bare, but is sometimes covered with a green plastic insulation — depending upon the manufacturer. The jacket or covering consists of rubber, plastic, or fiber. Most will also have markings on this jacket giving the manufacturer's name or trademark, the wire size, and the number of conductors. For example, "NM 12-2 W/GRD" indicates that the jacket contains two No. 12 AWG conductors along with a grounding wire; "NM 12-3 W/GRD" indicates three conductors plus a grounding wire. This type of cable may be concealed in the framework of buildings, or in some instances, may be run exposed on the building surfaces. It may not be used in any building exceeding three floors above grade; as a service-entrance cable; in commercial garages having hazardous locations; in theaters and similar locations; places of assembly; in motion picture studios; in storage battery rooms; in hoistways; embedded in poured concrete, or aggregate; or in any hazardous location except as otherwise permitted by the NEC. Nonmetallic sheathed cable is frequently referred to as Romex on the job. See Figure 4-15.

Type AC (Armored) Cable: Type AC cable — commonly called "BX" — is manufactured in two-, three-, and four-wire assemblies, with varying sizes of conductors, and is used in locations similar to those where Type NM cable is allowed. The metallic spiral covering on BX cable offers a greater degree of

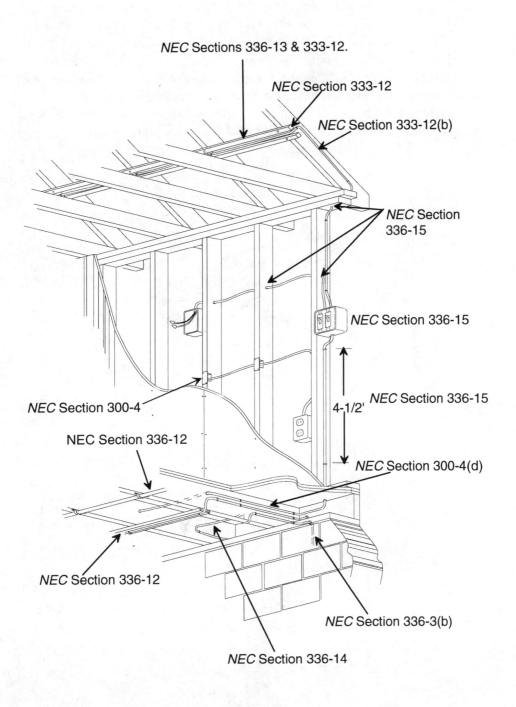

NEC Sections 336-13 & 333-12.

NEC Section 333-12

NEC Section 333-12(b)

NEC Section 336-15

NEC Section 336-15

NEC Section 300-4

NEC Section 336-15

4-1/2'

NEC Section 336-12

NEC Section 300-4(d)

NEC Section 336-12

NEC Section 336-3(b)

NEC Section 336-14

Figure 4-15: NEC installation requirements for Type NM cable.

mechanical protection than with NM cable, and the metal jacket also provides a continuous grounding bond without the need for additional grounding conductors.

BX cable may be used for under-plaster extensions, as provided in the NEC, and embedded in plaster finish, brick, or other masonry, except in damp or wet locations. It may also be run or "fished" in the air voids of masonry block or tile walls, except where such walls are exposed or subject to excessive moisture or dampness or are below grade. This type of cable is a favorite for connecting line-voltage devices above acoustical ceilings in commercial installations. See Figure 4-16.

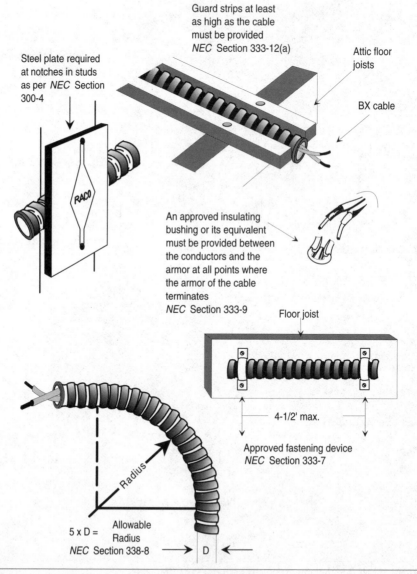

Figure 4-16: *NEC* installation requirements for Type AC cable.

Type NMC Cable: This type of cable is similar in appearance and used as conventional Type NM cable except that Type NM cable is suitable for dry locations only while Type NMC cable is permitted for dry, moist, damp, or corrosive locations.

Underground Feeder Cable: Type UF cable may be used underground, including direct burial in the earth, as a feeder or branch-circuit cable when provided with overcurrent protection at the rated ampacity as required by the NEC. When Type UF cable is used above grade where it will come in direct contact with the rays of the sun, its outer covering must be sun resistant. Furthermore, where Type UF cable emerges from the ground, some means of mechanical protection must be provided. This protection may be in the form of conduit or guard strips. Type UF cable resembles Type NM cable in appearance. The jacket, however, is constructed of weather resistant material to provide the required protection for direct-burial wiring installations.

Shielded Nonmetallic-Sheathed Cable: Type SNM cable consists of a conductor assembly which is enclosed in a PVC jacket followed by an overlapping layer of copper tape, a wire shield and, finally, a nonmetallic sheath. This is a rugged assembly as is indicated in the description given in NEC Article 337. This cable is intended for use in cable trays and other raceways and is suitable for use in hazardous locations under certain conditions as prescribed in NEC Articles 500 and 516.

ELECTRICAL CIRCUITS

A variety of materials is used to transmit electrical energy, but copper, due to its excellent cost-to-conductivity ratio, still remains the basic and most ideal conductor. Electrolytic copper, the type used for most electrical applications, can have three general characteristics:

- Method of stranding

- Degree of hardness (temper)

- Bare, tinned, or coated

Method of Stranding: Stranding refers to the relative flexibility of the conductor and may consist of only one strand or many thousands, depending on the rigidity or flexibility required for a specific need. For example, a small-gauge wire that is to be used in a fixed installation is normally solid (one strand), whereas a wire that will be constantly flexed requires a high degree of flexibility and would contain many strands.

- Solid is the least flexible form of a conductor and is merely one strand of copper.

- Stranded refers to more than one strand in a given conductor and may vary from 3 to 37 depending on size.

- Flexible simply indicates that there are a greater number of strands than are found in normal stranded construction.

Degree of Hardness: Temper refers to the relative hardness of the conductor and is noted as soft drawn-annealed (SD), medium hard drawn (MHD), and hard drawn (HD). Again, the specific need of an installation will determine the required temper. Where greater tensile strength is indicated, MHD would be specified over SD, and so on.

Bare, Tinned, or Coated: Untinned copper is plain bare copper that is available in either solid, stranded, or flexible and in the various tempers just described. In this form it is often referred to as red copper.

Bare copper is also available with a coating of tin, silver, or nickel to facilitate soldering, to impede corrosion, and to prevent adhesion of the copper conductor to rubber or other types of conductor insulation. The various coatings will also affect the electrical characteristics of copper.

Conductor Size: The American Wire Gauge (AWG) is used in the United States to identify the sizes of wire and cable up to and including No. 4/0 (0000), which is commonly pronounced in the electrical trade as "four-aught" or "four-naught." These numbers run in reverse order as to size; that is, No. 14 AWG is smaller than No. 12 AWG and so on up to size No. 1 AWG. To this size (No. 1 AWG), the larger the gauge number, the smaller the size of the conductor. However, the next larger size after No. 1 AWG is No. 1/0 AWG, then 2/0 AWG, 3/0 AWG, and 4/0 AWG. At this point, the AWG designations end and the larger sizes of conductors are identified by circular mils (cmil). From this point, the larger the size of wire, the larger the number of circular mils. For example, 300,000 cmil is larger than 250,000 cmil. In writing these sizes in circular mils, the "thousand" decimal is replaced by the letter k, and instead of writing, say, 500,000 cmil, it is usually written 500 kcmil.

Properties of Conductors

Various NEC tables define the physical and electrical properties of conductors. Electricians and security technicians use these tables to select the type of conductor and the cable jacket or size of raceway to enclose the conductors in specific applications.

NEC tables tabulate properties of conductors as follows:

- Name

- Operating temperature

- Application

- Insulation

- Physical properties

- Electrical resistance

- ac resistance and reactance

NEC Table 310-13 gives the name, operating temperature, application, and insulation of various types of conductors, while tables in NEC Chapter 9 (Tables 5, 6, 7, 8 and 9) give the physical properties and electrical resistance.

Conductor Insulation

Thermoplastic is a popular and effective insulation material used on conductors for security systems. The following thermoplastics are widely used as insulation materials:

Polyvinyl Chloride (PVC): The base material used for the manufacture of TW and THW insulation.

Polyethylene (PE): An excellent weatherproofing material used primarily for insulation of control and communication wiring.

Cross-linked Polyethylene (XLP): An improved PE with superior heat- and moisture-resistant qualities. Used for THHN, THWN, and XHHW wire.

Nylon: Primarily used as jacketing material. THHN building wire has an outer coating of nylon.

Teflon: A high temperature insulation. Widely used for telephone and security-system wiring in a plenum (where other insulated conductors require conduit routing).

Letter Coding

Conductor insulation as applied to building wire is coded by letters. The letters generally, but not always, indicate the type of insulation or its environmental rating. Some types of cable have the number of conductors, wire size, and other information inscribed on the cable jacket. The conductor insulation in the table in Figure 4-17 apply to those used in NEC wire tables.

Letter	Description	Letter	Description
A	Asbestos	RH	Heat-Rated Rubber
B	Braid	RHW	Weather-Rated, Heat-Rated Rubber
E	Ethylene or Entrance		
F	Fluorinated or Feeder	THW	Weather-Rated, Heat-Rated Thermoplastic
H	Heat Rated or Flame Retardant		
I	Impegnated	THWN	Weather-Rated, Heat-Rated Thermoplastic with Nylon Cover
N	Nylon	XHHN	Heat-Rated, Flame-Retardant, Weather-Rated, Cross-Linked Polyethylene
P	Propylene		
R	Rubber		
S	Silicon or Synthetic	USE	Underground Service Feeder
T	Thermoplastic	ZW	Weather-Rated Modified Ethylene Tetrafluorethylene
U	Underground		
V	Varnished Cambric	V	Varnished Cambric
W	Weather Rated	TA	Thermoplastic and Asbestos
X	Cross-Linked Polyethylene	TBS	Thermoplastic Braided Silicon
Z	Modified Ethylene Tetrafluorethylene	SA	Silicon Asbestos
		AVB	Asbestos Varnished and Braided
TW	Weather-Rated Thermoplastic	SIS	Synthetic Impregnated
UF	Underground Feeder	FEP	Fluorinated Ethylene Propylene
FEPW	Weather-Rated Thermosplastic		

Figure 4-17: Letter codes for conductor insulation.

Low-voltage, control circuit transformers are used extensively in security-system control circuits to obtain a lower voltage than is available from the main power supply. For example, many control circuits operate at 24 V, and normally 120 V is the lowest voltage rating used in any building's electrical system. Therefore, a control transformer is used to reduce the 120-V circuit to the required 24 V. In selecting such a transformer, Class 2, low-voltage control systems are limited to transformers with a maximum output capacity of 75 volt-amperes (VA) (watts). If a control transformer has a smaller output capacity than is required to service the system, it will eventually fail. Therefore, security systems requiring the use of a transformer to reduce voltage in the control circuits should be checked to ensure that the rating of the transformer will not be exceeded when the system is in use.

Electrical Line Current Capacity

Electrical conductors must be sized according to the NEC and also good wiring practices. Besides the information given in various NEC tables as to the allowable amperes that will safely flow through any given wire size, the wire or conductor should also be sized to limit the voltage drop to a maximum of 2 percent in any electrical circuit. This ensures efficient operation of both controls and equipment.

Even when sizing wire for low-voltage security systems, the voltage drop should be limited to 3 percent because excess voltage drop causes:

- Failure of controls to activate

- Control contact chatter

- Erratic operation of controls

- Control coil burnout

- Contact burnout

A table that may be used to size low-voltage wire is shown in Figure 4-18. To use, assume a load of 35 VA with a 50-ft run for a 24-V control circuit. Referring to the table, scan the 50-ft column. Note than No. 18 AWG wire will carry 20 VA and No. 16 wire will carry 43 VA, while still maintaining a maximum of 3 percent voltage drop. In this case, No. 16 wire should be used.

When the length of wire is other than listed in the table, the capacity may be determined by the following equation:

$$VA\ capacity = \frac{Length\ of\ circuit\ (from\ table)}{Length\ of\ circuit\ (actual)} \times VA\ (from\ table)$$

The 3 percent voltage-drop limitation is imposed to assure proper operation when the power supply is below the rated voltage. For example, if the rated 240-V supply is 10 percent low (216 V), the transformer does not produce 24 V, but only 21.6 V.

AWG	Length of Circuit, One Way in Feet											
Wire Size	25	50	75	100	125	150	175	200	225	250	275	300
20	29	14	10	7.2	5.8	4.8	4.1	3.6	3.2	2.9	2.6	2.4
18	58	29	19	14	11	9.6	8.2	7.2	6.4	5.8	5.2	4.8
16	86	43	29	22	17	14	12	11	9.6	8.7	7.8	7.2
14	133	67	44	33	27	22	19	17	15	13	12	11

Figure 4-18: Table showing length of circuit, one way in feet.

When normal voltage drop is taken from this 21.6 V, it approaches the lower operating limit of most security controls. If it is assured that the primary voltage to the transformer will always be at rated values or above, the control circuit will operate satisfactorily with more than 3 percent voltage drop. However, during extremely hot or cold weather, the use of electricity is increased, and many power companies must reduce the voltage by, say 10 percent, so that their generators can carry the additional load. You can usually tell when the voltage is reduced on power lines because heating elements and microwave ovens take longer than usual to produce the required amount of heat.

During the installation of low-voltage circuits, it is suggested than one extra line be run for emergency purposes. This extra line can be substituted for any one of the existing lines that may be defective. Also, it is possible to parallel this extra line with the existing line carrying the full load of the control circuit if the length of run affects control operation caused by voltage drop. In many cases this will reduce the voltage drop and permit satisfactory operation.

INSTALLING SYSTEMS IN EXISTING BUILDINGS

Many changes and advances in developing complete security/alarm systems for building operation and protection have taken place in the past few years. Numerous existing buildings are currently having security and fire-alarm systems installed — either to replace their obsolete systems or to provide protection they never had.

The materials used for installing a complete alarm system in an existing building are essentially the same as those used in new structures. However, the methods used to install the equipment and related wiring can vary tremendously and require a great deal of skill and ingenuity. Each structure is unique.

When concealed wiring is to be installed in a finished existing building, the installation must be planned so that the least amount of cutting and patching is necessary. In most cases, this means giving special consideration to the routing of conductors. Unlike the wiring of a new building where the installer would try to conserve as much material as possible, the amount of material used (within reason) is secondary in existing buildings. The main objective in security/fire-equipment installations in existing buildings is to install the wiring in the least amount of time with the least amount of cutting and patching of the existing finishes of the building.

Prior to any actual work on an existing building, the contractor or the installers should make a complete survey of the existing conditions in the areas where the security system will be installed. If the majority of the work can be done in exposed areas (as in an unfinished basement or attic), the job will be relatively simple. On the other hand, if most of the wiring must be concealed in finished areas, there are many problems to be solved. The initial survey of the building should determine the following:

1. The best location for the alarm control panel.

2. The type of construction used for exterior and interior walls, ceilings, floors, etc.

3. The location of any chases that may be used for routing the conductors and the location of closets, especially those located one above the other, for possible use in fishing wires.

4. The material used for wall and ceiling finishes — plaster, drywall, paneling, etc.

5. Location of moldings, baseboards, etc., that may be removed to hide conductors.

6. Location of decorations or other parts of the building structure that cannot be disturbed.

7. Location of any abandoned electrical raceways that new alarm-system wires might be fished into. Don't overlook similar possibilities. For example, old abandoned gas lines were recently used to fish security-system wires in an old building in Washington, D.C.

8. The location of all doors and windows, coal chutes, and similar access areas to the inside of the building.

As indicated previously, the most difficult task in running wires in existing buildings is the installation of concealed wiring in finished areas with no unfinished areas or to provide access to them in the area in question. In cases like these, the work is usually performed in one of two ways, namely, by deliberately cutting the finished work so that the new wiring can be installed. Of course, these damaged areas must be patched once the wiring is installed. The second way is to remove a small portion of the finished area (only enough to give access to voids in walls, ceilings, etc.) and then fish the wires in. The removed portions are then replaced after the wiring is complete.

Where outlet boxes are used, they should be designed for installation in the type of finish in the area. Means of securing the boxes to some structural member — like mounting ears or holding devices — should also be given consideration.

Another method of providing outlets in a finished area is to remove the existing baseboard and run the conductors in the usual groove between the flooring and the wall and then replace the baseboard. This method requires less work (cutting and patching) than most other methods when the finished area must be disturbed. There is also a type of metal baseboard on the market which may be installed along the floor line and used as a raceway. Most types are provided with two compartments for wires — one for power and one for low-voltage wiring. Using this metal baseboard provides a simple means of routing wires for security/fire-alarm systems with very little cutting or patching. In most cases, wires can be fished from the baseboard up to outlets on the wall, especially if they are under 3 ft above the floor.

Figure 4-19: A flashlight and mirror used in combination are useful for viewing conditions inside of partitions.

However, if this is not practical, matching surface molding can be installed to blend in very nicely with the baseboard.

When a lot of cutting and patching is required in a finished area, many installers like to hire a carpenter to do the work. The carpenter may know some tricks that will help the alarm-system installers get the system in with the least amount of difficulty. Also, any cutting or patching will be done in a professional manner.

Before doing any actual cutting of an existing building to install security/fire-alarm components, the installer should carefully examine the building structure to ascertain that the wires may be routed to the contacts and other outlets in a relatively easy way. See Figure 4-19. It is possible that a proposed outlet location, for example, could be moved only a foot or two to take advantage of an existing chase. Perhaps a smoke detector or similar component was originally located in a ceiling with insulation, which would make the fishing of cables very difficult. If the detector could be located on a ceiling containing no insulation, the job would be greatly simplified.

When cutting holes in ceilings for outlets, a drop cloth or paper should be spread underneath to catch all dust and dirt. Sometimes an old umbrella can be opened and hung upside down under the spot in the ceiling where the hole is being made to catch the debris and keep it off the rugs and furniture.

Holes for wires and components can be cut through plaster with a chisel, through wood with a keyhole saw after first drilling two or four pilot holes, and in brick or other masonry with a masonry chisel or rotary hammer. To locate the exact spot to cut these openings, it is best to first cut a very small hole in the center of the spot where the larger one will be made. This hole may then be used to locate the area between studs or — in the case of very old homes — the cracks between the plaster laths. It is then possible to shift the mark for the outlet openings so that all obstacles can be avoided and to provide proper anchoring of the outlet box or component.

There are a number of ways to pull and fish wires into walls and openings in finished buildings and, with a little ingenuity and careful thought, workers should be able to solve almost any problem of this kind that they may encounter.

When pulling wires into spaces between the studs in walls, a flashlight placed in the outlet box hole is often a great help when feeding the wires in or catching them as they are pushed near the opening. Under no circumstances should a candle or other open flame be used for this purpose. If one must see farther up or down the inside of a partition, a flashlight and mirror used in combination as shown in Figure 4-19 is a great help. Many installers like to make their own mirror by gluing a small 2- × 3-in compact mirror on a handle resembling a wooden tongue depressor. Any type of small flashlight may be used.

Where it becomes necessary to remove floor boards during a security/fire-alarm installation, it should be done with the greatest of care so that the edges are not split. Split edges make a poor appearance on the finished job when the boards are replaced. Special saws may be purchased for cutting into floors or other surfaces without drilling holes to start the saw. Then if the tongue (on tongue-and-groove boards) is split off with a thin sharp chisel driven down in the crack between the boards, the board from which the tongue was removed can be pried up carefully without damaging the rest of the floor.

New Installation Techniques For Existing Structures

A few years ago, the Diversified Manufacturing and Marketing Co. (Burlington, NC 27215) patented a system which attaches a drill bit to a long flexible spring steel shaft and is known as D'versiBit. This system makes it possible to manipulate easily a drill bit in walls to accomplish complex installation maneuvers in existing buildings. The D'versiBit can be inserted into the wall cavity through a small opening and positioned accurately for drilling from midwall to attic or basement, from windows and doorways to basement or attic, etc. The development of this system makes penetration and cable retrieval a much simpler operation than it used to be. Following is a list of tools available for use with the D'versiBit system.

Bits: The three types of bits available for this system are shown in Figure 4-20 on the next page. The auger bit (Figure 4-20a) is for starting and drilling a clean entrance hole, the combination bit (Figure 4-20b) is designed for greater durability, and the masonry bit (Figure 4-20c) has a carbide tip for drilling in cement blocks and plaster. All three of these bits are designed for use with standard electric drill motors.

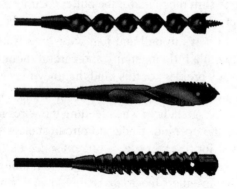

Figure 4-20: Three types of bits available for the D'versiBit system.

Alignment Tool: The special alignment tool shown Figure 4-21 provides total control of the flexible shaft, and may be used to hold the bit and shaft steady and true toward any desired destination.

Line Recovery Devices: After the drilling is completed, the system quickly converts to a line recovery system using the grips as shown in Figure 4-22. These grips attach to holes located in the bit tip or in the shaft end. This feature enables even one person to quickly fish wires or cables through partitions.

Shaft Extensions: The standard lengths of the flexible shaft are 54 in and 72 in, but shaft extensions (Figure 4-23) are available to provide extra distance drilling capabilities. One or more can be attached in special situations, such as from the basement to a smoke sensor in the attic.

The basic shaft is $3/16$ -in which will accommodate both $3/8$-in and $1/2$-in drill bits in the three styles mentioned previously. For larger bits — such as $3/4$-in

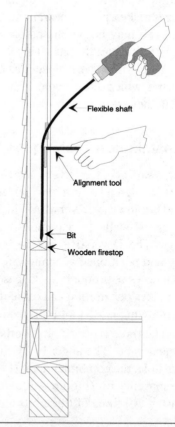

Flexible shaft

Alignment tool

Bit

Wooden firestop

Figure 4-21: Special alignment tool provides total control of the flexible shaft.

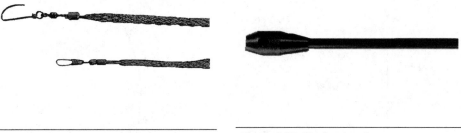

Figure 4-22: Line recovery devices.   **Figure 4-23: Shaft extension**

and 1-in sizes — a $\frac{1}{4}$-in shaft is required. This larger shaft reduces the flexibility for complex drilling.

Operation Procedures

When drilling with the flexible shaft of the D'versiBit, run the drill motor only when actually drilling. Never run the drill when sliding the bit up or down in the wall cavity as wires — either signal wires or existing electric power wiring — may be cut during the process. Also make certain that the bit is sharp since a dull bit is one of the greatest causes of bit breakage.

If at all possible, a reversible drill motor should be used to withdraw the bit from the wall. The motor should be running only when the bit is actually passing through a wood member. When drilling, force is exerted in one direction. When the bit is being removed, it is removed at a different angle and force is exerted from a different direction. This is why the reverse is used. If the flexible shaft is being used with drill motors with no reverse, it would be better to exert force to pull the bit from the hole with the motor running, because chances of an easy recovery without damage are much better with the motor running.

When drilling from an attic or crawl space, be certain not to select an area directly above or below a door since this will result in property damage. It is also good to keep a slight tension on the wire when it is being pulled from overhead so that it will not get tangled with the bit and become damaged.

The shaft should not be bowed any more than absolutely necessary to accomplish the job. Excessive bowing will decrease the life of the flexible shaft. Drill motors, of course, should be adequately grounded or else have insulated handles.

Practical Applications of the D'versiBit

Assume that an outlet box for an infrared photoelectric detector is to be installed above a countertop in a residential kitchen to sense entry of unauthorized persons

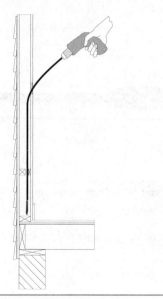

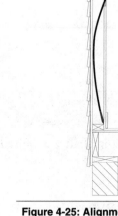

Figure 4-24: The first hole cut acts as a guide for drilling through the floor plate.

Figure 4-25: Alignment tool used to snap the bit back to the inside wall.

through the kitchen door. If, upon investigation of the space inside of the partitions, it is found that a 2- by 4-in wood member (fire-stop) blocks the route from the outlet hole to the basement area where the alarm control station is located, an alignment tool must be used.

The flexible shaft containing a drill bit is placed through a cut outlet-box opening and then the special alignment tool is attached to the shaft as shown in Figure 4-23. By keeping the alignment tool in the same position on the shaft and by lifting the handle, the shaft will bow back toward the operator. As the bit is lowered into the wall cavity, the operator can feel the bit strike the inside wall. When the bit is aligned correctly on the wooden member, the alignment tool is removed while keeping downward pressure on the bit so that it will not slip out of place, and the hole is drilled through the fire-stop. This hole will then act as a guide for drilling through the floor plate as shown in Figure 4-24.

In the case of a wall cavity without fire-stops or purlins, the alignment tool is used to snap the bit back to the inside wall (Figure 4-25) at which time downward pressure on the drill motor will keep the bit point in place and cause the shaft to bow. Power and pressure is then transmitted from the back wall which allows proper angle drilling to miss the joist boxing.

After the bit has penetrated into the basement area as shown in Figure 4-25, the operator has access to the hole in the drill bit itself for attaching the recovery grip and pulling the wire up to the outlet location — all without damage to the existing finish.

Figure 4-26: Recovery grip attached to the bit tip eyelet.

Figure 4-26 shows how the recovery grip is attached to the bit tip eyelet. The swivel located between the cable and the head of the grip prevents the wire or cable from becoming twisted during the fishing process.

Figure 5-27 shows the grip after it has been attached to the bit tip with the line inserted ready for recovery. The operator then operates the drill motor in reverse — due to the angle of the pull — applies a slight pull, and the wire can be pulled easily through the holes due to the reverse cutting action of the bit. If desired, the drill motor can be removed from the shaft and a recovery grip attached to the chuck end of the shaft for pulling the wires downward toward the basement. While this example shows the method of routing wires or cables from an outlet to a basement, the same procedure would apply for drilling from an outlet opening to an attic space.

To install contacts on windows for a burglar-alarm system, drill from the location of the contact through the casement, lintels, and plates with a $\frac{3}{8}$-in shaft. Attach a recovery grip to the end of the bit, insert the wire to keep the grip from becoming tangled, reverse the drill motor, and bring the wire toward the operator as the bit is being withdrawn. See Figure 4-28.

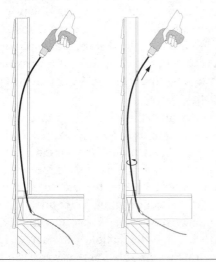

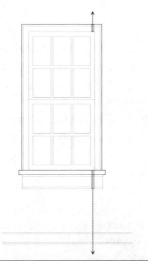

Figure 4-27: Grip attached to the bit tip with the line inserted rady for recovery.

Figure 4-28: Drilling through the window casing.

Burglar alarm contacts or door switches installed at doors are simple projects when one uses the flexible shaft. First cut or drill the entrance hole in the normal manner and then insert the flexible shaft with bit into the entrance hole, slanting the bit as much as possible in the desired direction of travel. Continue by drilling through the door casing and floor jamb into the cavity of the wall as shown in Figure 4-29. The drill is then stopped until it strikes the next stud which will deflect the bit either up or down, depending on the direction of the drilling. Continue to push the bit until it strikes the top of the bottom plate and then drill through the plate into the basement or attic. The recovery grip is then attached to the bit and the wire or cable may be drawn back toward the operator by reversing the drill motor and keeping a slight tension on the wires as they are being pulled to prevent tangling.

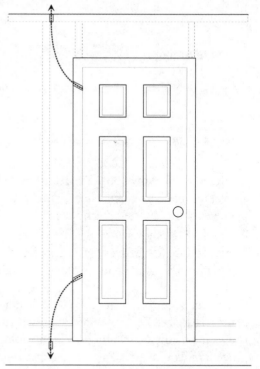

Figure 4-29: Drilling through the door jamb into the cavity of the wall.

With conventional tools, the routing of wires from one outlet to another requires either channeling the wall, using wire mold, or running the wires down to the baseboard, removing the baseboard, and then installing the wires behind it. Instances like these occur when the crawl space is too shallow for workers to crawl into or the house is built on a concrete slab. However, with the flexible shaft, it is possible to drill through the wall horizontally through several studs (Figure 4-30) and then pull the wires back through the holes to the openings.

The installation of an outside annunciator under the eave of a house with an extremely low pitch to the roof would cause several problems in getting wires to the outlet. With the flexible shaft, a hole can be drilled through the boxing as shown in Figure 4-31. As soon as the bit penetrates the boxing, it is pushed into the attic as far as it will go. A recovery grip is then attached to the bit, the wire or cable inserted, and then pulled backward toward the outlet opening. The outlet box and annunciator (horn, bell, etc.) are installed under the eave and the other end of the cable is connected to the alarm system. Also, because the flexible shaft is more rigid than the conventional fish tape, it will penetrate attic insulation if any exists.

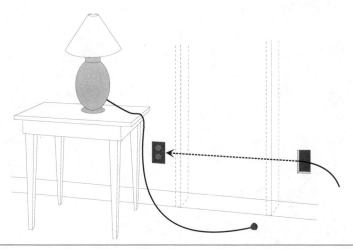

Figure 4-30: With the flexible shaft, it is possible to drill through the wall horizontally through several studs.

If it becomes necessary to install wiring in an attic and run cable from this area to the basement, the installation can be greatly simplified by using a flexible shaft. First drill through the top plate into the wall cavity — making sure that the drilling is not being done above a window or doorway or any other obstruction such as existing wiring, ductwork, etc. Once through the top plate, the drill motor is turned off and the bit is pushed into the cavity of the wall as far as it will go. If no fire-stops are encountered, the bit is pulled back and an extension is attached to the shaft. With the extension installed, the bit is again lowered into the wall cavity until a fire-stop is encountered. The bit is then positioned and used to drill through the wooden member. Once the wooden member is penetrated, the drill motor is again stopped and the bit is lowered further until the bottom plate is reached. Continue drilling through the bottom plate in the basement or crawl space. Fasten the appropriate recovery grip, insert the wire or cable, and pull up the wire with the flexible shaft. The drill motor should be reversed only when the bit is passing through one of the wooden members.

Those who use this device often are certain to discover many other useful techniques for installing wiring in existing structures.

Figure 4-31: Method of drilling a hole through boxing by using a flexible shaft.

Chapter 5

Residential Security Systems

A wide variety of security systems and accessories are available to take care of almost every conceivable residential application. This fact sometimes poses a problem for the security technician in choosing the most feasible system for the given application. This chapter covers the design of several types of residential occupancies — giving reasons for choosing the various systems.

THE ESSENTIALS

When planning the design of a security system for residential occupancies, the first decision to be made — and often the hardest — is what the system must accomplish. That is, identify the threat — whether it is personal risk encountered in a home due to burglary or psychological harassment or loss of property and money due to burglary, or some other threat. Furthermore, the security technician must decide what type of alarm should be provided from the following list:

- Scare an intruder with an alarm sounder

- Call for help from neighbors

- Summon police or others over telephone lines

- Combination of the above

The allotted budget is another factor to consider. Many residential security systems can be installed for less than $1000 while others may run into the thousands of dollars. The best way to determine the amount of protection needed is to consider the threat of personal risk or bodily injury and the possible loss of property. Then determine how much this protection is worth to the homeowner. When this figure is determined, you will have a good guide to how much of an alarm system is needed.

With the threat determined, the system goals and a general budget figure for the system cost established, the design may begin.

Basic Information

A form such as the one in beginning with Figure 5-1 should be used by the security system contractor or installer to ensure that all necessary information concerning the design will be obtained. Contractors should have a supply of such forms printed with their letterhead on top of the page. Manufacturers of security/fire-alarm equipment also furnish such forms at little cost.

Begin filling out the form with the customer's name, address, city, state, and zip code. Be sure to include the actual date that this survey is taken. Continue with the size of family, including all adults and children. Some adults are reluctant to give their age so an estimate in this category is okay; that is, "young couple," "middle-aged," etc. The number and weight of pets may seem ridiculous, but all of this information is pertinent for obtaining and installing the best security system. For example, if pressure-mat detectors are used in the home, they must be calibrated so that a dog or cat walking over the mats at night will not set off the alarm. The same is true for motion detectors. Knowing the type, size, and weight of pets will help you to get the right system for each individual family and premises.

Construction Information

The next part of the form (Figure 5-2 on page 154) deals with the construction of the building or premises. This information may be collected either by actual measurement or by obtaining existing architectural drawings along with a plot plan if these are available.

Many security technicians prefer to use graph paper as a sketch pad and then draw a rough sketch (to scale) of the property and floor plan of the building. Each square on the graph paper represents a predetermined size; that is, 1 ft, 2 ft, 10 ft, etc. Consequently, if one wall of the building was, say, 30 ft in length, a line drawn with a straightedge through 30 squares on the graph paper would then equal 30 ft on the building. The remaining walls are drawn in a similar fashion. Once the outside walls of the building are drawn on the graph paper, the interior partitions are sketched in to complete the drawing.

Reliable Security Services
4457 Royal Oak Drive
Front Royal, Virginia 22630
(703) 555-1212

SECURITY SURVEY
for

Name_____Date of Survey_____

Address_____

City_____State____Zip_____

Telephone (home)_____(work)_____

Family Size:
   Adults_____Ages_____

   Children_____Ages_____

   Pets_____Weight_____Height_____

Normal bedtime_____How many in family smoke?_____

Name of closest relative_____Telephone_____

Name of insurance agent_____

   Company_____Telephone_____

Figure 5-1: Cover page used for initial survey of project.

CONSTRUCTION INFORMATION

Age of home:_____ Lot size:_____ Ft. wide:_____ Ft. deep:_____

       Acre(s)_____

Building measurements: _____ Ft. long _____ Ft. wide _____ Ft. High

Walls: Wood _____ Shingle ___ Stone ___ Brick ___ Metal siding ___
      Other: _____

Interior walls: Wood _____ Plaster _____ Plasterboard _____
      Flagstone _____ Brick _____ Fiberboard _____
      Other: _____

Ceilings: Wood ___ Plaster ___ Plasterboard ___ False ___ Acoustic ___
      Other:_____

Roof: Wood shingle ___ Tar paper ___ Tile ___ Asphalt shingle ___
      Rock ___ Slate ___ Pitched ___ Flat ___ Multistory _____
      Other: _____

Floors: Wood ___ Concrete ___ Tile ___ Flat stone ___ Carpet ____
      Other: _____

Attic: Full ___ Partial ___ None ___

Attic crawl space: Good ___ Average ___ Poor ___ None _____

Crawl space under house: Good ___ Average ___ Poor ___ None ___

Basement: Full ___ Partial ___ None ___
      Basement dimensions:_____x_____

Garage: Attached ___ Free standing ___ Garage dimensions: ___x_____

Garage walls: Wood ___ Unfinished ___ Plasterboard ___ Brick ___
      Stone ___ Other _____

Type of insulation: Walls_____Floor_____Ceiling_____

Figure 5-2: Form used for construction information on a proposed residential project.

Referring again to Figure 5-2, note that the age of the home is requested, along with the lot size (width and depth of the lot) and total number of acres or a percentage of an acre. A plot plan (Figure 5-3) should also be prepared at the same time that the form is being completed. The plot plan should show the relation of the building to the property lines, all nearby roads, alleys, bushes, trees, and other pertinent information that can aid in the design of the security system. Also note any fire hydrants, the closest fire department, and the nearest police station.

Many modern residences will have an existing plot plan that may be used by the security technician in his or her design. If the homeowners do not have this plan available, check with the land developer, the architect, or the land surveyor. A plot plan may also be attached to the property deed in the deed office for the area. If such a plan already exists, using it will save the security technician much time and usually such a plan will be more accurate than can be made by the technician without using surveying instruments.

Once the plot plan is obtained or sketched, trouble spots should be indicated on the drawing. Burglars almost always prefer doors for entrance since doors are usually required for removing such items as television sets from the home. Even if some other means of entry is used, burglars will use doors to exit. Furthermore, they need a concealed approach route and a hiding place for the vehicle to be loaded with the stolen goods. Therefore, back alleys and hidden carports are the obvious vehicle hiding places. All such areas should be clearly indicated on your plot plan. With this knowledge in mind, choose the most vulnerable door in the building as deserving the best physical and burglar-alarm protection. A dead latch and dead-bolt locks should be used on a solid wood or steel door with no windows in it, if possible. If this point of entry is a sliding glass door, care must be taken so that the door cannot be lifted out of the track and the door should be capable of being securely key-locked and pinned into the closed position using appropriate hardware.

Obviously, this most vulnerable entry point must be alarmed with the best equipment available. Similarly, other doors of the home must have some sort of protection.

Windows should be analyzed in a similar manner to doors. In most premises there are one or more windows which may face a side yard, a fence, or a wall where no casual observer is likely to see someone making forced entry. First, protect the window from being forced open and then install a dependable security system.

The form in Figure 5-4 is designed to furnish security technicians with intrusion security information. Review the information included in this form as you continue with this chapter.

Most security systems use a closed-loop protective circuit where a pair of wires is connected to the alarm control and is then run around the perimeter of a building and finally returned to the alarm control panel. Closed-circuit detectors are connected in series in this loop. A small current flows through the wiring and detectors and any interruption of this current by the detector operation (cutting the wires or

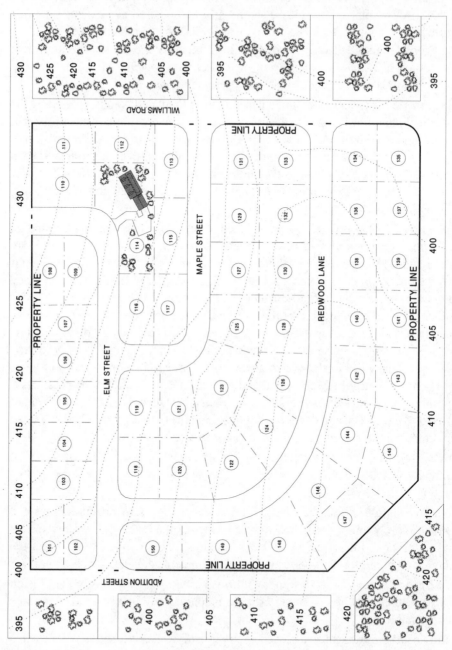

Figure 5-3: Typical plot plan as prepared by a land surveyor.

INTRUSION SECURITY INFORMATION

Distance to neighbor on:

    Right ____ft. Left ___ft. Front ___ft. Rear ___ft.

Type of public lighting: Street ___ Flood ___ Other _____None ___

Type of private lighting: Front _____ Side _____ Rear _____
    What lights are left on at night?_____

Visibility onto property from street:
    Good ___ Average ___ Poor ___ Why?_____

Hours home is normally vacant:_____

Number of entrances:
    Doors_____ Sliding glass doors_____ Windows_____ Other_____

Doors: Wood ___ Metal ___ Glass ___ Single ___ Double ___Hollow ___
    Solid:_____ Other:_____

Door frames: Wood ___ Metal ___ Aluminum ___ Other _____

Locks: Single-key ___ Sliding-bolt ___ Double-key ___ Dead-bolt ___
    Padlock ___ Night latch ___ When last rekeyed?_____
    Other: _____

Windows: Sliding ___ Double-hung ___ Single hung ___ Casement ___
    Louver ___ Fixed ___ Other _____

Glass: Single-strength ___ Double-strength ___Plate ___ Frosted ___
    Tempered ___ Thermal pane ___ Other _____

Storm windows: Yes ☐　　No ☐

Glass framing: Wood ___ Metal ___ Other_____ ___

Grilles or Screening: Standard screens___ Iron bars ___ Other _____

Garage door: Single ___ Double ___ One-piece overhead ___
    Sectional overhead ___ Swing out ___ Other _____

Outbuildings: Number_____Type _____

Figure 5-4: Form used to obtain intrusion security information.

shorting the wire pair together) will sound the alarm. Restoring the loop to its original condition, such as closing the alarm door after entry, will not stop the alarm condition. Only operating the appropriate control will do this.

Magnetic contacts or switches are by far the most commonly used detection devices for openings such as windows and doors. They consist of two pieces — a magnet and a magnetically operated switch enclosed in plastic cases. The magnet is mounted on the edge of the door while the switch section is mounted directly adjacent to the magnet on the door frame. When the magnet is located near the switch section, the switch is turned on and electricity flows through the switch contact. Moving the magnet away from the switch, such as opening a door, turns the switch off.

Since this is a closed-circuit system, the current through the loop will cease and the alarm will sound on opening. Magnetic switches are very successful because they are noncritical in alignment between the magnet and switch section and are extremely reliable in operation. Many switches are rated for hundreds of millions or even billions of switch operations. There is little mechanical motion in this switch, so replacement will be extremely infrequent under the worst of circumstances. By their nature, they are free from false alarms and are easy to troubleshoot and replace in the event one fails.

Magnetic contacts are also the best method of protecting windows and other openings. To protect glass from breakage in windows or sliding glass doors, a special lead foil is the common means of protection. This foil is put in series with the same burglar circuit that connects the doors and windows. The alloy in the foil is of such composition that any break in the glass will break the foil and thereby set off the alarm.

It may also be advisable to include an extra door switch or two on some of the interior doors that are likely to be opened in the event an intruder somehow penetrates the perimeter circuit. Such doors might include those to a gun closet, fur storage vault, or just between two rooms that have to be traversed to find any valuable property. The intruder is likely to have his guard down at this point and not to be looking for such a switch. Motion detectors — such as ultrasonic, infrared, audio, etc. — are also good insurance for the interior circuit.

Routing the circuit wires around the perimeter in an effective manner is one of the most important parts of a security/fire-alarm system. A pair of either 22-AWG or 24-AWG wires should be run all the way around the home from the control panel and then back. All detectors are then connected to this perimeter loop.

Wire concealment can be a major problem for the installer. If the house is under construction, the pair of wires can be located at some set distance within the partitions and walls. The installer can then cut into the wall at this distance when the walls are finished to get to the wires for the final connections. For existing construction, much fishing is necessary to route the wires to the various detectors, but Chapter 4 gives several solutions to these problems.

Concealment is important for aesthetic reasons, for making it impossible for the intruder to locate the presence of the system, and for reliability in the sense of minimizing damage to the wires.

Residential Fire-Alarm System

Heat and smoke detectors should be included in any residential security/fire-alarm system. They are generally connected to the system as shown in Figure 5-5. The fire-detection circuit should be fully supervised as required by UL. The circuit itself should act as a detector in the event of a malfunction; that is, a trouble bell or buzzer should activate in the control unit to alert the occupants of the situation.

The primary location for installing smoke detectors is outside each bedroom area. Since fire travels upward, the top of each stairwell is another important location. The NFPA also recommends that smoke detectors be installed on each living level of a multistory house.

Heat detectors should be installed in each enclosed living area including bathrooms, closets, attics, and basements. Any number of detectors can be used with most fire-alarm systems.

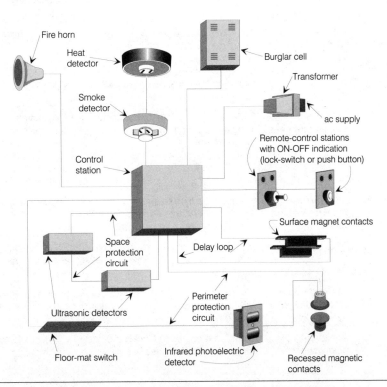

Figure 5-5: Various components of a residential security/fire-alarm system.

Rate-of-rise heat detectors should be mounted on the ceiling not less than 6 inches from a side wall. Exact detector location can be determined by an evaluation based on good engineering judgment, supplemented if possible by field tests.

The chart in Figure 5-6 shows some of the heat/smoke detectors supplied by NuTone. The model number, a description of each component, suggested use, and dimensions are given to assist security technicians.

Model No.	Description	Suggested Use	Specifications
S-120	135°F fixed-temperature heat detector.	Surface-mount on ceiling in ordinary living areas with normal room temperatures.	1.75 inches in diameter, .75 inch deep. Distance range: 10 ft in all directions. Detector covers area up to 20 x 20 ft.
S-121	200°F fixed-temperature heat detector.	Surface-mount on ceiling in areas where temperatures are higher than normal: furnace or boiler rooms; attics.	Same as above.
S-122	Rate-of-rise/135°F fixed-temperature heat detector.	Surface-mount on ceiling in ordinary living areas with normal room temperatures.	4.5 inches in diameter, 1.75 inches deep. Distance range: 25 ft in all directions. Detector covers area up to 50 x 50 ft.
S-123	Rate-of-rise/200°F fixed-temperature heat detector.	Surface-mount on ceiling in areas where temperatures are higher than normal: furnace or boiler rooms. Note: Use S-121 or S-125 in areas where temperatures consistently exceed 150°F.	Same as above.
SA-124	135°F fixed-temperature heat detector.	Surface-mount on ceiling in ordinary living areas with normal room temperatures.	1.75 inches in diameter, .75 inch deep. Distance range: 15 ft in all directions. Detector covers area up to 30 x 30 ft.
SA-125	200°F fixed-temperature heat detector.	Surface-mount on ceiling in areas where temperatures are higher than normal: furnace or boiler rooms; attics.	Same as above.
S-245	Smoke detector.	Surface-mount on 4-inch square or octagonal wiring box, primarily outside bedrooms.	5.5 inches square x $2\frac{5}{8}$ inches deep.
S-245H	Smoke detector with 135°F heat sensor.	Surface-mount on 4-inch square or octagonal wiring box, primarily outside bedrooms.	5.5 inches square x $2\frac{5}{8}$ inches deep.
S-240	Smoke-detector supervisory module.	Installs in wiring box at location of last smoke detector in series.	2 inches x 2 inches x 1 inch.

Figure 5-6: Heat-smoke detector selection guide.

While no regularly scheduled maintenance is necessary for most heat/smoke detectors, periodic cleaning of the detection chambers may be required when detectors are located in abnormally dirty or dusty environments.

RESIDENTIAL SECURITY-SYSTEM EQUIPMENT

The diagram in Figure 5-7 shows a variety of components designed for use in a residential security/fire-alarm system. The following is a brief description of each component and its function within the system.

Surface Magnetic Detector: The surface magnetic detector (Figure 5-8) is one of the most versatile entry detectors for residential alarm systems and should be

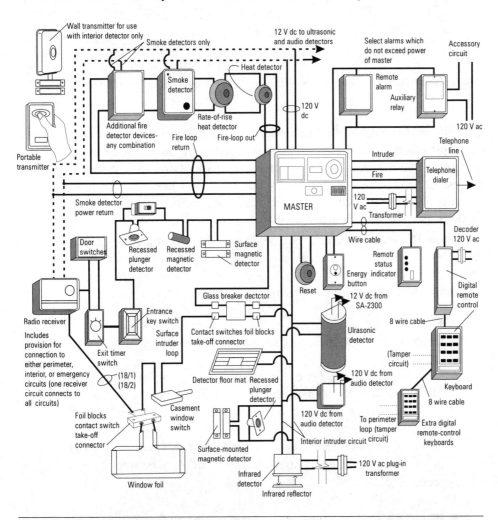

Figure 5-7: Variety of components designed for use in a residential security/fire-alarm system.

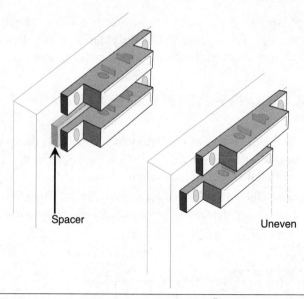

Spacer

Uneven

Figure 5-8: The surface magnetic detector is one of the most versatile entry detectors for residential alarm systems.

considered first as a method of protecting any movable door or window. These detectors can be mounted on wood, metal, and even glass, if necessary. They can be mounted with screws, double-sided tape, or epoxy. Obviously, the tape and epoxy are useful on glass, aluminum, or any other surface where screws cannot be used. However, when using tape or epoxy, make certain that the surface is clean, dry, smooth, and at least 65°F when applied.

Recess-Mounted Magnetic Detector: Where the appearance of surface-mounted detectors is objectionable, recess-mounted detectors may be used. These detectors are more difficult to install — requiring greater care on the technician's part — but few problems develop if the following precautions are taken:

- Be careful not to damage or destroy any weatherproofing seal around windows, doors, or other openings.

- If a recessed-mounted entry detector is installed in the window sill, you must prevent water seepage to the switch by applying a sealant under the switch flange and around the switch body.

- When drilling holes to accept each half of the detector, be sure the holes line up and there is no more than $\frac{1}{4}$-in space between the two sections of the detector.

- Be certain there is enough space between the window and its frame (or door and its frame) when each is closed; that is, there must be enough

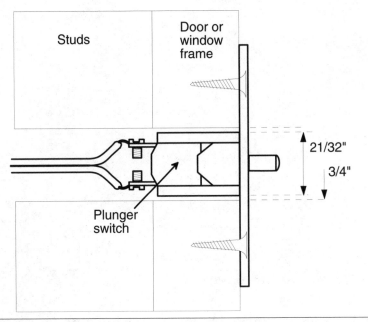

Figure 5-9: Cross-sectional view of a recess-mounted entry detector.

space (usually equaling $\frac{1}{16}$ inch) for the protrusion of both sections when they meet.

- If the window frame is not thick enough to accept the magnetic section of the detector, the detector can be mounted in the side frame.

The recessed plunger detector shown in Figure 5-9 is mounted so that the door or window will contact the plunger at the tip and push the plunger straight in. Therefore, the area of the window or the door that depresses the plunger should have no slots, cutouts, or step-downs into which the plunger might slip. The surface area should also be hard and free of rubber or vinyl that might be weakened by the plunger and consequently allow the plunger to open. For protecting doors, plunger-type detectors should only be mounted in the door frame on the hinge-side of the door.

In cases where it is difficult to protect a window or door by mounting any of the direct-type detectors, the area directly inside the door or window can be protected with interior "space" detectors, such as a floor-mat detector (Figure 5-10) or an ultrasonic motion detector (Figure 5-11), both shown on the next page.

Floor-mat detectors are easily concealed under the rugs at doors, windows, top or bottom of stairways, or any other area onto which an intruder is likely to step. A light pressure on the mat triggers the alarm. Obviously, if pets are allowed to roam throughout the house, the mats should be calibrated to withstand the weight of the pets without triggering the alarm. Some types, however, cannot be calibrated.

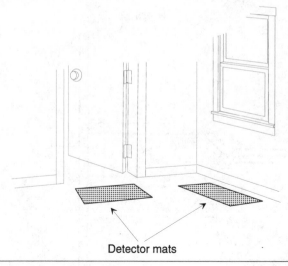

Detector mats

Figure 5-10: Application of floor-mat detectors.

Therefore, if the mats cannot be calibrated, they will be useless in homes where pets are allowed to roam.

There are also rolls of super-thin floor matting that can be cut to any desired length. These rolls can be used on stair treads and in areas near sliding glass doors or other large glass areas, entrance foyers, etc.

Other space detectors include ultrasonic motion detectors, audio detectors, and infrared detectors. Care must be used with any of these units because the protected area is limited both in width and depth — depending upon the particular unit.

The ultrasonic motion detector can be used in large glass-walled rooms that might otherwise be difficult to

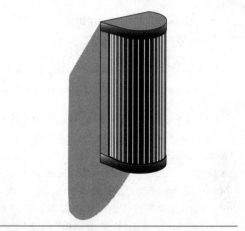

Figure 5-11: Ultrasonic motion detector.

protect and in hallways or entries or in virtually any area an intruder would have to pass through in moving about a home. They are especially useful as added protection (when conventional detectors are used also) to monitor a "valuables" room or area.

Most ultrasonic motion detectors are designed for mounting on either the wall or ceiling. It emits inaudible high-frequency sound waves in an elliptical pattern that ranges from 12 ft to 35 ft by 5 ft by 20 ft for most residential models. When an intruder moves within the secured area, movement interrupts the established pattern of sound waves and sounds the alarm.

Some designs of motion detectors can be rotated up to 180° for maximum coverage of the area being monitored as shown in Figure 5-12.

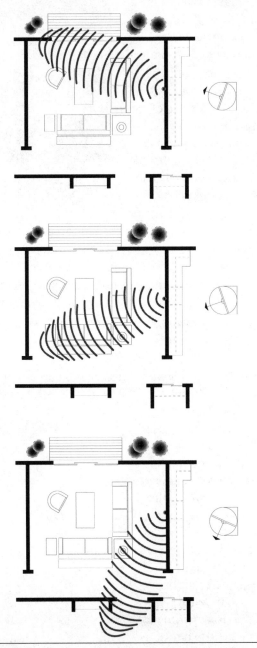

Figure 5-12: Motion detector rotating up to 180° for maximum coverage of the area being monitored.

Another type of motion detector is the audio detector (Figure 5-13). This type senses certain sharp sounds known to be present in forced entry, such as wood splintering or glass breaking. When these sounds are received through the unit's miniature microphone, the detector triggers the control unit to sound an alarm.

Audio detectors are best utilized in areas that are seldom used, such as an attic, garage, or closed-off wing of the house. It can be used in other areas, but when such areas are subject to much daytime activity, it is recommended that the detector only be armed at night when the family retires or is away from home.

Figure 5-13: Audio detector.

Infrared detectors are another type of motion detector. A combination transmitter-receiver is used to project an invisible pulsating beam at a special bounce-back reflector on an opposite wall. Any interruption of the beam activates the system alarms. Infrared detectors can be wired to either the perimeter or interior circuit, but for faster response, it is recommended that it be connected to the interior circuit.

Infrared detectors are designed for indoor areas such as entries, hallways, rooms, etc. Most cover a span from 3 ft to 75 ft, so it may be used in practically any indoor area or room.

Perimeter Detectors: Refer again to Figure 5-7 and note the various detectors available on the perimeter intruder loop. The glass-break detector, for example, is an excellent means of monitoring large areas of glass such as sliding glass doors, picture windows, and the like. These detectors, as the name implies, respond only to glass breaks and not to shock or vibrations. Therefore, they are relatively free from false alarms. The area which each will protect varies from manufacturer to manufacturer, but most will average about 10 ft² of protection. A small cube like the one in Figure 5-14 connects to the emergency circuit and the supervised perimeter circuit if they are mounted on movable windows.

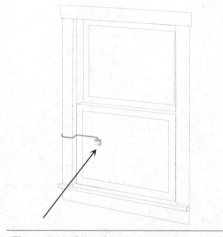

Figure 5-14: Glass-break detector.

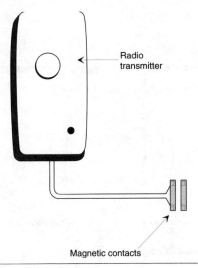

Radio transmitter

Magnetic contacts

Figure 5-15: Wall-mounted radio transmitter.

Window foil tape is used mostly in commercial and industrial buildings but are sometimes used in residential systems — especially on basement windows. If an intruder breaks the glass, the tape tears, opening the circuit, and causes the alarm to sound.

Where the building construction makes it difficult to install wires, radio controlled intruder detection systems are available. Such systems are also useful for linking outbuildings in a range of 150 ft or more, depending on the type used.

Wall-mounted radio transmitters (Figure 5-15) are easily mounted behind drapes at windows, above doors, and similar locations. Any number of transmitters can be used and each can be wired to an unlimited number of detectors as previously described.

When a detector senses forced entry, the transmitter sends a signal via radio waves to the radio receiver. It signals the control unit to sound an alarm — either audible or a silent alarm to a local police station.

PRACTICAL APPLICATIONS

To better understand the procedures necessary to design a suitable residential security/fire-alarm system, the floor plan of a single-story residence is shown in Figure 5-16 on the next page; the legend or symbol list used with this drawing is shown in Figure 5-17.

The obvious starting place for the design of the system is at the normal entrances, such as the front door opening into the vestibule, the sliding glass door in the dining area, and the kitchen door that opens onto the carport. These types of doors can be

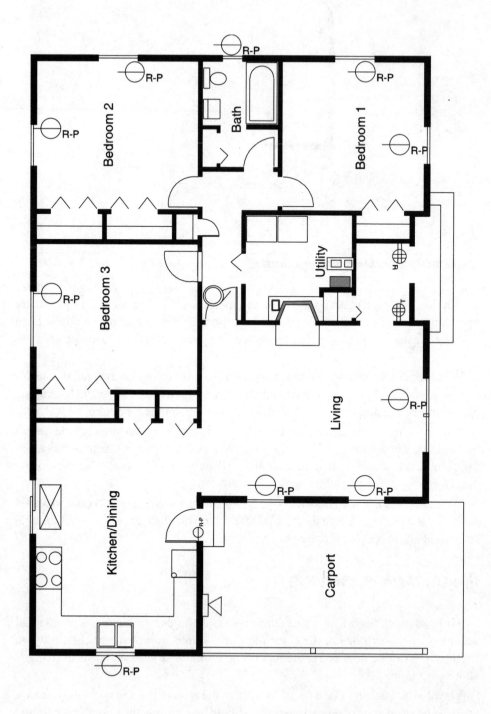

Figure 5-16: Floor plan of a single-story residence to be supplied with a security system.

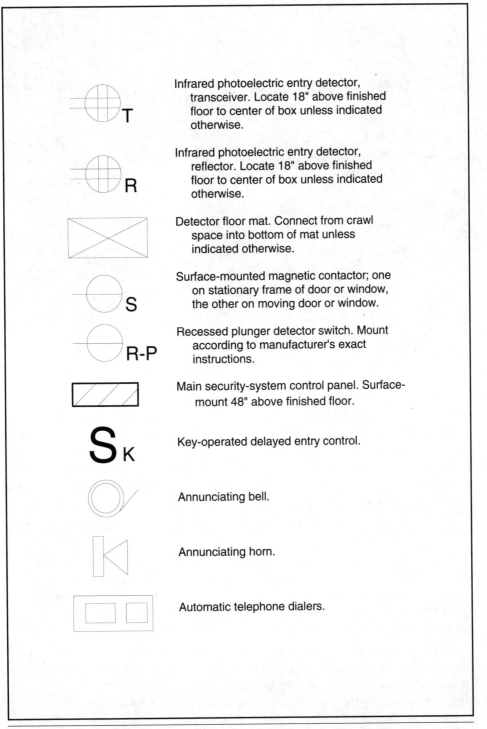

Infrared photoelectric entry detector, transceiver. Locate 18" above finished floor to center of box unless indicated otherwise.

Infrared photoelectric entry detector, reflector. Locate 18" above finished floor to center of box unless indicated otherwise.

Detector floor mat. Connect from crawl space into bottom of mat unless indicated otherwise.

Surface-mounted magnetic contactor; one on stationary frame of door or window, the other on moving door or window.

Recessed plunger detector switch. Mount according to manufacturer's exact instructions.

Main security-system control panel. Surface-mount 48" above finished floor.

Key-operated delayed entry control.

Annunciating bell.

Annunciating horn.

Automatic telephone dialers.

Figure 5-17: Security symbols used with the floorplan drawing in Figure 5-16.

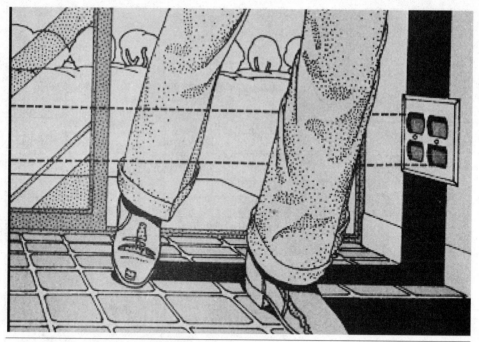

Figure 5-18: Transceivers and reflectors are located approximately 18 inches above the floor so that an intruder will break the beam.

protected by several methods, but in this case, infrared photoelectric entry detectors were used at the front door as shown in Figure 5-18. The transceivers are positioned at the locations indicated by appropriate symbol (1) and the reflectors are located directly opposite the transceivers on the opposite wall. Each of these units resembles a conventional quadruplex receptacle as shown in Figure 18. The centers of these outlets are located approximately 18 in above the finished floor so that an intruder will break the beam as shown.

If pets are allowed to roam in the home, the mounting height should be increased to keep the beam out of reach of pets, say, 36 in above the finished floor.

The sliding glass doors at the rear of the building could also be protected with photoelectric entry detectors. In fact, magnetic contacts are usually not recommended for sliding doors since the doors often become out of alignment, and the contacts will not function properly. In this case, however, the owners wanted a floor-mat entry detector as shown in Figure 5-19.

A scatter rug is a good medium for concealing floor-mat entry detectors, but there is always the problem of concealing the connector cord. In the case of the home under consideration, the scatter-rug connection was made in the crawl space beneath the floor — running the security circuit up through the floor and connecting directly to the floor-mat entry detector.

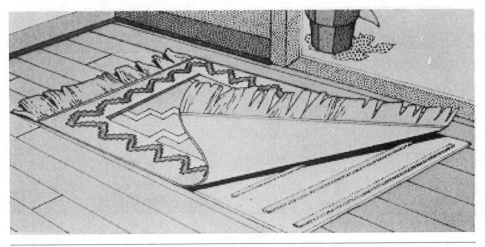

Figure 5-19: A scatter rug is a good medium for concealing floor-mat entry detectors.

Floor-mat entry detectors may also be used on stairways as shown in Figure 5-20. Furthermore, they are recommended for use in other interior locations that are likely to be used by intruders.

The kitchen door leading onto the carport is protected by conventional recessed magnetic contactors as shown in Figure 5-21. Again, either infrared photoelectric entry detectors or a floor-mat entry detector could have been used instead.

The items described thus far may be termed interior protective devices. Now, perimeter protection must be provided to ensure an intruder-proof home. Window foil is recommended for use on all windows, but many homeowners object to its

Figure 5-20: Floor-mat detectors may also be located on stairways.

appearance and prefer to go with magnetic detectors (preferably the recessed plunger type) on windows instead.

Figure 5-22 shows some possible locations for recessed magnetic detectors on doors and windows. These are the preferred type of magnetic detectors for new construction. However, when existing buildings are to be protected, the surface-mounted magnetic detectors are easier to install.

Of course, the system will need a delayed-entry control (Figure 5-23) and some means of sounding an alarm. A bell (Figure 5-24), horn (Figure 5-25), or telephone dialer (Figure 5-26) may be used.

If the security/fire-alarm system is operated by conventional house cur-

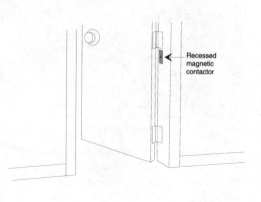

Figure 5-21: Recessed plunger-type detectors should be located on the hinge side of the door.

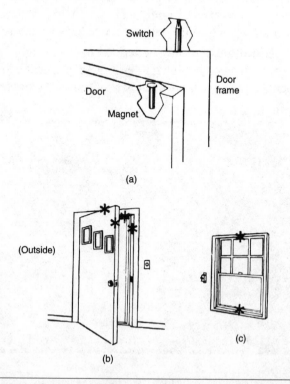

Figure 5-22: Some of the possible locations for recessed magnetic entry detectors.

Figure 5-23: A key-operated delayed entry control.

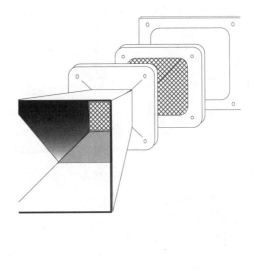

Figure 5-25: A horn is often used to alert neighbors that an intruder is on the premises.

Figure 5-24: A bell may be used as a means of sounding the alarm.

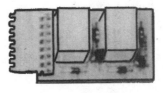

Figure 5-26: A telephone dialer is one means of notifying law-enforcement agencies without scaring off the intruder..

rent, you should install a battery backup system. Also, the security technician should consider some possible causes of false or unwanted alarms, as presented in the following list:

- Severe electrical storms

- Faulty smoke detector

- Faulty wiring; wire connections, staple cutting through insulation, insulation broken by severe bending, closely spaced bare wires which may touch if jarred by vibration of refrigerator, washer, dryer, furnace, etc.

- Electrical transients from heavy-duty appliances, such as refrigerators, relays, etc.

- The use of low-temperature heat detectors in a high-temperature environment, such as an attic or furnace room

- Concentration of sunlight on a heat detector or smoke detector

- Accidental activation of an intruder detector (opening protected door or window, exerting 80 pounds or more of pressure on floor mat, depressing an emergency alarm pushbutton)

- A momentary activation of an entry detector switch on the perimeter or interior detection circuit, caused by a severe vibration

- Shortwave or citizens band (CB) radio operating with excessive power near the home

Chapter 6
Commercial and Industrial Security Systems

The design of commercial and industrial systems is very similar to residential systems except that heavier-duty equipment is normally used and the goals are somewhat different from residential demands. This chapter covers the basic techniques necessary to design and calculate the material requirements for typical commercial and industrial occupancies.

The floor plan of a small commercial building is shown in Figure 6-1. A burglar-alarm panel and a telephone dialer (Figure 6-2) are located in the storage area. The relay-type control panel has one protective circuit, output for 6 V dc alarm-sending devices, and a silent holdup alarm with telephone dialer to dial emergency numbers and deliver voice messages.

Glass on the front door is protected with window foil connected to foil blocks which are then connected to the protective circuit wiring in the alarm system. Door cords are used to provide a flexible connection from the foil blocks on the door and window to a solid contact point adjacent to the door. See Figure 6-3. Flexible door cords also may be used on moving windows and money clips installed in cash drawers.

The large display window is again protected with foil connected to foil blocks, while the office area is protected by an ultrasonic motion detector as shown in Figure 6-4. A surface-mounted door contact (Figure 6-5) is used to protect the rear door of the building. Legal entry is permitted by use of a key lock.

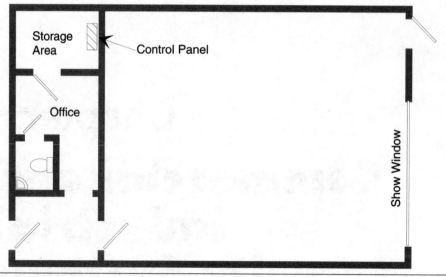

Figure 6-1: Floor plan of a small commercial building.

Figure 6-2: Relay-type control panel utilizing one protective circuit and having output for alarm-sounding devices and other detection/alarm capabilities.

Security Equipment for Commercial Applications

Magnetic contacts are used on doors and windows in closed-protective circuits, in direct-wire systems, and also in open-circuit applications. Movable elements within the protective switch unit of the magnetic contacts usually consist of a single flexible contact arm that provides a solid metal circuit path from the terminal

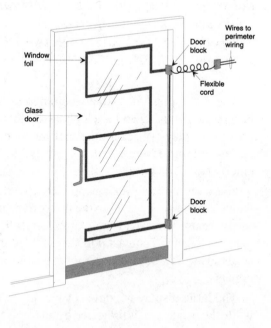

Figure 6-3: Glass door with security devices installed.

176

Figure 6-4: Ultrasonic motion detector.

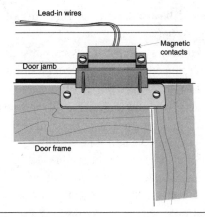

Figure 6-5: Surface-mounted door contact.

screw to the contact-point end. The circuit continuity should not depend upon conduction across a hinge joint or through a coil spring.

When magnetic contacts are mounted on either noncoplanar or ferromagnetic surfaces, magnet and/or switch units should be held away from their respective mounting surfaces as necessary to:

- Bring switch and magnet into close proximity when the door, window, etc. is closed.

- Reduce the shunting effect of ferromagnetic materials so that positive switch pull-in occurs when the magnet approaches to within $\frac{1}{4}$-in of the switch.

Mechanical contacts are used as emergency, panic, or fire-test switches. Ball contacts and plunger contacts (Figure 6-6) are used in both closed- and open-circuit applications.

Mercury contacts are sometimes used in low-energy alarm or signal systems to detect tilting of any horizontally hinged windows, door, cover, access panel, and the like. Due to the different items to be protected, it is best to install mercury contacts that can be adjusted to sensitivity after installation.

For combined detection of either opening or breakthrough, cord-mounted contacts with foil connected to takeoff terminals

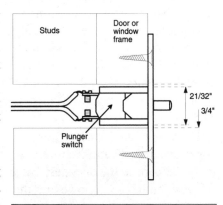

Figure 6-6: Cross-sectional view of plunger contacts.

should be used. Wiring diagrams of mercury contact connections are shown in Figure 6-7.

Holdup switches are usually installed under counters or desks in banks or stores, where an employee observing a holdup may be able to signal for help.

In banks and similar places where large amounts of money are exchanged, a money-clip alarm device is sometimes used. This device automatically triggers an alarm when all bills are removed from a cash drawer. A bill inserted in the clip holds its switch in the normal position. Additional bills on top of the clip keep it concealed. Bills may be added or removed as required for normal business operations as long as one remains in the clip. However, the removal of all bills trips the clip switch to signal an alarm.

Money-clip alarm devices should be installed in the largest bill compartment of cash drawers and connected to the building alarm system by means of a retractable door cord. If exceptionally busy working conditions create the possibility of a false alarm since the bill in the clip might be accidentally removed, two money clips should be used at each station and wired so that both must be emptied to cause an alarm.

Window foil is used extensively in commercial applications. For fixed windows, the connections to the building alarm system is usually made through foil blocks. For movable windows and doors, a retractable door cord must be used, or plunger contacts may be installed as shown in Figure 6-8.

Ultrasonic motion detectors for commercial applications are essentially the same as the ones described for residential use. However, the range of detection is sometimes extended on the units designed for

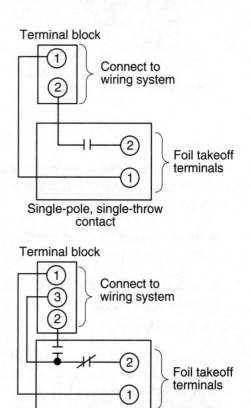

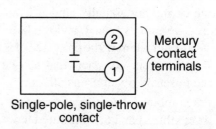

Figure 6-7: Wiring diagram of mercury contact connections.

commercial use. For example, a typical coverage pattern of a motion detector is shown in Figure 6-9. Note the coverage here is 15 ft wide by 30 ft deep.

Commercial telephone dialers are available that dial emergency numbers and deliver voice messages. Most distinguish between burglar and fire-alarm channels. A typical wiring diagram is shown in Figure 6-10.

Digital Alarm Transmitters

Digital alarm transmitters are relatively popular in the larger commercial establishments. Such devices can be programmed on memory chips to meet the exact requirements of any business.

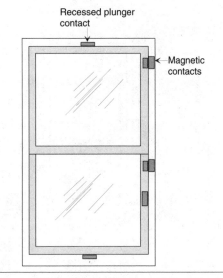

Figure 6-8: Location of plunger contacts in movable window.

In a typical model, each line (corresponding to an alarm code) is limited to 13 characters. A blank space between two words on the same line will take up one character.

These units are specifically designed for central-station monitoring of commercial buildings. The unit consists of a transmitter, a special module, and a subscriber control station.

One type of module has three input zones as follows:

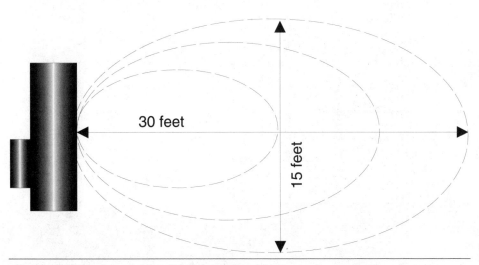

30 feet

15 feet

Figure 6-9: Typical coverage pattern of a motion detector.

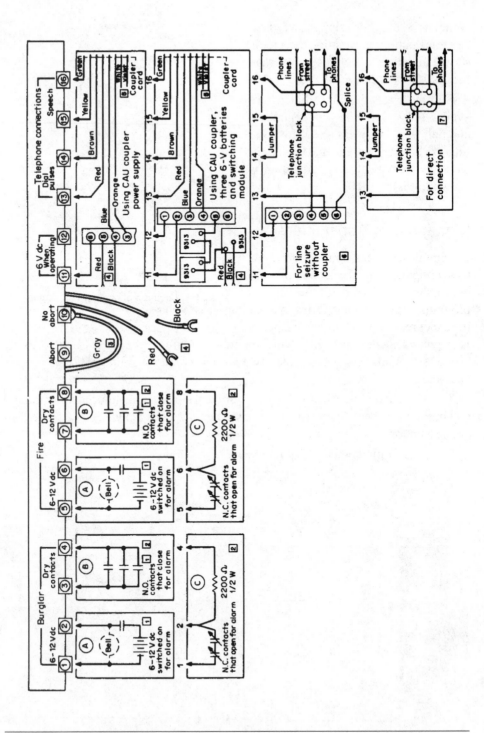

Figure 6-10: Wiring diagram of a commercial telephone dialer.

- Zone A: Two-wire, closed-circuit input generally used for a foil circuit. This zone may be 24-hour or key-controlled by the subscriber control station.

- Zone B: Three-wire, closed-circuit and open-circuit input for perimeter doors and windows. This zone is armed and disarmed by the subscriber control station. It can be connected to the detector contacts so that an open or a crossed circuit will produce an alarm.

- Zone C: Three-wire, closed circuit and open-circuit input for internal protection devices, such as ultrasonic motion detectors, infrared beams, passive infrared detectors, and the like. They may be wired so that either an open or a crossed circuit will produce an alarm.

Six output leads are provided from the module to trip the control as follows:

1. Zone A open
2. Zone B open or crossed
3. Zone C open or crossed
4. System armed (closed—night)
5. System disarmed (open—day)
6. Alarm circuit restored

Zones A and B may be connected to the same channel of the transmitter, thereby using only five channels for the module. If this is done, a daytime foil break will be reported as "perimeter alarm—day." The sixth channel may then be used for 24-hour reporting of fire alarm, holdup alarm, or equipment supervisory monitoring. A holdup alarm may also be connected to the same channel of the transmitter as Zone C. If this is done, a holdup would be indicated as "interior alarm—day."

When the subscriber leaves, an interior alarm will be tripped (which will be reported) and the perimeter door circuit will be tripped (which will be reported). A restore signal will be reported only when all three zones have returned to normal.

The subscriber control station consists of a key switch and two LED's mounted in a stainless steel plate. One LED indicates that all three zones are good. When the subscriber turns the key to arm the system, the second LED comes on, indicating that the transmitter is reporting the closing signal. This LED goes out when the signal is received at the central station.

Because the transmitter can report multiple signals on the same call, it is practical to locate the subscriber control station near the exit door. Consequently, if the subscriber arms the system and leaves immediately, the closing (interior alarm), perimeter alarm, and restore signal will all be transmitted on a single call. This will take about 30 seconds (including dialing time). The receiver at the central station will be tied up for about 15 seconds after it answers the call.

Surveillance cameras are being used extensively in banks and stores to prevent holdups, pilferage, and burglaries. Since thieves are notoriously camera-shy, the presence of a surveillance camera is often sufficient to make a would-be robber change his or her mind. If a business should be robbed, a surveillance camera provides sharp evidence to aid police and courts.

Most surveillance cameras can be adjusted to take individual still pictures at preset intervals to keep a continuous eye on the premises. The Super 8 Kodak Surveillance camera, for example, provides continual recorded surveillance for up to 180 hours with each 100 ft roll of film. There are up to 7200 individual photographs to assist in positive identification and apprehension. This camera can be activated by a switch on the camera, by remote control, or automatically by relay from the external alarm system.

Video tapes have been substituted for film in recent years, but the principle is basically the same.

Miscellaneous Security Equipment

Vibration detectors are often used on buildings to detect vibrations caused by forced entry. Such detectors have been used on a variety of construction materials such as hollow tile, plaster and lath, brick, concrete, metal ceilings, wood, and concrete block with brick veneer. Once mounted in place, they may be adjusted with a set screw for the desired sensitivity.

Some establishments maintain a security fence equipped with fence-guard detectors. This type of detector will detect climbing, cutting, or any other penetration of the fenced area. Most of these detectors operate on standard closed-circuit controls as described previously.

Fence-guard detectors use a vertical-motion detector that is sensitive to movement created by climbing or cutting the fence. Normal side motions such as wind or accidental bumping do not affect the detector and cause false alarms. They are normally mounted about midway up the fence, and every 10 ft of fence length. Most of these devices set off the alarm if they are tampered with or if the wire is cut. they may be connected to a control panel and the alarm will "sound" in the form of a bell or horn, or it will silently dial the local law-enforcement agency.

Outdoor microwave detectors are used for protecting large outdoor areas like parking lots, construction sites, and building perimeters. In operation, a solid circular beam of microwave energy extends from a transmitter to the receiver over a range of up to 1500 ft. Any movement inside of this beam (Figure 6-11) will activate the alarm.

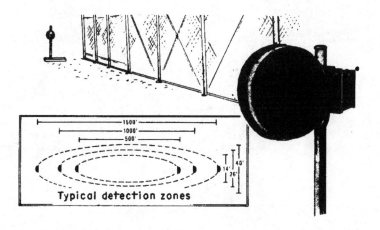

Figure 6-11: A solid circular beam of microwave energy extends from a transmitter to the receiver over a range of up to 1500 ft.

Thermistor Sensors

The continuous linear thermal sensor is a small-diameter coaxial wire that is capable of sensing temperature changes along its entire length. The sensor is made up of a center conductor and an outer stainless steel sheath. The center conductor is electrically insulated from the outer sheath by a ceramic thermistor material.

The term thermistor is derived from the words "thermal resistor." Thermistors are actually thermally-sensitive semiconductor devices and consist of two basic types:

- NTC (negative temperature coefficient)

- PTC (positive temperature coefficient)

An NTC will decrease its resistance as the temperature increases. The PTC thermistor will increase its resistance as the temperature increases. Of the two types, the NTC thermistor is the most widely used.

Thermistors are highly nonlinear devices and are therefore difficult to use for measuring temperature. Devices utilizing thermistors must be calibrated for the particular type of thermistor being used. If the thermistor is ever replaced, it has to be an exact replacement or the circuit will no longer operate correctly.

Thermistors are used as set-point detectors as opposed to actual temperature measurement. A set-point detector is a device that activates some process or circuit when the temperature reaches a certain level.

183

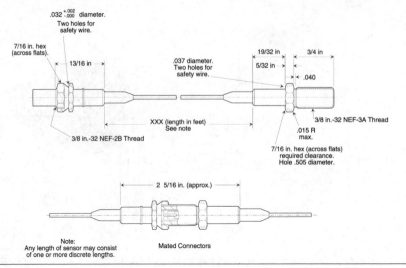

Figure 6-12: Using connectors to supply desired length of sensor cable.

Since the thermistor has a negative coefficient of resistance, in our case, the electrical resistance between the center wire and the outer sheath decreases exponentially as the surrounding temperature increases.

The changing resistance is monitored by one of several control panels which then can actuate extinguishing systems or any other electrically controlled devices.

Such sensors have a diameter of approximately 0.080 in and therefore have a small mass which permits them to sense changes in temperature rapidly. They can sense temperatures from 70°F up to 1200°F, if the thermistor material is properly selected.

Since electrical resistance is measured across two wires (center to sheath), the sensor has the ability to detect a high temperature on a short wire as well as a lower temperature on a longer one.

The element is mounted by clamps spaced along their lengths and the detectors, being all solid state, have only two electrical failure modes: open-circuit and short-circuit. Both of these conditions can be caused only by mechanical means and are minimized by rigid mounting. Figure 6-12 shows the construction and mounting details.

Ultraviolet-Radiation Devices

Ultraviolet-radiation fire detectors combine large-scale integration circuit techniques with an ultraviolet detection assembly to form a simple, yet flexible, fire-detection system.

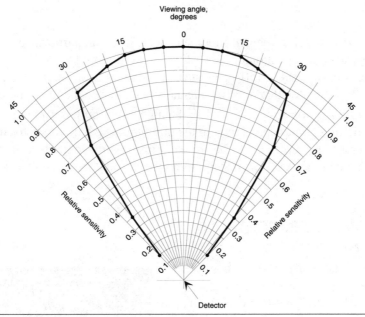

Figure 6-12: Viewing angle of an ultraviolet detector.

The basis of this type of system is a gas-detection tube employing the Geiger-Mueller principle to detect radiation wave lengths of a certain length. It should be noted that visible radiation does not extend into the detector's sensitive area. Similarly, radiation from artificial lighting sources does not extend into the detector's sensitive area.

Welding arcs and lightning strikes, however, will generate radiation to which the detectors are sensitive and precautions must be taken to minimize these effects.

The ultraviolet-radiation detector's focus of sensitive points is a 60-degree spherical cone whose apex lies at the detector tube. Figure 6-12 indicates the relationship between viewing angle and relative sensitivity. The sensitivity of the detector tube is a characteristic of its cathode material and is fixed, but its Vage-pulse output rate is directly proportional to flame size; that is, it increases when larger flame fronts are presented to the detector. The pulse output rate is also inversely proportional to the distance of the flame front from the detector tube — the pulse output rate decreases as the distance from the detector tube to the flame front increases.

To illustrate, a 1 ft^2 hydrocarbon fire will cause a pulse output rate of 3 pulses per second at a viewing distance of 30 ft. This same fire will cause a tube pulse output rate of 20 pulses per second at a viewing distance of 20 ft. In a like manner, a 1 ft^2 flame front must be located at a distance of 5 ft to create a pulse output rate of 30 pulses per second, a 16 ft^2 fire will create the same pulse output rate at a distance of 25 ft.

Firestat

A *firestat* is a safety device mounted in the fan compartment of a heating, ventilating, and air-conditioning (HVAC) system to stop the fan if the return air temperature reaches about 160°F. Most firestats are bimetal actuated and utilize a normally closed switch that must be manually reset before the fan can operate.

The reason for stopping the fan when the high return air temperature exists is to prevent agitation of any open flame in the building, which in turn helps to prevent the spreading of any fire that may be present. Firestats are required on all residential and commercial HVAC systems; in some areas, other safety devices are also required.

SECURITY-SYSTEM CONTROLS

A typical burglar/fire-alarm control panel is shown in Figure 6-13. This particular panel is designed for combined burglar-, fire-, and panic-alarm systems. This panel, and most others, operate on low-voltage, alternating current from a plug-in transformer. Many systems also have a rechargeable or dry cell battery pack for backup power should the ac source fail.

A wiring diagram for a rechargeable 6-V dc power supply is shown in Figure 6-14. Note that the transformer is connected to a 120-V ac supply for it pri-

Figure 6-13: Typical burglar/fire-alarm control panel.

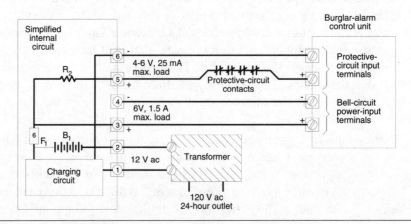

Figure 6-14: Wiring diagram for a rechargeable 6-V dc power supply.

mary connection; the transformer then supplies 12-V ac from its secondary. One terminal from the transformer connects to the charging circuit (1) while the other lead connects to one side of the battery (B1). Fuse F1 and resistor R2 offer 6-A circuit protection in this case. R2 also provides short-circuit protection.

The protective-circuit contacts from terminal 5 utilize a 100-W, 2-W resistor in the positive feed to each circuit to keep a cross or short-circuit on any one zone from affecting other zones.

Fire-Alarm Control Panels

The heart of any fire-alarm system is the master control panel. To this panel are connected various detector and alarm circuits, as shown in Figure 6-15. In this case, the primary power is taken from an unswitched single-phase, three-wire, 120/240-V ac distribution line. The initiating and alarm circuits are connected to the neutral ground and one leg of the main or ungrounded side of the circuit. The trouble-indicating circuits are connected to the neutral ground and to the ungrounded or opposite leg of the circuit.

When an automatic detector or manual station is activated, the contacts close to complete a circuit path and apply 120 V ac to the alarm control circuits in the main panel. This includes a synchronous motor on some systems, which immediately operates cam assemblies that cause the alarm circuit switch contacts to make and break in a code sequence (if a code sequence is used). Additional cam-controlled switches stop the motor and alarm signals after a predetermined time lapse and actuate the alarm buzzer on the main panel.

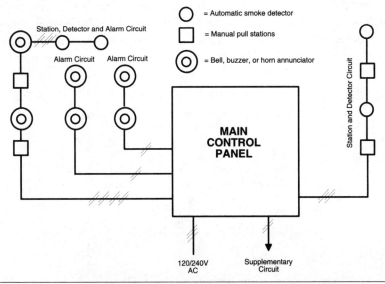

Figure 6-15: Wiring diagram of a fire-alarm main control panel with its connecting detector circuits.

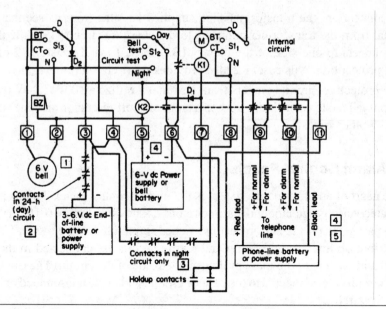

Figure 6-16: Schematic drawing of a day-night police control panel.

Most control panels contain a supplementary relay control for connection to an external auxiliary circuit providing its own electrical power. The relay usually has a single-pole, double-throw contact, which operates in step with the master code signal. The circuit may be used to activate other auxiliary alarms or controls, such as a city fire-department connection, fan shutdown, or door release.

A schematic drawing of a day-night police panel is shown in Figure 6-16 while key switch operating sequences are depicted in Figure 6-17. In general, any DAY circuit contact opening sounds the buzzer in the panel but does not ring the alarm bell or disturb police. A holdup contact closure sends a silent police alarm.

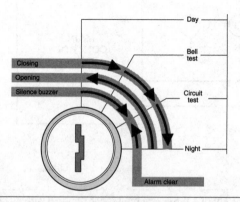

Figure 6-17: Connection detail of entry/exit delay module.

On the BELL TEST circuit, the bell can be rung for a test to check the power source and wiring without disturbing the police, but the holdup circuit remains armed during this test.

During the CIRCUIT TEST sequence, the holdup circuit remains armed and the meter shows the current through DAY and NIGHT circuits combined when all contacts are closed. A reading on this particular circuit should be from 2 to 6 mA.

Any contact opening (or cross) in the DAY or NIGHT circuits rings the alarm bell and sends the police alarm. This alarm latches on until the key switch is turned back to CIRCUIT TEST or beyond.

Entry/Exit Delay Module

Solid-state entry/exit delay modules eliminate the need to install a shunt lock across any entry/exit door contacts in a security system. Door contacts are connected to the module, which in turn is wired into the protective circuit. Separately adjustable exit and entry delay periods allow the user to turn the system on and leave and then enter and shut the system off without causing alarms.

The module is installed in the alarm system control cabinet as shown in Figure 28. It operates on current from the system's bell battery or power supply and is controlled by the switch functions available in any conventional control unit. It works like a normally closed contact in the negative side of the protective circuit, with all the protective contacts except the entry/exit door contacts wired into the

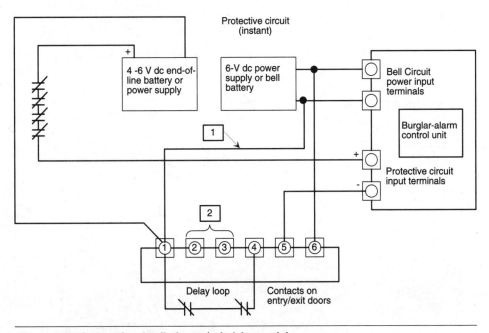

Figure 6-18: Connection detail of entry/exit delay module.

positive side of the circuit. Opening of any positive-side contacts causes an instant alarm, but the module opens the negative side to cause an alarm only when one of the following occurs:

1. Door contacts have opened once and are still open when the exit delay expires.
2. Door contacts open after the exit delay expires when there was not an exit during the exit delay period.
3. Door contacts open after a proper exit and the system is not shut on before the entry delay expires.

Ultrasonic Motion Detectors

Ultrasonic detectors work by flooding an area with ultrasonic energy and monitoring the "sound" that returns to the detector from the covered area. In the absence of motion, the received sound is all of a single frequency. Movement of an object in the protected space shifts the frequency of some of the reflected sound, changing the output of the receiving transducer. But such frequency shifts can also be caused by certain environmental factors that must be taken into consideration at installation if false alarms are to be avoided.

Chapter 7

Printreading for Technicians

Anyone involved in the installation or maintenance of security systems will often encounter several types of drawings. This chapter introduces the layout of drawings and the symbols used on them. It further describes the various types of drawings and how to read them.

ARCHITECTURAL DRAWINGS

In all large construction projects and in many of the smaller ones, an architect is commissioned to prepare complete working drawings and specifications for the project. These drawings usually include:

- A plot plan indicating the location of the building on the property.

- Floor plans showing the walls and partitions for each floor or level.

- Elevations of all exterior faces of the building.

- Several vertical cross sections to indicate clearly the various floor levels and details of the footings, foundation, walls, floors, ceilings, and roof construction.

- Large-scale detail drawings showing such construction details as may be required.

For projects of any consequence, the architect usually hires consulting engineers to prepare structural, electrical, and mechanical drawings — the latter encompassing pipe-fitting, instrumentation, plumbing, heating, ventilating, and air conditioning drawings.

Plot Plan

This type of plan of the building site is as if the site is viewed from an airplane and shows the property boundaries, the existing contour lines, the new contour lines (after grading), the location of the building on the property, new and existing roadways, all utility lines, and other pertinent details. Descriptive notes may also be found on the plot plan listing names of adjacent property owners, the land surveyor, and the date of the survey. A legend or symbol list is also included so that anyone who must work with site plans can readily read the information. See Figure 7-1.

Floor Plans

The plan view of any object is a drawing showing the outline and all details as seen when looking directly down on the object. It shows only two dimensions — length and width. The floor plan of a building is drawn as if a slice was taken through the building — about window height — and then the top portion removed to reveal the bottom part where the slice was taken. See Figure 7-2.

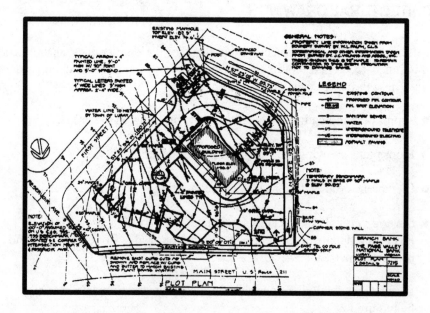

Figure 7-1: A typical plot plan.

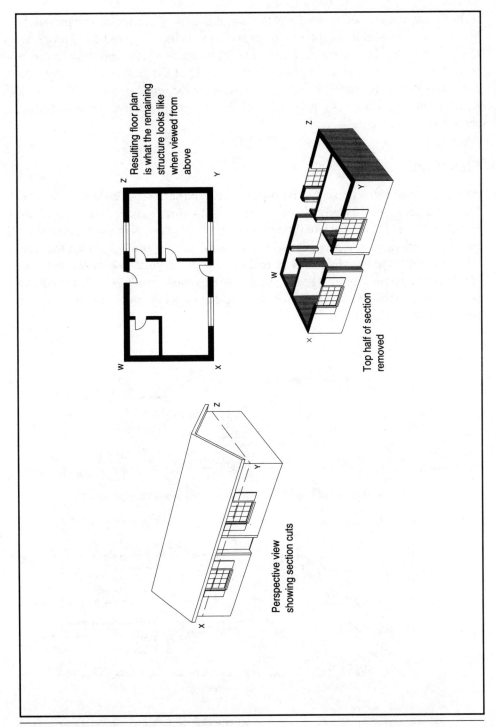

Resulting floor plan is what the remaining structure looks like when viewed from above

Top half of section removed

Perspective view showing section cuts

Figure 7-2: Principles of floorplan layout.

Let's say that we first wanted a plan view of a home's basement. The part of the house above the middle of the basement windows is imagined to be cut away. By looking down on the uncovered portion, every detail, partition, and the like can be seen. Likewise, imagine the part above the middle of the first floor windows cut away and a drawing made looking straight down at the remaining part. This would be called the first floor plan. A cut through the second floor windows would be the second floor plan, etc.

Elevations

A plan view may represent a flat surface, a curved surface, or a slanting one, but for clarification it is usually necessary to refer to elevations and sections of the building. The elevation is an outline of an object that shows heights and may show the length or width of a particular side, but not depth. Figure 7-3 shows the front and rear elevation drawings for a building, while Figure 7-4 shows the side elevations of the same building. Note that these elevation drawings show the heights of windows, doors, porches, the pitch of roofs, etc. — all of which cannot be shown conveniently on floor plans.

FRONT ELEVATION

REAR ELEVATION

Figure 7-3: Front and rear elevations of a building.

LEFT ELEVATION

RIGHT ELEVATION

Figure 7-4: Side elevations of the building in Figure 7-3.

Elevation drawings are quite useful to security-system technicians for determining the number and sizes of all windows and doors. The types of windows and doors are also visible — giving the necessary information to select the kind of door and window contacts to use on the system.

Sections

A section or sectional view of an object is a view facing a point where a part of an object is supposed to be cut away, allowing the viewer to see the object's inside. The point on the plan or elevation showing where the imaginary cut has been made is indicated by the section line, which is usually a very heavy double dot-and-dash line. The section line shows the location of the section on the plan or elevation. It is, therefore, necessary to know which of the cutaway parts is represented in the sectional drawing when an object is represented as if it was cut in two. Arrow points are thus placed at the ends of the sectional lines.

In architectural drawings it is often necessary to show more than one section on the same drawing. The different section lines must be distinguished by letters, numbers, or other designations placed at the ends of the lines as shown in Figure 7-5, in which the sections are lettered A-A and B-B. These section letters are generally heavy and large so as to stand out on the drawings. To further avoid confusion, the same letter is usually placed at each end of the section line. The section is named according to these letters — that is, Section A-A, Section B-B, and so forth.

A longitudinal section is taken length-wise while a cross section is usually taken straight across the width of an object. Sometimes, however, a section is not taken along one straight line. It is often taken along a zigzag line to show important parts of the object.

A sectional view, as applied to architectural drawings, is a drawing showing the building, or portion of a building, as though cut through, as if by a saw, on some imaginary line. This line may be either vertical (straight up and down) or horizontal. Wall sections are nearly always made vertically so that the cut edge is exposed from top to bottom. In some ways the wall section is one of the most important of all the drawings to construction workers, because it answers the questions on how a structure is built. The floor plans of a building show how each floor is arranged, but the wall sections tell how each part is constructed and usually indicate the material to be used. The security technician needs to know this information when laying out the security/fire-alarm system to determine the location and mounting techniques of the alarm devices, the routing of the conductors, estimating the quantity of materials, and choosing wiring methods that comply with the latest edition of the NEC.

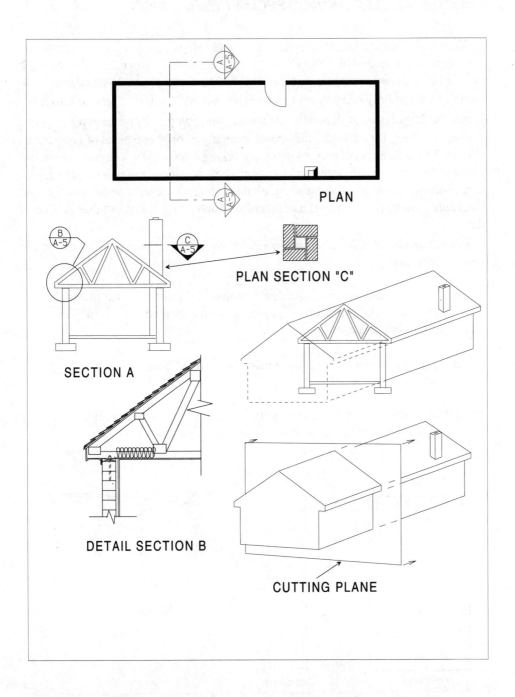

PLAN

PLAN SECTION "C"

SECTION A

DETAIL SECTION B

CUTTING PLANE

Figure 7-5: The principles of showing sections on working drawings and prints.

ELECTRICAL/ELECTRONICS SECURITY DRAWINGS

The ideal electrical/electronics drawing should show in a clear, concise manner exactly what is required of the workers. The amount of data shown on such drawings should be sufficient, but not overdone. This means that a complete set of drawings could consist of only one $8\frac{1}{2} \times 11$ in sheet, or it could consist of several dozen 24 $\times$ 36 in (or larger) sheets, depending on the size and complexity of the given project. A shop drawing, for example, may contain details of only one piece of equipment (Figure 7-6), while a set of security-system working drawings for a large commercial installation may contain dozens of drawing sheets detailing the layout and location of all security devices in the building, along with equipment, controls, connection diagrams, schematic diagrams, equipment schedules and a host of other pertinent data.

In general, electrical/electronics working drawings for a given project serve three distinct functions:

- To give contractors an exact description of the project so that materials and labor may be estimated in order to form a total cost of the project for bidding purposes.

- To give workers on the project instructions as to how the security system is to be installed.

- To provide a "map" of the security system once the job is completed to aid in maintenance and troubleshooting for years to come.

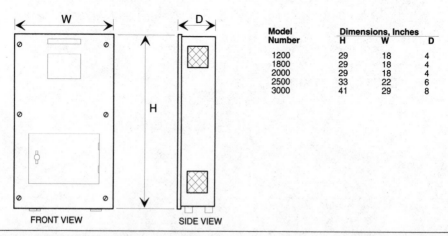

Model	Dimensions, Inches		
Number	H	W	D
1200	29	18	4
1800	29	18	4
2000	29	18	4
2500	33	22	6
3000	41	29	8

FRONT VIEW   SIDE VIEW

Figure 7-6: A shop drawing of a fire-alarm control panel. This gives the necessary dimensions for "roughing-in" the panel during the construction or renovation of the building.

Security-system drawings from manufacturers and consulting engineering firms will vary in quality from sketchy, incomplete drawings to neat, very complete drawings that are easy to understand. Few, however, will cover every exact detail of the system. Therefore, a good knowledge of installation practices must go hand-in-hand with interpreting security-system working drawings.

Sometimes security-system contractors will have drafters prepare special supplemental drawings for use by the contractors' employees. On certain projects, these supplemental drawings can save supervision time in the field once the project has begun.

DRAWING LAYOUT

Although a strong effort has been made to standardize drawing practices in the industry, seldom will working drawings — prepared by different architectural or engineering firms — be identical. Similarities, however, will exist between most sets of prints, and with a little experience, you should have little trouble interpreting any set of drawings that might be encountered.

Most drawings used for building construction projects will be drawn on drawing paper from 11×17 in to 24×36 in size. Each drawing sheet will have border lines framing the overall drawing and a title block as shown in Figure 7-7. Note that the type and size of title blocks vary with each firm preparing the drawings. In addition, some drawing sheets will also contain a revision block near the title block, and

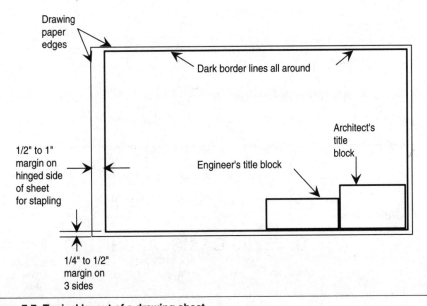

Figure 7-7: Typical layout of a drawing sheet.

199

perhaps an approval block. This information is normally found on each drawing sheet, regardless of the type of project or the information contained on the sheet.

Title Block

The title block for a print or technical drawing is usually boxed in the lower right-hand corner of the drawing sheet; the size of the block varies with the size of the drawing and also with the information required. See Figure 7-8.

In general, the title block of a security-system drawing should contain the following:

- Name of the project

- Address of the project

- Name of the owner or client

- Name of the architectural and/or engineering firm

- Date of completion

- Scale(s)

- Initial of the drafter, checker, and designer, with dates under each

- Job number

- Sheet number

- General description of the drawing

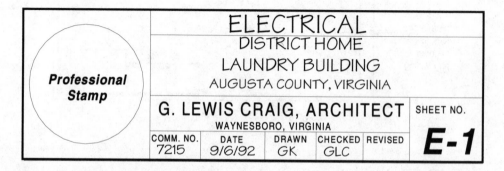

Figure 7-8: Typical architect's title block.

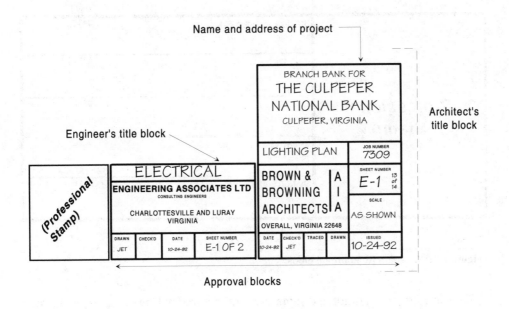

Figure 7-9: Completed engineering and architectural title blocks.

Every architectural/engineering firm has its own standard for drawing titles, and they are often preprinted directly on the tracing paper or else printed on "stick-on" paper which is placed on the drawing.

Often the consulting engineering firm will also be listed, which means that an additional title block will be applied to the drawing — usually next to the architect's title block. In some cases, the security equipment supplier will also appear. Figure 7-9 shows completed architectural and engineering title blocks as they appeared on an actual drawing.

Approval Block

The "approval block," in most cases, will appear on the drawing sheet as shown in Figure 7-10. The various types of approval blocks — drawn, checked, etc. — will be initialed by the appropriate personnel. This type of approval block is usually part of the title block and appears on each drawing sheet.

Figure 7-10: One type of approval block used on electrical drawings.

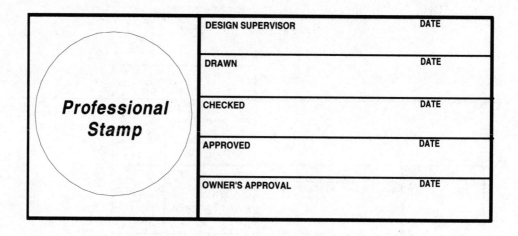

Figure 7-11: An alternate approval block.

On some projects, authorized signatures are required before certain systems may be installed, or even before the project begins. An approval block such as the one shown in Figure 10-11 indicates that all required personnel has checked the drawings for accuracy, and that the set meets with everyone's approval. Such approval blocks usually appear on the front sheet of the print set and may include:

- Professional stamp — registered seal of approval by the architect or consulting engineer.

- Design supervisor's signature — the person who is overseeing the design.

- Drawn (by) — signature or initials of the person who drafted the drawing and the date it was completed.

- Checked (by) — signature or initials of the person(s) who reviewed the drawing and the date of approval.

- Approved — signature of initials of the architect/engineer and the date of the approval.

- Owner's approval — signatuare of the project owner or the owner's representative along with the date signed.

REVISIONS				
REV	DESCRIPTION	DR	APP'D	DATE
1	FIXTURE No. 3 IN LIGHTING-FIXTURE SCHDL	BD	GLC	10/12/92

Professional Stamp	ELECTRICAL DISTRICT HOME LAUNDRY BUILDING AUGUSTA COUNTY, VIRGINIA	
	G. LEWIS CRAIG, ARCHITECT WAYNESBORO, VIRGINIA	SHEET NO.

COMM. NO.	DATE	DRAWN	CHECKED	REVISED	E-1
7215	9/6/92	GK	GLC		

Figure 7-12: One method of showing revisions on working drawings.

Revision Block

Sometimes security-system drawings will have to be partially redrawn or modified during the installation of a system. It is extremely important that such modifications are noted and dated on the drawings to ensure that the workers have an up-to-date set to work from. In some situations, sufficient space is left near the title block for dates and description of revisions. In other cases, a revision block is provided (again, near the title block) as shown in Figure 7-12. But these two samples are by no means the only types or styles of revision blocks that will be seen on electrical working drawings — not by any means. Each architect/engineer/designer/drafter has his or her own method of showing revisions, so expect to find deviations from those shown.

DRAFTING LINES

All drafting lines have one thing in common — they are all the same color. However, good easy-to-read contrasting lines can be made by varying the width of the lines or else "breaking" the lines in some uniform way.

Figure 7-13 on the next page shows common lines used on architectural drawings. However, these lines can vary. Architects and engineers have strived for a common "standard" for the past century, but unfortunately, their goal has yet to be reached. Therefore, you will find variations in lines and symbols from drawing to drawing, so always consult the legend or symbol list when referring to an architectural or

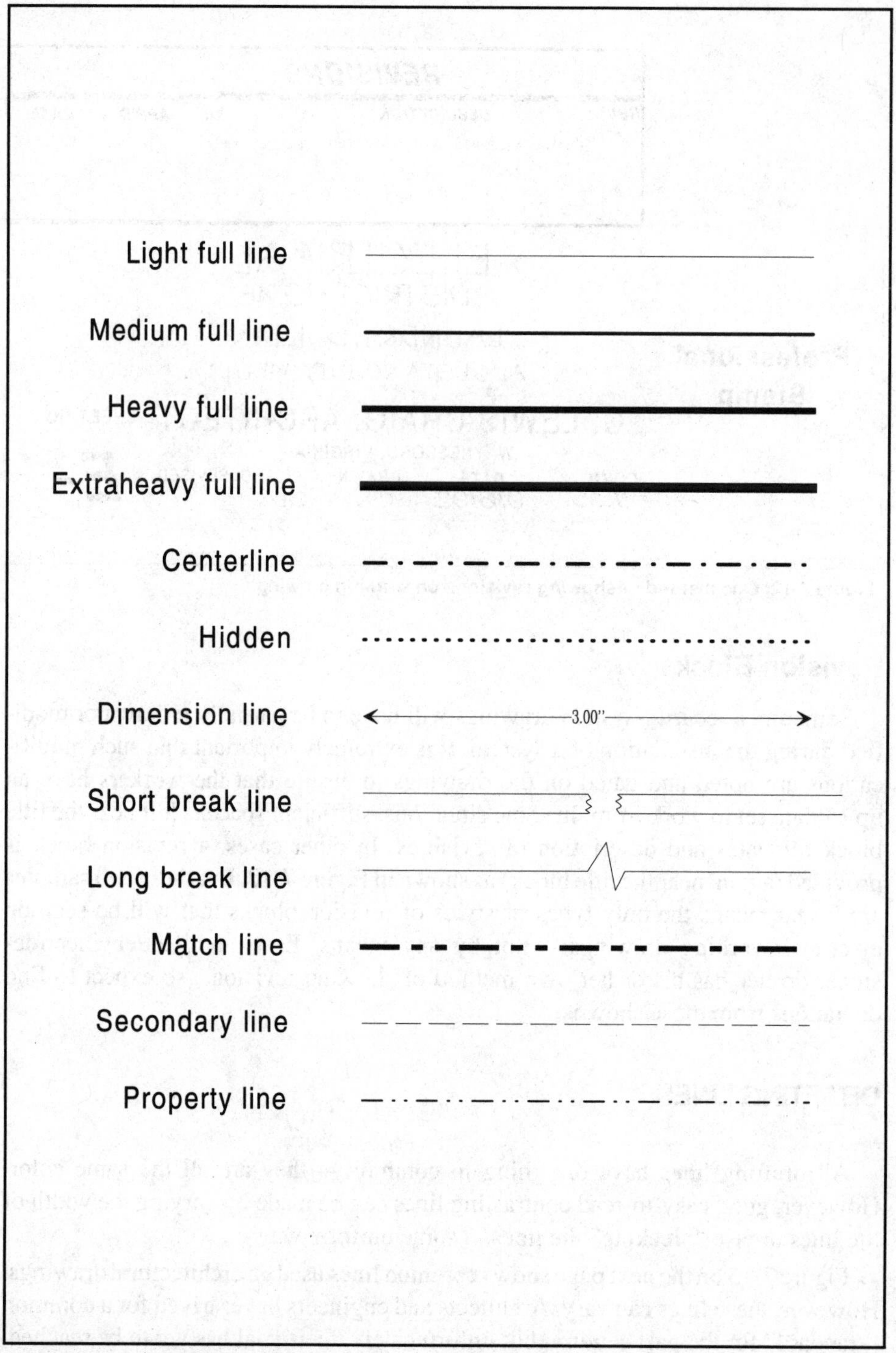

Light full line

Medium full line

Heavy full line

Extraheavy full line

Centerline

Hidden

Dimension line ————————3.00"————————→

Short break line

Long break line

Match line

Secondary line

Property line

Figure 7-13: Typical drafting lines.

electrical drawing. Also carefully inspect each drawing to ensure that line types are used consistently.

A brief description of the drafting lines shown in Figure 7-15 follows:

Light Full Line - This line is used for section lines, building background (outlines), and similar uses where the object to be drawn is secondary to the electrical system.

Medium Full Line - This type of line is frequently used for hand lettering on a drawing. It is further used for some drawing symbols, circuit lines, and the like.

Heavy Full Line - This line is used for borders around title blocks, schedules and for hand lettering drawing titles. Some types of symbols are frequently drawn with the heavy full line.

Extraheavy Full Line - This line is used for border lines on architectural/engineering drawings.

Centerline - A centerline is a broken line made up of long and short dashes alternately spaced. It indicates the centers of objects such as, hole, pillars, or fixtures. Sometimes, the centerline indicates the dimensions of a finished floor.

Hidden Line - A hidden line consists of a series of short dashes closely and evenly spaced. It shows the edges of objects that are not visible in a particular view. The object outlined by hidden lines in one drawing is often fully pictured in another drawing.

Dimension Lines - These are thinly drawn lines used to show the extent and direction of dimensions. The dimension is usually placed in a break inside of the dimension lines. Normal practice is to place the dimension lines outside the object's outline. However, sometimes it may be necessary to draw the dimensions inside the outline.

Short Break Line - This line is usually drawn freehand and is used for short breaks.

Long Break Line - This line which is drawn partly with a straightedge and partly with freehand zigzags, is used for long breaks.

Match Line - This line is used to show the position of the cutting plane. Therefore, it is also called cutting plane line. A match or cutting plane line is an extraheavy line with long dashes alternating with two short dashes. It is used on drawings of large structures to show where one drawing stops and the next drawing starts.

Secondary Line - This line is frequently used to outline pieces of equipment or to indicate reference points of a drawing that is secondary to the drawing's purpose.

Property Line - This is a line made up of one long and two short dashes alternately spaced. It indicates land boundaries on the site plan.

Other uses of the lines just mentioned include the following:

Extension Lines - Extension lines are lightweight lines that start about $1/16$ in away from an object's edge and extend out. A common use of extension lines is to create a boundary for dimension lines. Dimension lines meet extension lines with arrowheads, slashes, or dots. Extension lines that point from a note or other reference to a particular feature on a drawing are called *leaders*. They usually end in either an arrowhead, a slash or a dot and may include an explanatory note at the end.

Section Lines - These are often referred to as *cross-hatch lines*. Drawn at a 45-degree angle, these lines show where an object has been cut away to reveal the inside.

Phantom Lines - Phantom lines are solid, light lines that show where an object will be installed. A future door opening or a future piece of equipment can be shown with phantom lines.

Electrical Drafting Lines

Besides the architectural lines shown in Figure 7-13, consulting electrical engineers, designers, manufacturers of security equipment and components and their drafters use additional lines to represent circuits and their related components. Again, these lines may vary from drawing to drawing, so check the symbol list or legend for the exact meaning of lines on the drawing with which you are working. Figure 7-14 shows lines used on some electrical drawings.

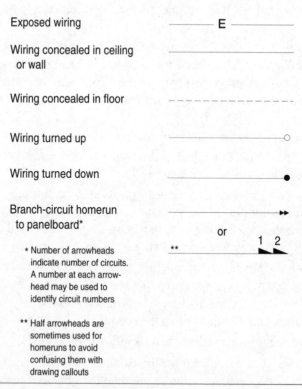

Exposed wiring

Wiring concealed in ceiling
  or wall

Wiring concealed in floor

Wiring turned up

Wiring turned down

Branch-circuit homerun
  to panelboard*

    * Number of arrowheads
    indicate number of circuits.
    A number at each arrow-
    head may be used to
    identify circuit numbers

    ** Half arrowheads are
    sometimes used for
    homeruns to avoid
    confusing them with
    drawing callouts

Figure 7-14: Circuit lines used on electrical drawings.

ELECTRICAL SYMBOLS

The electrician must be able to correctly read and understand electrical working drawings which includes a thorough knowledge of electrical symbols and their application.

An electrical symbol is a figure or mark that stands for a component used in the electrical system. For example, Figure 7-15 on the next page shows a list of electrical symbols that are currently recommended by the American National Standards Institute (ANSI). It is evident from this list of symbols that many have the same basic form, but, because of some slight difference, their meaning changes. A good procedure to follow in learning symbols is to first learn the basic form and then apply the variations for obtaining different meanings.

It would be much simpler if all architects, engineers, security equipment manufacturers, electrical designers, and drafters used the same symbols. However, this is not the case. Although standardization is getting closer to a reality, existing symbols are still modified and new symbols are created for almost every new project.

The electrical symbols described in the following paragraphs represent those found on actual electrical working drawings throughout the United States and Canada. Many are similar to those recommended by ANSI and the Consulting Engineers Council/US; others are not. Understanding how these symbols were devised will help you to interpret unknown electrical symbols in the future.

Some of the symbols used on security-system drawings are abbreviations, such as WP for weatherproof and AFF for above finished floor. Others are simplified pictographs. In some cases, the symbols are combinations of abbreviations and pictographs. Several symbols used on security-system drawings are shown in Figure 7-16 beginning on page 209.

Circuit and feeder wiring symbols are getting closer to being standardized. Most circuits concealed in the ceiling or wall are indicated by a solid line; a broken line is used for circuits concealed in the floor or ceiling below; and exposed raceways are indicated by short dashes or else the letter E placed in the same plane with the circuit line at various intervals.

The number of conductors in a cable, conduit or raceway system may be indicated in the panelboard schedule under the appropriate column, or the information may be shown on the floor plan.

Symbols for communication and signal systems, as well as symbols for light and power, are drawn to an appropriate scale and accurately located with respect to the building; this reduces the number of references made to the architectural drawings. Where extreme accuracy is required in locating outlets and equipment, exact dimensions are given on larger-scale drawings and shown on the plans.

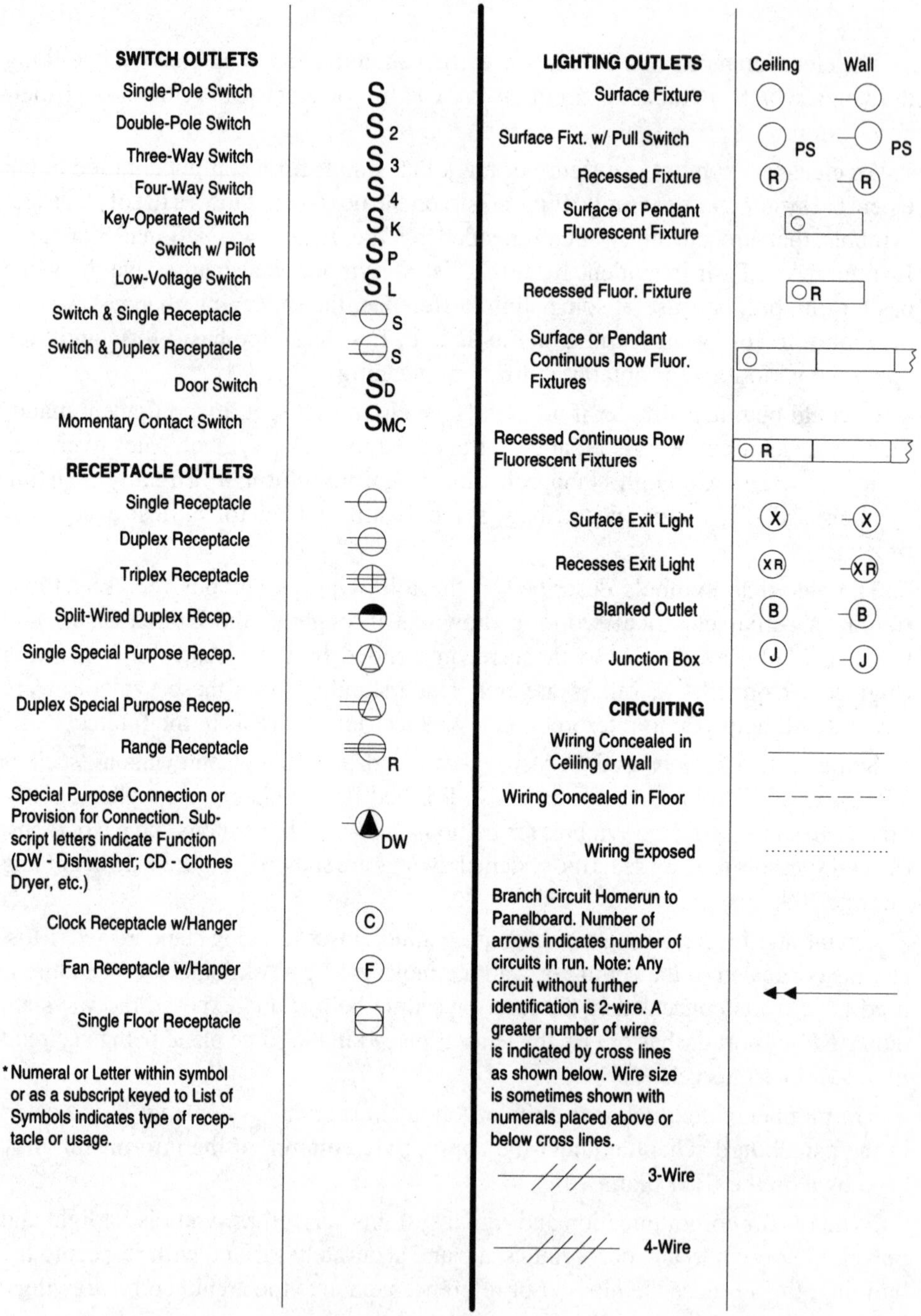

SWITCH OUTLETS

Single-Pole Switch

Double-Pole Switch

Three-Way Switch

Four-Way Switch

Key-Operated Switch

Switch w/ Pilot

Low-Voltage Switch

Switch & Single Receptacle

Switch & Duplex Receptacle

Door Switch

Momentary Contact Switch

S
S_2
S_3
S_4
S_K
S_P
S_L
$\ominus S$
$\ominus S$
S_D
S_{MC}

RECEPTACLE OUTLETS

Single Receptacle

Duplex Receptacle

Triplex Receptacle

Split-Wired Duplex Recep.

Single Special Purpose Recep.

Duplex Special Purpose Recep.

Range Receptacle

R

Special Purpose Connection or
Provision for Connection. Sub-
script letters indicate Function
(DW - Dishwasher; CD - Clothes
Dryer, etc.)

DW

Clock Receptacle w/Hanger

C

Fan Receptacle w/Hanger

F

Single Floor Receptacle

* Numeral or Letter within symbol
or as a subscript keyed to List of
Symbols indicates type of receptacle or usage.

LIGHTING OUTLETS

	Ceiling	Wall
Surface Fixture		
Surface Fixt. w/ Pull Switch	PS	PS
Recessed Fixture	R	R
Surface or Pendant Fluorescent Fixture		
Recessed Fluor. Fixture	R	
Surface or Pendant Continuous Row Fluor. Fixtures		
Recessed Continuous Row Fluorescent Fixtures	R	
Surface Exit Light	X	X
Recesses Exit Light	X R	X R
Blanked Outlet	B	B
Junction Box	J	J

CIRCUITING

Wiring Concealed in
Ceiling or Wall

Wiring Concealed in Floor

Wiring Exposed

Branch Circuit Homerun to
Panelboard. Number of
arrows indicates number of
circuits in run. Note: Any
circuit without further
identification is 2-wire. A
greater number of wires
is indicated by cross lines
as shown below. Wire size
is sometimes shown with
numerals placed above or
below cross lines.

3-Wire

4-Wire

Figure 7-15: Electrical symbols recommended by ANSI.

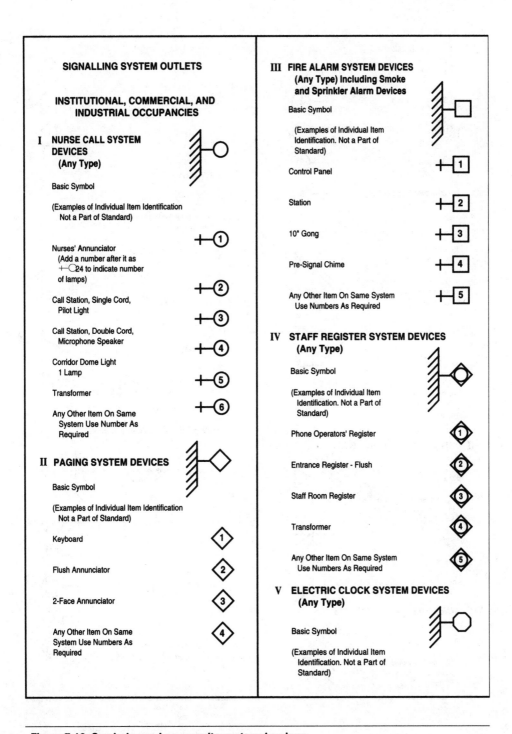

SIGNALLING SYSTEM OUTLETS

INSTITUTIONAL, COMMERCIAL, AND
INDUSTRIAL OCCUPANCIES

I   NURSE CALL SYSTEM
    DEVICES
    (Any Type)

Basic Symbol

(Examples of Individual Item Identification
 Not a Part of Standard)

Nurses' Annunciator
(Add a number after it as
 24 to indicate number
 of lamps)

Call Station, Single Cord,
Pilot Light

Call Station, Double Cord,
Microphone Speaker

Corridor Dome Light
1 Lamp

Transformer

Any Other Item On Same
System Use Number As
Required

II PAGING SYSTEM DEVICES

Basic Symbol

(Examples of Individual Item Identification
 Not a Part of Standard)

Keyboard

Flush Annunciator

2-Face Annunciator

Any Other Item On Same
System Use Numbers As
Required

III FIRE ALARM SYSTEM DEVICES
    (Any Type) Including Smoke
    and Sprinkler Alarm Devices

Basic Symbol

(Examples of Individual Item
 Identification. Not a Part of
 Standard)

Control Panel

Station

10" Gong

Pre-Signal Chime

Any Other Item On Same System
Use Numbers As Required

IV STAFF REGISTER SYSTEM DEVICES
    (Any Type)

Basic Symbol

(Examples of Individual Item
 Identification. Not a Part of
 Standard)

Phone Operators' Register

Entrance Register - Flush

Staff Room Register

Transformer

Any Other Item On Same System
Use Numbers As Required

V   ELECTRIC CLOCK SYSTEM DEVICES
    (Any Type)

Basic Symbol

(Examples of Individual Item
 Identification. Not a Part of
 Standard)

Figure 7-16: Symbols used on security-system drawings.

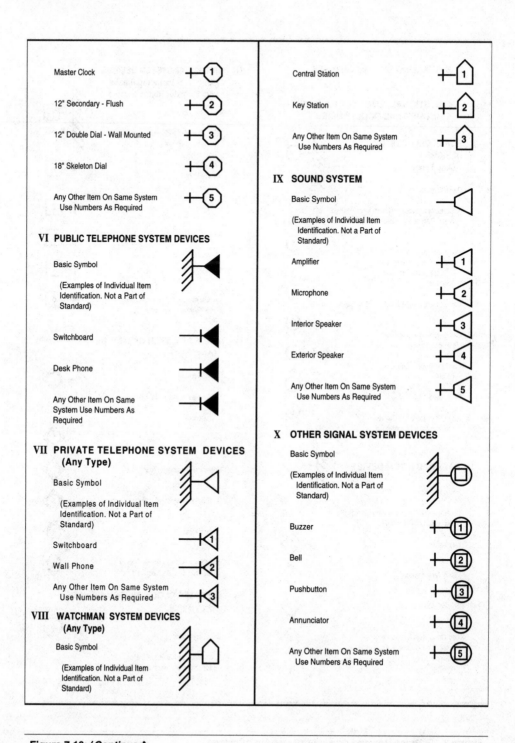

Figure 7-16: (*Continued*).

Each different category in an electrical system is usually represented by a distinguishing basic symbol. To further identify items of equipment or outlets in the category, a numeral or other identifying mark is placed within the open basic symbol. In addition, all such individual symbols used on the drawings should be included in the symbol list or legend.

SCALE DRAWINGS

In most architectural and electrical construction drawings, the components are so large that it would be impossible to draw them actual size on a usable drawing sheet. Consequently, drawings are made to some reduced scale — that is, all the distances are drawn smaller than the actual dimension of the object itself, all dimensions being reduced in the same proportion. For example, if a floor plan of a building is to be drawn to a scale of $\frac{1}{4}'' = 1'\text{-}0''$, each $\frac{1}{4}''$ on the drawing would equal 1 ft on the building itself; if the scale is $\frac{1}{8}'' = 1'\text{-}0''$, each $\frac{1}{8}''$ on the drawing equals 1 ft on the building, and so forth.

When architectural and engineering drawings are produced, the scale decided upon is very important. Where dimensions must be held to extreme accuracy, the scale drawings should be made as large as practical with dimension lines added. Where dimensions require only reasonable accuracy, the object may be drawn to a smaller scale (with dimension lines possibly omitted) since the object can be scaled with the appropriate scale.

In dimensioning drawings, the dimension written on the drawing is the actual dimension of the building, not the distance that is measured on the drawing. To further illustrate this point, look at the floor plan in Figure 7-17; it is drawn to a scale

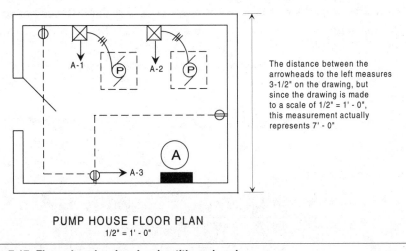

The distance between the arrowheads to the left measures 3-1/2" on the drawing, but since the drawing is made to a scale of 1/2" = 1' - 0", this measurement actually represents 7' - 0"

PUMP HOUSE FLOOR PLAN
1/2" = 1' - 0"

Figure 7-17: Floor plan showing drawing title and scale.

of $\frac{1}{2}'' = 1' - 0''$. One of the walls is drawn to an actual length of $3\frac{1}{2}''$ on the drawing paper, but since the scale is $\frac{1}{2}'' = 1' - 0''$ and since $3\frac{1}{2}''$ contains 7 halves of an inch ($7 \times 0.5 = 3\frac{1}{2}$), the dimension shown on the drawing will therefore be $7'- 0''$ on the actual building.

From the previous example, we may say that the most common method of reducing all the dimensions (in feet and inches) in the same proportion is to choose a certain distance and let that distance represent one foot. This distance can then be divided into 12 parts, each of which represents an inch. If half inches are required, these twelfths are further subdivided into halves, etc. We now have a scale that represents the common foot rule with its subdivisions into inches and fractions, except that the scaled foot is smaller than the distance known as a foot and, likewise its subdivisions are proportionately smaller.

When a measurement is made on the drawing, it is made with the reduced foot rule or scale; when a measurement is made on the building, it is made with the standard foot rule. The most common reduced foot rules or scales used in security-system drawings are the architect's scale and the engineer's scale. Sometimes drawings may be encountered that use a metric scale, but the principle of using this scale is similar to the architect's or engineer's scales. All types are covered in the next section.

Architect's Scale

Figure 7-18 shows two configurations of architect's scales — the one on the left is designed so that $1'' = 1' - 0''$; the one on the right has graduations spaced to represent $\frac{1}{8}'' = 1' -0''$. Now let's zoom in for a closer look.

Note on the one-inch scale in Figure 7-18 that the longer marks to the right of the zero (with a numeral beneath) represent feet. Therefore, the distance between the zero and the numeral 1 equals 1 ft. The shorter mark between the zero and 1 represents $\frac{1}{2}$ of a foot, or 6 in.

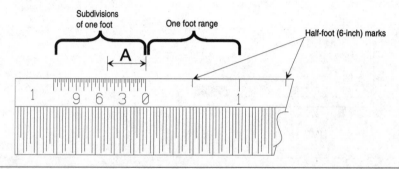

Figure 7-18: A close-up view of the 1-inch architect's scale.

Referring again to Figure 7-18, look at the marks to the left of the zero. There are four different lengths of marks in this group. The longest marks are spaced three scaled inches apart and have the numerals 0, 3, 6, and 9 for use as reference points. The next longest group of lines each represent scaled inches, but are not marked with numerals. In use, you can count the number of marks to the left of the zero to find the number of inches, but after some practice, you will be able to tell the exact measurement at a glance. For example, the measurement "A" represents 5″ because it is the fifth "inch" mark to the left of the zero; it is also one "inch" mark short of the 6-in line on the scale.

The next size line that is shorter than the "inch" line is the half-inch line, and the shortest lines in the group represent $\frac{1}{4}''$. On smaller scales, however, the basic unit is not divided into as many divisions. For example, the smallest subdivision on the $\frac{1}{8}'' = 1' - 0''$ scale represents 2 in.

Types of Architect's Scales

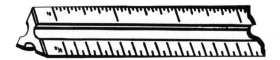

Figure 7-19: Typical triangular architect's scale.

Architect's scales are available in several types, but the most common include the triangular scale and the "flat" scale. The quality of architect's scales also vary from cheap plastic scales (costing a dollar or two) to high-quality wooden-laminated tools such as produced by Keffel&Esser, Dietzgen, and others.

The triangular scale (Figure 7-19) is frequently found in drafting and estimating departments or engineering and security-system contracting firms, while the flat scales are more convenient to carry on the job site by workers.

Triangular-shaped architect's scales (Figure 7-20) have 12 different scales — two on each edge — as follows:

- Common foot rule (12 in)

- $\frac{1}{16}'' = 1' - 0''$

- $\frac{3}{32}'' = 1' - 0''$

- $^3\!/_{16}'' = 1' - 0''$

- $^1\!/_8'' = 1' - 0''$

- $^1\!/_4'' = 1' - 0''$

- $^3\!/_8'' = 1' - 0''$

- $^3\!/_4'' = 1' - 0''$

- $1'' = 1' - 0''$

- $^1\!/_2'' - 1' - 0''$

- $1^1\!/_2'' = 1' - 0''$

- $3'' = 1' - 0''$

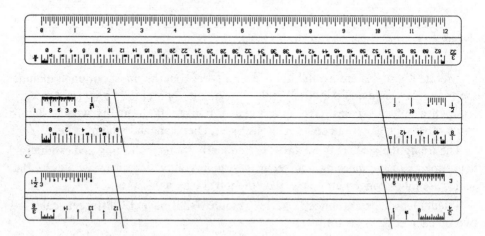

Figure 7-20: The various scales on a triangular architect's scale.

Two separate scales on one face may seem confusing at first, but after some experience, reading these scales becomes "second nature."

In all but one of the scales on the triangular architect's scale, each face has one of the scales spaced exactly one-half of the other. For example, on the 1-in face, the 1-in scale is read from left to right, starting from the zero mark. The half-inch scale is read from right to left — again starting from the zero mark.

On the remaining foot-rule scale ($\frac{1}{16}'' = 1'-0''$), each $\frac{1}{16}''$ mark on the scale represents one foot.

The "flat" architect's scale shown in Figure 7-21 is ideal for workers on most projects. It is easily and conveniently carried in the shirt pocket, and the four scales ($\frac{1}{8}$-, $\frac{1}{4}$-, $\frac{1}{2}$-, and 1-inch) are adequate for the majority of projects that will be encountered.

The partial floor plan shown in Figure 7-21 is drawn to a scale of $\frac{1}{8}'' = 1'-0''$. The dimension in question is found by placing the $\frac{1}{8}''$ architect's scale on the drawing and reading the figures. It can be seen that the dimension reads 24′ -6″.

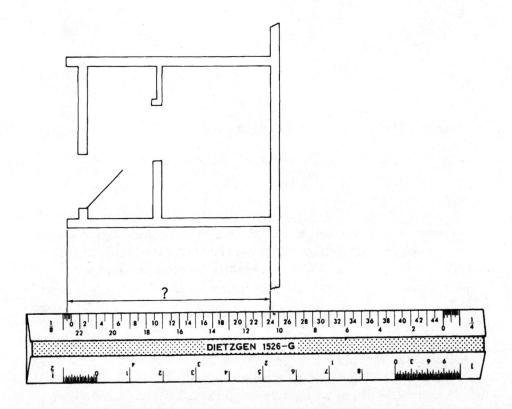

Figure 7-21: Using the 1/8" architect's scale to determine dimensions on a drawing.

215

Every drawing should have the scale to which it is drawn, plainly marked on it as part of the drawing title. However, it is not uncommon to have several different drawings on one print sheet — all with different scales. Therefore, always check the scale of each different view found on a drawing sheet.

Engineer's Scale

The civil engineer's scale is used fundamentally in the same manner as the architect's scale, the principal difference being that the graduations on the engineer's scale are decimal units rather than feet, as on the architect's scale.

The engineer's scale is used by placing it on the drawing with the working edge away from the user. The scale is then aligned in the direction of the required measurement. Then, by looking down over the scale, the dimension is read.

Civil engineer's scales are common in the following graduations:

- $1'' = 10$ units

- $1'' = 20$ units

- $1'' = 30$ units

- $1'' = 40$ units

- $1'' = 60$ units

- $1'' = 80$ units

- $1'' = 100$ units

The purpose of this scale is to transfer the relative dimensions of an object to the drawing or vice versa. It is used mainly on site plans to determine distances between property lines, manholes, duct runs, direct-burial cable runs, and the like.

Site plans are drawn to scale using the engineer's scale rather than the architect's scale. On small lots, a scale of, say, 1 in = 10 ft or 1 in = 20 ft is used. This means that 1 in (actual measurement on the drawing) is equal to 10 ft, 20 ft, and so on, on the land itself.

On larger drawings, where a large area must be covered, the scale could be 1 in = 100 ft or 1 in = 1000 ft, or any other integral power of 10. On drawings with the scale in multiples of 10, the engineering scaled marked 10 is used. If the scale in 1 in - 200 ft, the engineer's scale marked 20 is used, and so on.

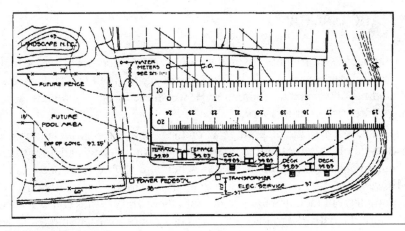

Figure 7-22: Engineer's scale.

Although site plans appear reduced in scale, depending on the size of the object and the size of the drawing sheet to be used, the actual true-length dimensions must be shown on the drawings at all times. When you are reading the drawing plans to scale, think of each dimension in its full size and not in the reduced scale it happens to be on the drawing. See Figure 7-22.

Security technicians frequently encounter plot plans when installing security systems in industrial establishments or when a network system is installed in shopping malls or tract development houses.

The Metric Scale

Metric scales (Figure 7-23), are divided into centimeters (cm), with the centimeters divided into 10-divisioned millimeters (mm), or into 20-divisioned half-millimeters. Scales are available with metric divisions on one edge while inch divisions are inscribed on the opposite edge. Many contracting firms that deal in international trade have adopted a dual-dimensioning system expressed in both metric and English symbols. Furthermore, drawings prepared for government projects frequently require metric dimensions.

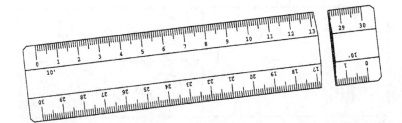

Figure 7-23: Metric scale.

SCHEMATIC DIAGRAMS

Earlier chapters thoroughly covered various types of electrical circuits, including series, parallel, and series-parallel. Consequently, you should already have a basic understanding of schematic diagrams. However, let's briefly review schematic drawings to refresh your memory.

In general, a schematic diagram is a "picture" of an electrical/electronic circuit that uses symbols to represent the various circuit components and lines to connect these components. Basic symbols used in schematic diagrams are shown in Figure 7-24. However, as you have already learned in an earlier chapter, this list is by no means complete. In fact, there are dozens of other symbols that you will encounter when using schematic diagrams — a different symbol for each of the components used in the circuit. If any variations are necessary, an exact description of each is usually listed in schedules or else noted on the drawings.

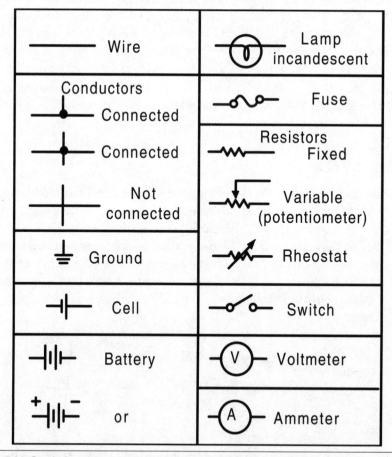

Figure 7-24: Symbols commonly used in electrical schematic diagrams.

Schematic diagrams indicate the scheme or plan according to which components are connected for a specific purpose. They are seldom, if ever, drawn to scale as an architectural drawing would be. They appear in diagrammatic form, and the symbols rarely look exactly like the component. In the better drawings, however, the components are arranged in a neat and logical sequence so that they are easily traced and can be clearly understood.

To serve all its intended purposes, the schematic diagram must be accurate. Also, it must be understood by all qualified personnel, and it must provide definite information without ambiguity.

The schematics for a security system should indicate all circuits in the system. If the drawings are accurate and well prepared, they will be easy to read and follow an entire closed path in each circuit. If there are interconnections, they will be clearly indicated.

In nearly all cases the conductors connecting the electronic symbols will be drawn either horizontally or vertically. Rarely are they ever slanted.

A dot at the junction of two crossing wires means a connection between the two wires. An absence of a dot, in most cases, indicates that the wires cross without connecting.

Schematic diagrams are, in effect, shorthand explanations of the manner in which an electrical/electronic circuit or group of circuits operates. They make extensive use of symbols and abbreviations.

Every component on a complete schematic diagram usually has a number to identify the component. Supplementary data about such parts are supplied on the diagram or on an accompanying list in the form of a schedule, which describes the component in detail or refers to a common catalog number familiar to the trade.

To interpret schematic diagrams, remember that each circuit must be closed in itself. Each component should be in a closed loop connected by conductors to a source of electric current such as a battery, transformer, or other power supply. There will always be a conducting path leading from the source to the component and a return path leading from the component to the source. The path may consist of one or more conductors. Other components may also be in the same loop or in additional loops branching off to other devices. Again, for each component, it must be possible to trace a completed conducting loop to the source.

The common flashlight is an example of a basic electric circuit. It contains a source of electrical energy (the dry cells in the flashlight), a load (the bulb) which changes the electrical energy into light energy, and a switch to control the energy delivered to the load; that is, to turn the light off and on.

SCHEDULES

A schedule, as applied to printreading, is a systematic method of presenting notes or lists of materials, equipment, components, and the like on a drawing in tabular

Component Identification	Name of Item	GE Catalog Number
S1	Switch	1087-BA
DS1	3-V lamp	9875-3 V
Battery (2)	1.5 V battery	4756-1.5 V

Figure 7-25: Component schedule for a common flashlight circuit.

form. When properly organized and thoroughly understood by both the drafter and those reading the drawings, schedules are great time-saving devices.

Refer again to the common flashlight circuit. In most cases, there are three major components in the circuit:

- Switch

- Battery

- Bulb

In a circuit as simple as this, the components could be easily indicated by note on the schematic. However, on more complex circuits, such notes would tend to make the drawing "muddy" and if there were many components of the same type, it would be easier to list them in a schedule such as the one in Figure 7-25.

A checklist schedule for an electronic security device is shown in Figure 7-26. This schedule allows the person installing the system to perform tests to ensure that correct connections have been made. The schedule is to be used with a voltmeter. Note that the person testing the circuit reads the top line of the schedule; he places the negative test lead to P102, pin 2 and the positive test lead to P102, pin 1. The voltmeter reading should show 70 V dc. If not, something in the circuit is at fault.

Negative Lead To:	Positive Lead To:	Meter Reading
P102, pin 2	P102, pin 1	70V dc
P102, pin 4	P102, pin 3	13 V dc
P102, pin 7	P102, pin 6	+20 V dc
P102, pin 7	P102, pin 8	-20 V dc
Heat Sink	S516, pin 3	5 V dc
Heat Sink	S516, pin 1	+20 V dc

Figure 7-26: Checklist schedule for a security-system component.

If the same information in this schedule was included in the written specifications, more time would be required to explain how the test is made. The person building the project would have to comb through pages of written specifications to find the explanation.

From the above explanation, it should also be obvious that schematic diagrams and schedules can be a great help in installing new security systems as well as troubleshooting existing systems.

RISER DIAGRAMS

Single-line block diagrams are used extensively to show the arrangement of security equipment and components on many security/fire-alarm installations. The riser diagram in Figure 7-27, for example, shows a riser diagram for a fire-alarm system used in a small commercial building. The heart of this system is the main or master control panel indicated by the large square in the drawing. To this panel are connected various detector and alarm circuits.

The primary power for this fire-alarm system is taken from an unswitched three-wire distribution line of 120/240 V ac. The initiating and alarm circuits are connected to the neutral ground and to one leg of the main circuit. Trouble-indicator circuits are connected to a neutral ground and also to the opposite leg of the circuit.

When an automatic detector or manual station is activated, the contacts close to complete a circuit path and apply 120-V power to the alarm control circuits in the main control panel. This includes a synchronous motor on some systems, which immediately operates various cam assemblies that cause the alarm circuit switch

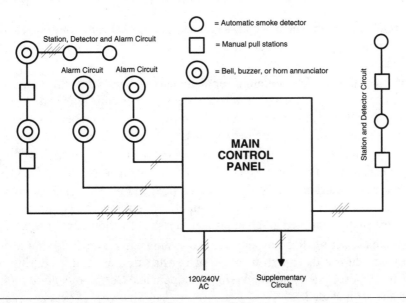

Figure 7-27: A riser diagram for a typical fire-alarm system.

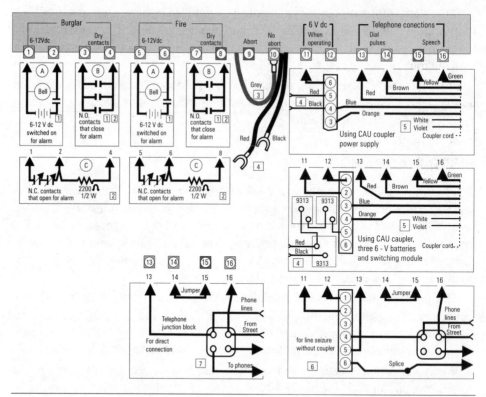

Figure 7-28: Schematic wiring diagrams should always be provided during the rough-in stage of any security system.

contacts to make and break in a code sequence. Additional cam-controlled switches stop the motor and alarm signals after, say, four complete rounds and actuate the alarm buzzer on the main panel.

Most fire-alarm panels contain a supplementary relay control for connection to an external auxiliary circuit to operate other devices or circuits related to the system. The relay usually has a single-pole, double-throw contact that operates in step with the master code signal. The circuit may be used to activate other auxiliary alarms or controls, such as a city fire-department connection, fan shutdown, or door release.

All of the electrical/electronic details are not shown on the riser diagram in Figure 7-27. The riser diagram merely shows the number and relation of the components to the main control panel, along with the number of circuits and conductors. Other details are usually furnished in schedules, written specifications, or wiring diagrams.

A schematic wiring diagram such as the one shown in Figure 7-28 should always be provided during the rough-in stage of construction as well as during actual connection of the system and the various components. Details of station mounting should also be included.

DRAWING DETAILS

A detail drawing is a drawing of a separate item or portion of a security system, giving a complete and exact description of its use and all the details needed to show the workers exactly what is required for the installation. The riser diagram in Figure 7-27 indicates the installation of four smoke detectors. This is a good example of where an extra, detailed drawing is desirable. Since there are several types of smoke detectors on the market, workers need to know the rough-in dimensions, mounting requirements, and circuit connections.

A detail drawing of the smoke detector such as shown in Figure 7-29 leaves little doubt as to the detector's dimensions and mounting requirements. The additional connection detail in Figure 7-30 further facilitates the installation of the smoke detectors.

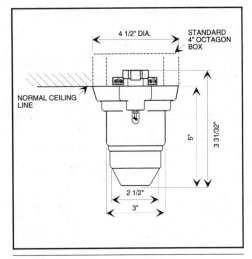

Figure 7-29: Details of smoke-detector mounting requirements.

Some security equipment manufacturers will sometimes provide pictorial drawings in the form of isometric or perspective views of the installation requirements of their equipment as shown in Figure 7-31. Even with these highly realistic drawings, schematic wiring diagrams must also be provided to detail the connections of each component in the system.

Many older fire-alarm systems are being updated with modern ionization, infrared, and photoelectric detection capabilities. A special control panel is added to the old system to accommodate the new detectors. In such situations, it is best to have

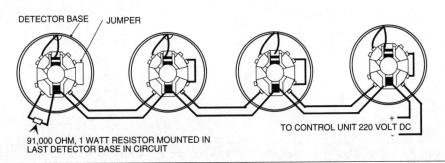

Figure 7-30: Wiring or connection details usually are provided during the rough-in stage as well as during the time of mounting the equipment.

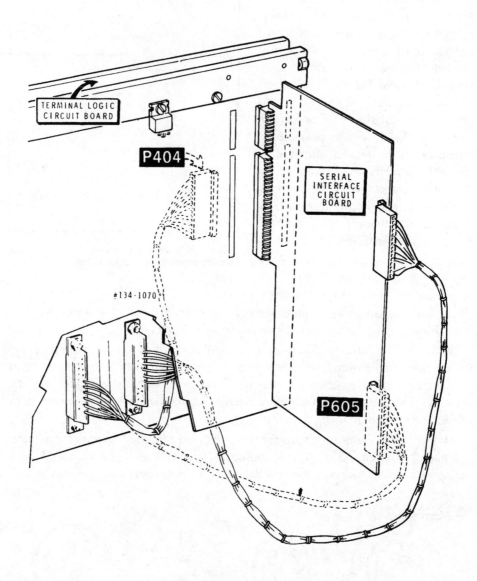

TERMINAL LOGIC
CIRCUIT BOARD

P404

SERIAL
INTERFACE
CIRCUIT
BOARD

#134-1070

P605

Figure 7-31: Even if highly detailed pictorial drawings are furnished with the security equipment, technicians still need a schematic wiring diagram to ensure correct connections.

complete schematic diagrams of the existing system as well as the new connections. Sometimes these drawings will be provided by the manufacturer or engineering firm; other times the security technician will have to make a survey of the building, and prepare these drawings from scratch. These drawings (with all necessary dimensions) are usually sketched on graph paper at the job site and then put into finished form in the drafting room. Once the drawings have been prepared, the new system may be integrated with the old quite easily by experienced workers.

Once the extent of the existing system has been determined, fire-alarm equipment manufacturers will usually provide security technicians with complete instructions for the installation or modification of the existing system — often at no charge if the equipment is purchased from the manufacturer doing the design drawings.

WRITTEN SPECIFICATIONS

The written specifications for a building or project are the written descriptions of work and duties required by the owner, the architect, and the consulting engineer. Together with the working drawings, these specifications form the basis of all contract requirements for the construction of the building or project, including the mechanical and electrical systems associated with the building. Those who use such construction drawings and specifications must always be alert to discrepancies between the working drawings and the written specifications. Such discrepancies occur particularly when:

- Architects or engineers use standard or prototype specifications and attempt to apply them without any modification to specific working drawings.

- Previously prepared standard drawings are changed or amended by reference in the specifications only and the drawings themselves are not changed.

- Items are duplicated in both the drawings and specifications, but an item is subsequently amended in one and overlooked on the other contract document.

In such instances, the person in charge of the project has the responsibility to ascertain whether the drawings or the specifications take precedence. Such questions must be resolved, preferably before the work is started, to avoid added cost to either the owner, the architect/engineer, the contractor, or the security/electronics technician.

How Specifications Are Written

Writing accurate and complete specifications for building construction and the building's related systems is a serious responsibility for those who design the buildings because the specifications, combined with the working drawings, govern practically all important decisions made during the construction span of every project. Compiling and writing these specifications is not a simple task, even for those who have had considerable experience in preparing such documents. A set of written specifications for a single project usually will contain thousands of products, parts and components, and methods of installing them, all of which must be covered in either the drawings and/or specifications. No one can memorize all of the necessary items required to accurately describe the various areas of construction. One must rely upon reference materials — manufacturer's data, catalogs, checklists, and, best of all, a high-quality master specification.

Specification Format

For convenience in writing, speed in estimating work, and ease in reference, the most suitable organization of the specification is a series of sections dealing successively with the different trades, and in each section grouping all the work of the particular trade to which the section is devoted. All the work of each trade should be incorporated into the section devoted to that trade. Those people who use the specifications must be able to find all information needed without taking too much time in looking for it.

The CSI Format

The Construction Specification Institute (CSI) developed the Uniform Construction Index some years ago that allowed all specifications, product information, and cost data to be arranged into a uniform system. This format is now followed on most large construction projects in North America. All construction is divided into 16 Divisions, and each division has several sections and subsections. The following outline describes the various divisions normally included in a set of specifications for building construction.

Division 1—General Requirements. This division summarizes the work, alternatives, project meetings, submissions, quality control, temporary facilities and controls, products, and the project closeout. Every responsible person involved with the project should become familiar with this division.

Division 2—Site Work. This division outlines work involving such items as paving, sidewalks, outside utility lines (electrical, plumbing, gas, telephone, etc.), landscaping, grading, and other items pertaining to the outside of the building.

Division 3—Concrete. This division covers work involving footings, concrete formwork, expansion and contraction joints, cast-in-place concrete, specially finished concrete, precast concrete, concrete slabs, and the like.

Division 4—Masonry. This division covers concrete, mortar, stone, masonry accessories, and the like.

Division 5—Metals. Metal roofs, structural metal framing, metal joists, metal decking, ornamental metal, and expansion control normally fall under this division.

Division 6—Carpentry. Items falling under this division include: rough carpentry, heavy timber construction, trestles, prefabricated structural wood, finish carpentry, wood treatment, architectural woodwork, and the like. Plastic fabrications may also be included in this division of the specifications.

Division 7—Thermal and Moisture Protection. Waterproofing is the main topic discussed under this division. Other related items such as dampproofing, building insulation, shingles and roofing tiles, preformed roofing and siding, membrane roofing, sheet metal work, wall flashing, roof accessories, and sealants are also included.

Division 8—Doors and Windows. All types of doors and frames are included under this division: metal, plastic, wood, etc. Windows and framing are also included along with hardware and other window and door accessories.

Division 9—Finishes. Included in this division are the types, quality, and workmanship of lath and plaster, gypsum wallboard, tile, terrazzo, acoustical treatment, ceiling suspension systems, wood flooring, floor treatment, special coatings, painting, and wallcovering.

Division 10—Specialties. Specialty items such as chalkboards and tackboards; compartments and cubicles, louvers and vents that are not connected with the heating, ventilating, and air conditioning system; wall and corner guards; access flooring; specialty modules; pest control; fireplaces; flagpoles; identifying devices; lockers; protective covers; postal specialties; partitions; scales; storage shelving; wardrobe specialties; and the like are covered in this division of the specifications.

Division 11—Equipment. The equipment included in this division could include central vacuum cleaning systems, bank vaults, darkrooms, food service, vending machines, laundry equipment, and many similar items.

Division 12—Furnishing. Items such as cabinets and storage, fabrics, furniture, rugs and mats, seating, and other similar furnishing accessories are included under this division.

Division 13—Special Construction. Such items as air-supported structures, incinerators, and other special items will fall under this division.

Division 14—Conveying Systems. This division covers conveying apparatus such as dumbwaiters, elevators, hoists and cranes, lifts, material-handling systems, turntables, moving stairs and walks, pneumatic tube systems, and also powered scaffolding.

Division 15—Mechanical. This division includes plumbing, heating, ventilating, and air conditioning and related work. Electric heat is sometimes covered under Division 16, especially if individual baseboard heating units are used in each room or area of the building.

Division 16—Electrical. This division covers all electrical requirements for the building including lighting, power, alarm and communication systems, special electrical systems, and related electrical equipment. This is the Division that security technicians will use the most. Division 16 contains the following main sections:

DIVISION 16—ELECTRICAL

 16050 Electrical Contractors

 16200 Power Generation

 16300 Power Transmission

 16400 Service and Distribution

 16500 Lighting

 16600 Special Systems

 16700 Communications

 16850 Heating and Cooling

 16900 Controls and Instrumentation

The above sections are further subdivided into many subsections. For example, items covered under Section 16400 — Service and Distribution — will usually include the project's service entrance, metering, grounding, service-entrance conductors, and similar details.

Chapter 8

Troubleshooting and Maintenance of Security Systems

Preventive maintenance of a security system is essential whether the system is basic, serving a small installation or is complex, incorporating supervisory circuits in a large, multifloor building.

Although modern security equipment is highly reliable, components can wear out or corrode in poor environments. Also, circuit parameters may change, and relays can go out of adjustment.

Because security systems are essentially electrical systems, they usually are maintained by electricians. Consequently, anyone involved in the electrical industry should have a working knowledge of fire-alarm systems along with other types of signaling systems installed in all types of building-construction projects.

Figure 8-1, on the following page, shows the parts of a basic fire-alarm system. Reliability of these components is assured by regular, thorough testing and maintenance programs.

RELAYS

The two types of relays commonly found in fire-alarm systems consist of sealed plug-in relays and nonsealed plug-in relays.

229

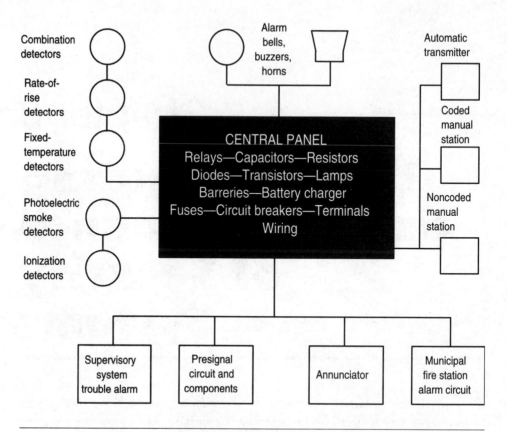

Figure 8-1: Components of a basic fire-alarm system.

Maintenance and adjustment of sealed relays (Figure 8-2) usually are performed only by the manufacturer. Because of this, spare relays should be kept on hand for replacement of malfunctioning units. Occasionally, relay contacts are burned or pitted by a circuit fault or transient high-current. When this happens, the relay should be sent back to the manufacturer for repair and readjustment. When it returns, it should be kept in reserve as a replacement part.

A major objection to the sealed plug-in relay is the reluctance of many users to maintain an adequate inventory of spare units for emergency use. The chief advantage of this type of relay is that it is impervious to contamination and it is highly reliable.

Figure 8-2: Sealed relay.

Nonsealed plug-in relays have the advantage of permitting adjustment in the field, although they are more susceptible to contamination. In general, relays require readjustment after many months to a few years of service. The adjustment may be one of armature gap, armature spring tension, contact gap or contact spring tension.

To clean relay contacts, use a contact burnishing tool, except where excessive pitting or burning has occurred. To remove pits or burns, a fine steel file should be used.

Armature spring tension on some relays can be varied by a screw or knurled nut with or without a locknut; on others by bending a soft brass or steel arm to which a spiral retractile spring is attached. In some instances, it may be necessary to slightly stretch the spring to reduce tension, or cut off a turn or two to increase tension.

Contact springs should be straight. Any excessive belly or waves can be removed by a spring bender or duck-bill pliers. Use a gram gauge to check gram tension as recommended by the relay manufacturer. Tension should never be less than 6 to 8 grams. Contact gap can be changed on some relays by a set screw and locknut; on others, by bending the spring tab which rests on the coil spool head or armature actuator insulator. Set contact gaps according to the manufacturer's specifications.

Pilot Lamps

Where lamps (Figure 8-3) are only occasionally illuminated, such as in an annunciator, their life will be essentially unlimited unless lamps are subject to considerable vibration from nearby equipment. Where lamps fail often because of vibration, install circuits and lamps rated at 6 or 12 V because these lamps will outlast lamps rated at 24, 32, or 48 V since their filaments are physically stronger.

When pilot lamps are on continuous operation, such as lighting a colored bullseye lens or a back-lighted panel, it is advantageous to use lamps rated at a higher voltage than the actual supply voltage. This greatly increases lamp life. Typical examples are 32-V lamps supplied at 24 V or 145-V lamps supplied at 120 V. This variation of rated lamp voltage to supply voltage permits ample illumination.

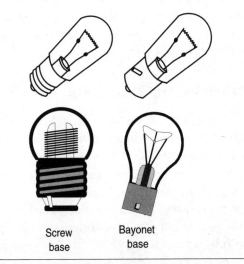

Screw base   Bayonet base

Capacitors

Ceramic capacitors require little maintenance other than a periodic

Figure 8-3: Basic types of pilot lamps.

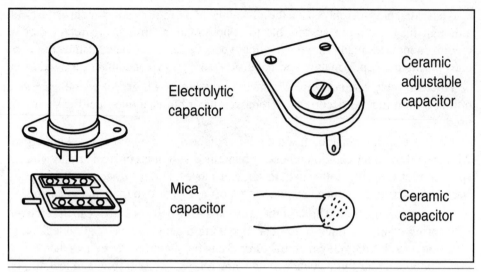

Figure 8-4: Various types of capacitors.

inspection to see that terminals are free of dirt, grease or moisture, and to check electrical connections. Failure of this type of capacitor is very infrequent. When a capacitor malfunction is suspected, the capacitor may be tested with an ohmmeter or, at rated voltage, with a voltmeter.

Electrolytic capacitors have a definite life, which varies depending on quality. The best grades should last for at least 7 years. Ambient or working temperature has a direct effect on capacitor life—the higher the temperature the shorter the life.

They can be tested in a manner similar to the dry paper or ceramic capacitors; however, polarity must be observed on full-voltage tests. Terminal areas and electrical connections should be checked when trouble is suspected. And the terminal areas should be kept clean to facilitate inspection and service of connections. See Figure11-4.

Resistors and Rheostats

Resistors and rheostats (Figure 8-5) require little maintenance. Usually loose or broken connections or an actual broken resistor will be the cause of trouble. During inspection, terminal-screw connections should be checked for tightness.

Slide bands on resistors and the wiping brushes of rheostats should make positive contact with the exposed turns of wire. These exposed turns should be kept clean. Carbon resistors which have been overheated because of operation at power levels beyond their rated value will change resistance substantially. In such instances, they must be replaced.

Diodes: Diodes may be checked with an ohmmeter or a dc voltmeter and a dc source. When using the ohmmeter, switch to the lowest scale and connect the diode

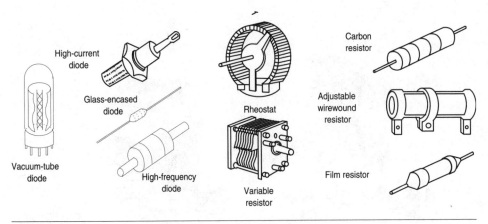

Figure 8-5: Several types of resistors, rheostats, and diodes.

so that a very low resistance reading is obtained. If a significantly higher reading is obtained when the meter leads are reversed, the diode checks out properly. If only a low resistance can be obtained, the diode is shorted. If only high resistance readings can be obtained, the diode is open.

Using the diode principle of unidirectional current flow, a dc voltage test can be set up.

Transistors

Transistors (Figure 8-6) require very little maintenance, except for checking lead connections. Transistor leads go directly to silicon crystal junctions. Therefore, when soldering, excessive heat must be prevented from reaching the crystal junction. A pair of pliers grasping the lead when applying heat should prevent this. In addition, when soldering, quick application of the iron tip and immediate removal from the lead are important.

Transistors are very susceptible to transient voltage spikes that may occur in the supply power line. Excessive spikes can cause undesirable transistor conduction as well as damage to the component. Double-anode zener diodes or similar voltage clippers effectively prevent these spikes from reaching the transistor.

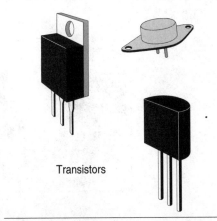

Transistors

Figure 8-6: Transistors are very susceptible to transient voltage spikes.

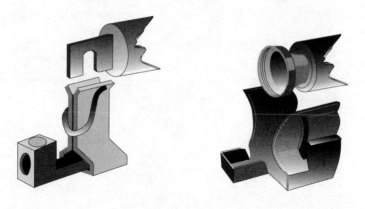

Figure 8-7: Periodic inspection of fuse clips is necessary to make sure that ferrules are in good contact with clips.

Overcurrent Devices

Important steps in fuse maintenance include a periodic check of fuse clips to make sure that ferrules are in good contact with clips. See Figure 8-7. Also look for corrosion or overheating at fuse clips. Hot fuses or clips usually indicate either poor contact or an overloaded fuse, probably close to blowing. A supply of fuses of proper ratings should always be kept on hand for fast replacement of blown fuses.

Molded-case circuit breakers (Figure 8-8) require little maintenance. They should be kept free of dust and grime to assure proper mechanical operation. Regular inspections of circuit breakers should be made, including dynamic tests. Every 3 or

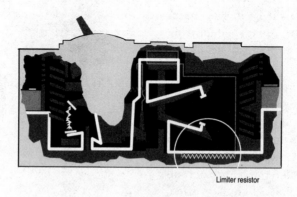

Limiter resistor

Figure 8-8: Molded-case circuit breakers require very little maintenance.

4 years, operating trip settings may be checked with special load-testing instruments. These tests are often performed by security maintenance contractors or special service organizations. When these tests are performed, it is advisable to load-test overcurrent protective relays.

Batteries

Batteries should be located in a clean, dry place preferably on shelves or racks, or in a cabinet. Maintenance includes regular checking of battery electrolyte level, specific gravity, voltage output, "ball" floats, and the battery exterior for dirt or corrosion of terminals.

When the electrolyte is low, bring the liquid up to proper level by adding distilled water (never tap water). Specific gravity and voltage should be checked at least twice a year. Batteries furnished with transparent glass or plastic cases often are equipped with colored ball floats which indicate discharge condition of the battery. When balls are floating at the top of the cell, the battery is in a fully or nearly fully charged condition. When the balls are "down," the battery is nearing complete discharge.

Be sure the battery is kept clean and dry. Terminals should be tight and free of corrosion. Terminals of lead-acid cells may be cleaned with a cloth moistened with aqueous ammonia. A coating of petroleum jelly will retard further corrosion of battery terminals.

Battery chargers should receive regular inspections to head off trouble. The need for more detailed maintenance will become apparent when batteries are not maintained at full charge. For example, lower than normal charge rates will cause the batteries to slowly discharge. When this happens, check input voltage to the charger, and inspect components such as selenium rectifiers for aging and rheostats for loose or corroded slide bands.

Wiring

The key to reliable operation of circuits between panels and remote devices is proper installation. Be sure conduits will not be subject to water or other contamination which could cause insulation breakdown. In addition, proper wire stripping and connections at terminals are important. Improper stripping sometimes results in nicks in solid conductors which later break from vibration or handling at terminals.

When an installation is completed, insulation resistance tests prove the initial reliability of the installation. Use a 500-V tester. The insulation resistance should be at least 1 mΩ and preferably higher. Annual insulation resistance tests should be made and records kept for comparison of readings. A continuing downward trend of readings over a period of a few years indicates failing insulation.

If frequent grounds or partial grounds are causing erratic operation, make a 500-V RMS or a 1250-V RMS breakdown test. These tests, with voltage applied between conductor and conduit, usually will break through weak spots in the insulation revealing the faulty conductor for immediate replacement. On circuits of 50 V or less, use the 500-V test level; on 51- to 125-V circuits, apply the 1250-V test. Portable test sets for the purpose are available. Instructions should be carefully followed to avoid damaging good wiring or components and to ensure safety.

Prior to the test, be sure to disconnect all equipment. Also, make certain that the normal power supply is removed and that all precautions are taken to prevent physical contact with conductors under test.

Control Cabinets

Control enclosures should be kept free of dust and grease on the face of the panel as well as inside. Dirt can cause faulty relay operation and can be a source of corrosion of metal parts. Connecting wires coming from conduits and cables should be neatly arranged at terminating points and laced into a fanned cable form with skinners opposite the terminals they serve. This saves time when looking for a wire during troubleshooting or replacement of circuits. Be sure control panel enclosure is of proper type for its environment. Check NEMA specifications to be sure.

MAINTENANCE OF FIELD DEVICES

Noncoded Manual Stations

Maintenance of various types of noncoded manual fire-alarm stations consists primarily of periodic operational tests, replacement of "break-glass" windows or glass rods, and inspection of terminals for loose or corroded connections. In supervised fire alarm systems, a broken connection will sound a trouble signal. See Figure 8-9.

A test program should be set up in which one station is operated each month (or in accordance with local codes). A different station should be operated each month thereafter until all stations have been tested within a period of a year or two depending on the number of stations installed. Where stations are installed in a presignal system, be sure to test both the presignal and general alarm function. In systems that send the alarm to a municipal fire department, check transmission of the alarm to the fire department if arrangements can be made for the test. When this is not possible, the alarm system should incorporate means to check this feature without actually transmitting the alarm to the fire department. Identification of each station, location, results of tests, etc., should be kept in a maintenance log.

Some stations are furnished with open-type contacts which should be checked and cleaned every year or two, depending on environment. In some stations, contacts

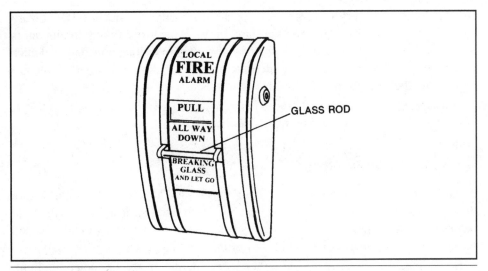

Figure 8-9: Manual fire-alarm station.

are enclosed in dust-tight housings, which preclude dust and dirt and eliminate contact cleaning procedures. Always keep on hand spare glass rods, plates and extra hammers, where applicable, for replacement.

Coded Manual Stations

Two general types of coded stations are the spring-driven type and the motor-driven type. When operating a spring-driven station, the pull handle usually winds a clock spring, which when released, unwinds and drives a gear train and code wheel. The code wheel makes or breaks contacts which transmit code pulses to the control unit. These components are usually enclosed in transparent glass housings, which provide good protection from dirt. However, some dust can penetrate the enclosure and the parts should be oiled with "watch oil" at least every 5 years. At this time, inspect terminals and conductors for tightness and corrosion and clean contacts, if required. Be sure to check extra contacts for annunciation if the station is furnished with this feature. Usually, these contacts must be reset after operation.

Some coded stations must be wound by a key to set the spring-driven operation. On these stations, pulling the lever, simply releases the spring that drives the code wheel. These stations must be rewound after operation.

Maintenance of motor-driven coded stations is similar, except that some are furnished with motors that may require attention. These motors are usually fractional-horsepower types rated in inch-ounces. They consume only 4 to 25 W of power. Those stations furnished with synchronous (hysteresis) motors will not require additional maintenance because these motors do not have brushes and normally bearings are the sealed type. However, stations equipped with dc motors should be checked every 1 to 2 years. Inspect brushes and commutator. Badly worn brushes will cause excessive sparking and erratic operation. Pitted commutators may be smoothed with an emery cloth or turned down in a lathe, polished, and mica undercut. If motors do not have sealed bearings, they should be oiled as recommended by the manufacturer.

A test program, log of records and general maintenance procedures similar to that described for noncoded stations should be observed.

Automatic Transmitters

These units are essentially manual stations but they have the additional feature of an electromagnetic trip circuit to initiate operation. These transmitters, which can be operated either manually or electrically from a remote location, should be tested for both modes of operation in a program similar to that described previously.

Some transmitters are equipped with a local trouble buzzer, an indicating light, and a silencing switch. Others have auxiliary contacts to close a circuit to a central annunciator. Some have both features. When inspecting transmitters, be sure to check these functions. On transmitters that sound a one-round signal as a trouble indication, be certain that the unit is reset after operation or testing.

Heat Detectors

One type of fixed-temperature heat detector operates when a low-melting-point metal allows electrical contacts to energize the alarm circuit. Maintenance consists of a testing program and periodic inspection of terminals and connections for looseness or corrosion. It is important that the detectors be replaced if they have been painted several times — to an extent that the paint has created excessive delay in operating time of the thermostats. This can be checked during testing.

The testing program should require that at least 2 of every 100 detectors be sent to a testing laboratory each year (after an initial no-test period of 5 years). Testing agencies such as UL or a similar facility will perform the prescribed tests. This type of detector is a "one-operation" device and must be discarded after testing; however, replacement cost is low and reliability of detectors is proved. If either of the first two detectors are faulty, more detectors must be tested to determine if a general condition of faulty detectors exists. A record of detector location, test results, etc. should be kept in a log.

The bimetal type of fixed-temperature detector can be tested without removal from the ceiling or disconnection from the alarm circuit. These units operate on the principle of heat-expansion of dissimilar metals to energize the alarm circuit; they return to their normal position after cooling ready for another operation.

These detectors may be tested using a portable cord and lamp socket furnished with a 60-or 75-W incandescent lamp. The lamp is held within a few inches of the

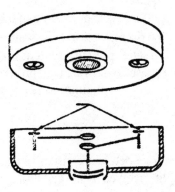

Figure 8-10: Typical fixed-temperature heat detector.

detector and the heat from the lamp should cause operation of the unit after a few seconds. See Figure 8-10.

Rate-of-Rise Detectors

Rate-of-rise detectors operate their contacts when the ceiling temperature rises faster than 12 – 15°/min. This assures operation over a wide range of variable ambient temperatures depending on rating of the detector.

These rate-of-rise detectors may be of the line type or spot type. Line-type detectors consist of small diameter copper or aluminum tubing which is attached to ceilings or walls near the ceiling. Both ends of the tubing terminate at a bellows-like switch assembly, which closes alarm circuit contacts on internal pressure increase. A slow increase of pressure is bled off through a small orifice; however, a rapid rise of 15 degrees per minute or more expands the bellows, and closes the contacts to the fire alarm circuit.

To test for proper operation, use the portable incandescent lamp set, previously described, held close to the tubing. Make this test at least twice a year. Annually, check the tubing for pinhole leaks with a special testing device provided by the manufacturer. These systems can be furnished with the fixed-temperature feature with the addition of special fittings installed in the tubing at 15-ft intervals.

Spot-type rate-of-rise heat detectors are available. One type uses the melting solder principle of operation; the other uses the bimetal principle. Another type of detector is the *rate anticipation* heat detector. These are similar to rate-of-rise detectors; however, they have no thermal lag beyond the instant that operating temperature is reached. The fixed-temperature detectors do have this time lag.

All heat detectors discussed should receive period inspection for corrosion and loose connections, and testing as previously described.

Sprinkler system actuators include pressure-operated water-flow switches, paddle-type switches installed in pipe risers, high and low water-level switches installed in gravity water tanks, and differential pressure switches on excess pressure pump systems. In general, contacts on these devices are well protected; however, mechanical linkages are subject to corrosion and should be checked every year or two.

Smoke Detectors

One type of photoelectric smoke detector consists of a photoelectric cell and an external light source. When light received by the cell drops to a predetermined value (such as when smoke blocks the light from the light source), relays will cause the alarm to sound. Because of this, it is important to keep the light source and cell lens clean. Also, the lamp in the light source should be replaced regularly before failure.

Another type has an internal light source feeding into a labyrinth. Any dust accumulation in the labyrinth may be removed by directing compressed air into the unit. This type is furnished with a 6-V, 5000-hour lamp which should be replaced before end of life.

The balanced-bridge type of smoke detector should be cleaned two or three times a year, or after being actuated by smoke a few times. The unit should be carefully disassembled and components cleaned with ethyl alcohol.

Ionization detectors will discover fires where flame predominates and smoke generation is negligible. This is because invisible gas-combustion products become ionized when they strike the detector head, triggering the detector mechanism. These units should be kept free of dust accumulation.

Smoke detectors should be tested at least once a year. The test is accomplished simply by blowing smoke from a cigar, pipe or other smoke generator toward the ceiling-mounted unit. A log should be kept to ensure that all detectors are tested on schedule.

Horns and Bells

Alarm horns (Figure 8-11) may be dc or ac. The dc alarm horns are usually of the vibrating diaphragm type. These horns are actuated by an armature which rapidly strikes a diaphragm. Connected in series with the armature actuating coil is a pair of contacts. The armature makes and breaks these contacts, alternately energizing and deenergizing the coil creating the vibrating motion. A tubular capacitor is generally connected across the contacts to suppress arcing. To obtain desired sound-level output, an adjusting screw can be set to obtain minimum to maximum stroke of the armature that strikes the diaphragm.

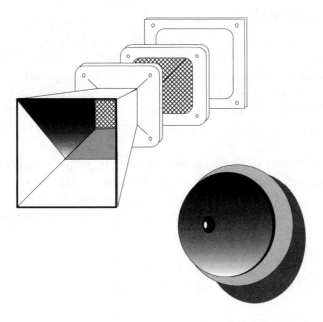

Figure 8-11: Annunciating devices.

The horns should be tested regularly, contacts inspected and any existing pits or burrs removed with a fine file. Contact gap should be checked and set according to manufacturer's specifications.

Some dc horns have a small high-speed dc motor which drives a wheel with projections that strike a diaphragm. Maintenance of this type of horn includes inspection of brushes for excessive wear and commutator for pitting or burning.

Most ac-powered vibrating diaphragm horns require no maintenance other than a periodic test. These horns do not have contacts because the zero and peak voltage created by the 60-cycle sine wave will alternately energize and deenergize the armature.

Trumpet-type ac horns are usually furnished with contacts to obtain the right armature speed and stroke force for their characteristic resonant operation. These contacts will require attention more frequently than contacts on dc vibrating diaphragm horns.

Alarm bells, both ac and dc types, operate on the same principles as described for ac and dc horns. Construction of operating mechanisms is similar to horns except that the armature drives a striker that strikes a gong shell. Testing, adjustment and maintenance are similar to that recommended for horns.

It should now be obvious that preventative maintenance for any type of security/fire-alarm system is mandatory for safe and efficient operation. In fact, some jurisdictions require periodic inspections by local fire wardens and electrical inspectors.

TROUBLESHOOTING

Troubleshooting covers a wide range of problems from such small jobs as finding a ground fault in a perimeter loop (sensor circuit) to tracing out defects in a complex control circuit. In any case, troubleshooting usually requires only a thorough knowledge of testing equipment and a systematic and methodical approach to the problem; that is, testing one part of the circuit or system after another until the trouble is located.

Those involved in the maintenance of security alarm systems should keep in mind that every electrical/electronic problem can be solved, regardless of its nature. The paragraphs that follow are designed to aid those involved in such work to better solve the more common security-system problems in a safe and logical manner.

Basic Electrical Problems

In general, there are only three basic electrical faults:

- A short circuit or ground fault

- An open circuit

- A change in electrical value

A ground fault is one of the most common causes of electrical problems. Such a condition can be caused by any number of faults, but in most cases the cause if faulty insulation on conductors which allows two conductors to touch (Figure 8-12A) and short out, or else the fault occurs between one "hot" wire and a grounded object as illustrated in Figure 8-12B.

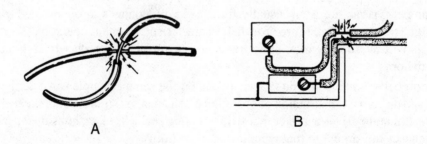

A   B

Figure 8-12: A ground fault or short circuit is one of the most common causes of problems in electrical systems.

An open circuit is an incomplete current path and is usually caused by either a blown or tripped overcurrent-protection device, a loose connection or broken conductor, or a faulty switch or control.

A change in electric value covers such items as low voltage, electrical surges, a change in resistance, and similar items.

TESTING INSTRUMENTS

To maintain and troubleshoot existing security systems, workers should know and apply modern testing techniques and have a good understanding of basic testing instruments.

The use of electrical/electronic testing instruments generally involves three applications:

1. Verifying proper operation of instruments and associated equipment.
2. Calibrating electronic instruments and associated equipment.
3. Troubleshooting electrical/electronic circuits and equipment.

For these applications, specific test equipment is selected to analyze circuits and to determine specific characteristics of discrete components.

The test equipment that a technician chooses for a specific task depends on the type of measurement and level of accuracy required. Additional factors that may influence selection include the following:

● Whether the test equipment is portable

● The amount of information that the test equipment provides

● The likelihood that the test equipment may damage the circuit or component being tested (some test equipment can generate enough voltage or current to damage an instrument or electrical circuit)

Meters

The functioning of conventional electrical measuring instruments is based upon electromechanical principles. Their mechanical components usually work on dc electricity. Mechanical frequency meters are an exception. A meter that measures ac has a built-in rectifier to change the ac to dc, and resistors to correct for the various ranges.

Today, many meters utilize solid-state digital systems for operation; they are superior because they have no moving parts. These meters will work in any position, unlike mechanical meters, many of which must remain in one position in order to be read accurately.

When using any testing instrument, always consider the operator's personal safety first. Know the voltage levels and shock hazards related to all equipment to be tested, and make certain that the instrument used has been tested and correctly calibrated; this should be done at least once a year. To prevent damage to the test instrument, select a range (on meters with different ranges) that ensures less than full-scale deflection on readouts in the cases of needle or digital instruments, respectively.

D'Arsonval Meter Movement

The conventional ammeter is based on the principle that the magnetic effect of electricity in a current-carrying conductor will rotate when placed in a magnetic field, the same as an electric motor. The readings on an ammeter of this kind have been calibrated by comparison with a primary standard instrument. This calibration provides assurance that the practical magnetic instruments used in everyday electrical measurements indicate the same amount of current as the standard instrument.

The basic d'Arsonval meter (Figure 8-13) operates on direct current (dc) only because alternating current (ac) continually reverses its direction and the meter coil will do likewise. However, by installing a rectifier that can convert ac to dc, the output is dc and the d'Arsonval meter can read it.

A moving-coil meter movement operates on the electromagnetic principle. In its simplest form, the moving-coil meter uses a coil of very fine wire wound on a light metallic frame. A permanent magnet surrounds the coil. The metallic frame is mounted on pivots to allow it and the coil to rotate freely between the poles of the

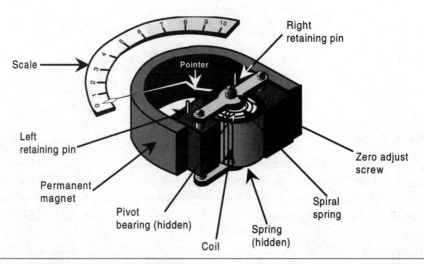

Figure 8-13: Major parts of a d'Arsonval meter.

permanent magnet. When current flows through the coil, it becomes magnetized, and the polarity of the coil is such that it is repelled by the field of the permanent magnet.

This will cause the coil frame to rotate on its pivots, and the distance it rotates is determined by the amount of current that flows through the coil. By attaching a pointer to the coil frame and adding a calibrated scale, the amount of current flowing through the meter can be measured.

Magnetic-Vane Meters

Another type of meter is called the magnetic-vane meter. It differs from the d'Arsonval meter in that the magnetic-vane meter contains a fixed coil and a movable iron vane, rather than the fixed magnet and moving coil used in the d'Arsonval meter.

Figure 8-14 shows a typical magnetic-vane meter. In this meter, two iron vanes are enclosed by a coil of wire. When there is current through the coil, the vanes are magnetized so that they repel each other regardless of whether the energizing current is direct or alternating. Usually one vane is fixed and the other is pivoted. The movable vane is provided with a pointer over a calibrated scale.

In recent years, digital-readout meters are rapidly taking the place of many of the needle-pointer-type meters. The accuracy of digital meters, in many cases, far exceeds that of analog or dial-type meters. Better than 0.5 percent accuracy is fairly standard for most digital meters. This improved accuracy is due to the carefully calibrated electronic circuitry contained in digital meters. Because of the readout on a digital meter, the precision of the reading accuracy by the operator is exact — not a close estimate.

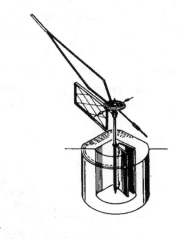

Digital meters also offer an advantage in poor lighting conditions when the face of an analog meter might be hard to see. LED (light-emitting diode) displays can easily be seen in low-light areas. They do however,

Figure 8-14: Working parts of a magnetic-vane meter.

consume more power and, therefore, the batteries may not last as long.

Digital meters are also smaller and are often less expensive to manufacture than the bulky analog meters of the past. Consequently, digital meters are quickly replacing the dial-type meters and you will probably see more and more digital type meters appear on job sites than any other types.

Ammeters

An electrical circuit is a complete conductive path through which electrons may move. The movement of electrons in an electrical circuit is called current and is measured in amperes with an ammeter.

Most ammeters operate on a magnetic principle or the magnetic effect of electric current to produce the movement of the meter pointer on the scale or the digital readout on electronic instruments. A basic dc ammeter consists of a permanent magnet that supplies a magnetic flux or field, a delicately balanced coil that rotates in the field, a pointer, and a scale. This meter design is the d'Arsonval type that was discussed previously.

Most basic d'Arsonval type ammeters will measure only small amounts of current. The typical range is in microamperes (0.000001 A) or milliamperes (0.001 A). Very few ammeters in use can measure very much current without additional modifications. To increase the range of the ampere level, a shunt is used as shown in Figure 8-15.

The meter is connected in parallel with the shunt. Shunts may be located inside the meter housing (internal shunt) and are generally used to measure currents up to 30 A. Ampere ratings over 30 A generate too much heat for internal shunts that could damage the meter. Consequently, other types of ammeters utilize external shunts with leads connecting the shunt to the meter. External-shunt ammeters are normally used to measure currents over 30 A. The use of a shunt allows the ammeter to derive current in amperes by actually measuring the voltage drop across the shunt.

To measure current above 10 mA, a shunt with an extremely low resistance is placed in series with the load and the meter is connected across the shunt to measure the resulting voltage drop proportional to current flow. A shunt has a relatively large wattage rating to enable it to carry a relatively large current. See Figure 8-16.

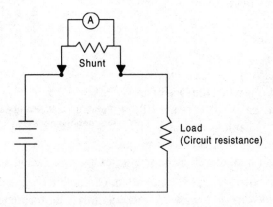

Figure 8-15: Ammeter shunt.

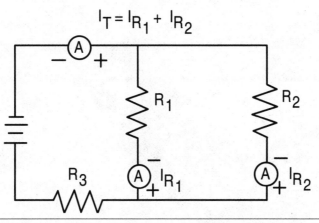

$$I_T = I_{R_1} + I_{R_2}$$

Figure 8-16: Ammeters connected at various areas of a parallel dc circuit.

As mentioned previously, alternating current can also be measured with a d'Arsonval-type meter if the alternating current is first changed to direct current by a rectifier. As the name implies, a rectifier is a device that rectifies, or converts ac to dc.

A thermocouple may also be used to adapt dc meters to the measuring of alternating current, but since thermocouple-equipped instruments are quite sensitive to overloads, their applications are usually limited to electronic circuits where overloads seldom occur.

CAUTION

Never connect an ammeter in parallel with a load. Because of the low resistance in the ammeter, a short circuit can occur. Consequently, ammeters must be connected in series with the load. Furthermore, proper polarity must be observed in a dc circuit; that is, the negative lead of the meter must be connected to the negative side of the load, while the positive lead (+) must be connected to the positive side of the load. If the meter is connected with the polarities reversed, the meter coil will move in the opposite direction and often damage the meter.

Clamp-on Ammeters

Figure 8-17 on the next page shows a clamp-on ammeter that can be used to measure current in an electrical circuit while the circuit carries the full load. Disconnection of the conductors is not necessary to make the test.

Although the exact operating procedures will vary with the manufacturers, most operate as follows when measuring current:

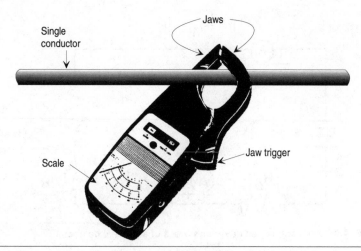

Figure 8-17: Typical clamp-on type ammeter. Both dial and digital scales are available.

Step 1. Make sure the battery-attachment case (for use when in the ohmmeter mode) is removed from the instrument.

Step 2. Release on pointer locks.

Step 3. Turn the scale selector knob until the highest current range appears in the scale window.

Step 4. Press the trigger button to open the jaws of the clamp before encircling one of the conductors under test with the transformer jaws.

Step 5. Release finger pressure on the trigger slowly to allow the jaws to close around the conductor and keep an eye on the scale while doing so. If the pointer jumps abruptly to the upper range of the scale before the jaws are completely closed, the current is probably too high for the scale used. Should this happen, remove the jaws immediately from the conductor and use either a higher scale or a range-extender attachment as discussed in the next section. If the pointer deflects normally, close the jaws completely and take the reading from the scale.

Although the clamp-on ammeter is very convenient to use, the operator may possibly be close to high voltage that is potentially dangerous. Therefore, special precautions must be taken to prevent accidental contact with live conductors and

---

CAUTION

Never encircle two or more conductors as shown in Figure 8-18A; only encircle one conductor as shown in Figure 8-18B.

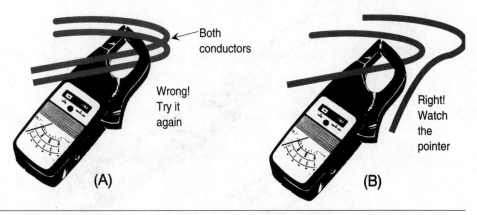

Figure 8-18: Right and wrong way to take current reading with a clamp-on ammeter.

parts. When using this type of instrument, the current-carrying conductor should be centered inside the iron-core clamp for greatest accuracy.

Extending the Range of Ammeters

The range of an ac ammeter can be extended by using a range extender as shown in Figure 8-19. This device permits taking a measurement of higher current beyond the range of the regular clamp-on ammeter. The model shown extends the current range ten times to allow an actual current reading of 1000 A on a 0- to 100-A meter scale. To illustrate its use, if the scale shows a reading of, say, 42 A, the actual current (using the range extender) would be 420 A because $42 \times 10 = 420$.

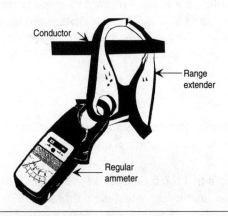

Figure 8-19: Clamp-on transformer extends ammeter range.

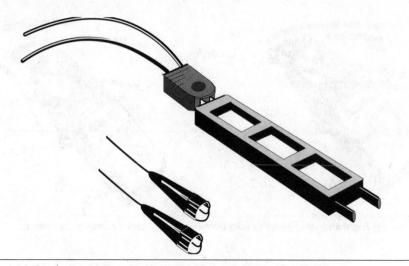

Figure 8-20: Current multiplier may be used with most clamp-on ammeters.

Current Multipliers

Sometimes it is desirable to use a current multiplier in conjunction with a clamp-on ammeter, such as the one shown in Figure 8-20. This device allows current measurement on low-current equipment since the load current shown has been multiplied either two, five, or ten times; that is, if the meter scale shows a reading of, say, 62 A and the 10X multiplier was used, the actual load current would be:

$$\frac{62}{10} = 6.2 \ A$$

If a current-multiplier attachment is not available, the same effect may be had by wrapping turns of wire around the jaws of the ammeter as shown in Figure 8-21 on the next page. In this illustration, the wires are wrapped around the jaws to multiply the current three times. If an attachment is available, and the device or apparatus to be tested has a plug-and-cord assembly, the load may be tested as shown in Figure 8-22.

Precautions

When using clamp-on ammeters, care must be taken to obtain accurate readings. Some items to be considered include:

1. Make certain that the frequency of the circuit under test is within the range of the instrument. Most are calibrated at 70 hertz (Hz).

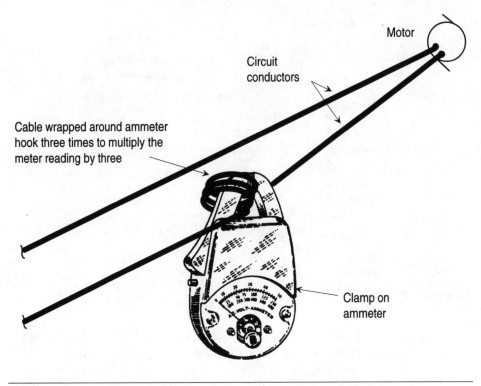

Motor

Circuit
conductors

Cable wrapped around ammeter
hook three times to multiply the
meter reading by three

Clamp on
ammeter

Figure 8-21: Wrapping turns of wire around meter jaws will increase the current reading.

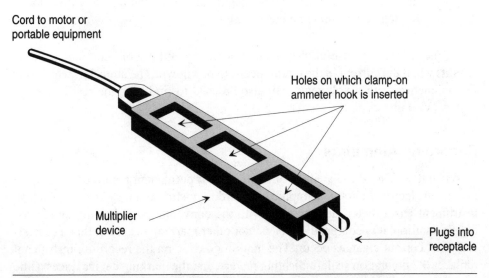

Cord to motor or
portable equipment

Holes on which clamp-on
ammeter hook is inserted

Multiplier
device

Plugs into
receptacle

Figure 8-22: Ammeter multiplying device for use on plug-in electrical equipment.

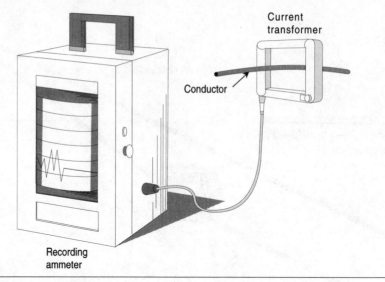

Figure 8-23: Recording ammeter.

Take care that stray magnetic fields do not affect the current reading; that is, arrange the meter leads as far away as possible from the conductors under test. Try to take current readings in a control panel at a location remote from magnetic relays that might influence the accuracy of the reading. Avoid taking current readings on conductors at a point close to a transformer.

3. When current readings are taken on high-voltage conductors, always use a hot-line extension pole specifically designed for use with a high-voltage clamp-on ammeter.

Ammeters are very useful instruments for testing and troubleshooting electrical circuits when the current in the circuit needs to be known. The ammeter, when used in conjunction with a voltmeter, can also be used to find both the resistance and volt-A (VA) in a circuit.

Recording Ammeters

When it is desired to have a continuous and/or permanent record of the current in a given electrical circuit, a graphic or recording instrument may be used. Such an instrument has a meter element similar to the conventional indicating ammeters, but, in addition, it is equipped with a pen or other marking device so that a curve is drawn as current changes occur. The marking device on the recording instrument replaces the pointer on scale-indicating meters, and the marking device traces a line on a chart representing the value of the A that the instrument is measuring. See Figure 8-23.

The charts are usually either circular or in strip form, depending on the type of instrument.

Voltmeters

The unit of electromotive force (emf) is the volt. One V is a form of pressure that, if steadily applied to an electrical circuit having a resistance of 1 Ω, produces a current of 1 A.

Voltmeters are used to accurately measure the pressure or voltage in various electrical circuits. Very low voltage values are measured in milliV (a V = 1000 mV) by a millivoltmeter with low resistance.

A voltmeter should be connected across the terminals at the place the voltage is to be measured. A voltmeter should never be connected across a circuit having a voltage higher than the rating of the instrument; that precaution must be observed particularly in the case of measurements with a millivoltmeter.

Several types of voltmeters are in common use. For example, the basic pointer-type ammeter can also be used to measure voltage. The meter coil has a fixed resistance, and, therefore, when current flows through the coil, a voltage drop will be developed across this resistance. According to Ohm's law, the voltage drop will be directly proportional to the amount of current flowing through the coil. Also, the amount of current flowing through the coil is directly proportional to the amount of voltage applied to it. Therefore, by calibrating the meter scale in units of voltage instead of current, the voltage in different parts of the circuits can be measured.

When connecting a voltmeter to a dc circuit, always observe the proper polarity. The negative lead of the meter must be connected to the negative terminal of the dc source, and the positive lead to the positive terminal. If the leads are connected to opposite terminals, the needle will move in the reverse direction. Since the voltage constantly reverses polarity in an ac circuit, there is no need to observe polarity when connecting voltmeters designed for use on ac circuits.

Many portable voltmeters are designed with two or more voltage ranges than can be read on a common scale, such as 0 – 150 V, 0 – 300 V, and 0 – 600 V. The change from one meter range to another is accomplished by the selection of internal shunts, resistors, or other auxiliary components by means of a switch or plug-in terminals. When using a multirange voltmeter, it is best to select a higher range than needed to assure that no damage will occur to the instrument. Then, if the initial reading indicates that a lower scale is needed to obtain a more accurate reading, the meter can be switched or otherwise adjusted to the next lowest range.

One of the reasons for using various ranges of voltmeters is that the greatest accuracy is obtained on the upper half of the scale. Therefore, if a single 0- to 600-V range were used, lower voltages would be harder to read and meter accuracy would be less.

Solid-state digital voltmeters are usually autoranging; that is, they do not have a selector switch for adjustment. The internal construction of the meter itself will select the proper resistance for the voltage being detected.

Voltmeter Applications

Besides measuring the voltage applied to an electrical circuit, voltmeters can be used for other electrical tests, such as troubleshooting circuits, circuit tracing, and measuring low resistance. For example, a common cause of electrical problems is low equipment voltage. This problem usually occurs because of one or more of the following reasons:

- Undersized conductors

- Overloaded circuits

- Transformer taps set too low

Low-Voltage Test

When making a low-voltage test, first take a reading at the main switch or service entrance. If, for example, the main service is 120/240, single-phase, three-wire, the voltage reading between phases (ungrounded conductors) should be between 230 and 240 V. If the reading is much lower than this, the fault lies with the utility company supplying the power, and they should be notified to correct the problem. However, if the reading at the main service switch is between 230 and 240 V, the next procedure is to check the voltage reading at various outlets throughout the system.

When a low-voltage problem is found on a circuit, leave the voltmeter terminals connected across the line and begin disconnecting all loads, one at a time, that are connected to the circuit. If the problem is corrected after several of the loads have been disconnected, the circuit is probably overloaded. Steps should be taken to reduce the load on the circuits or else increase the wire size to accommodate the load. As mentioned previously, loose connections can also cause low voltage; to check for this, the entire circuit should be deenergized, and each terminal in all disconnect switches, motor starters, and so on, should be checked for loose connections. A charred or blackened terminal screw is one sign to look for.

Megohmmeter

A typical megohmmeter (megger) is composed of a hand-driven or motor-powered ac generator and/or a transformer with voltage rectified to 100, 250, 500, and

1000 V dc, a cross-coil movement with 0 to 20,000 Ω and 0 to 1000 megohms (MΩ) scales, a carrying case, and test leads. The megger is used to measure the resistance in megohms to the flow of current through and/or over the surface of electrical equipment insulation. The test results are used to detect the presence of dirt, moisture, and insulation deterioration. The instrument also typically measures resistances up to 20,000 Ω.

The test set and the sample to which it is connected are sources of high-voltage electrical energy, and all persons making or assisting in the tests must use all practical safety precautions to prevent contact with energized parts of the test equipment and associated circuits. Persons actually engaged in the test must stand clear of all parts of the complete high-voltage circuit unless the set is deenergized and all parts of the test circuit are grounded. If the set is properly operated and all grounds are correctly made, no rubber gloves are necessary. As a routine safety procedure, however, some users require the use of rubber gloves in making connections to the high-voltage terminals and in manipulating the controls.

The instruction manuals accompanying the megger usually contain detailed instructions about preparing for tests and connecting the megger to various types of equipment.

Insulation Resistance Testing

To prepare for an insulation resistance test, first take the equipment or circuits to be tested out of service. Check between the equipment terminals and ground using the megger voltage ranges to be sure there is no voltage present. If possible, disconnect all leads to the unit being tested. When a motor or circuit is not completely isolated, make sure you are aware of all the components that will be tested when the megger is connected. Should an interconnected circuit be overlooked, the megger reading may be lower than expected.

The testing of wiring can be performed on all types of systems if two rules are kept in mind:

- Be sure all wiring is deenergized.

- Know what wiring is included in the test and make a record card of it.

WARNING!

Only qualified personnel should make tests with a megger, and then only after obtaining permission from their supervisor. Megger tests can be dangerous to personnel and harmful to equipment and wiring systems if improperly handled.

When a distribution panel is present, check the entire system to ground by attaching one megger lead to the dead post of the open main power switch and the other lead to a grounded conduit or grounded metal housing.

Individual circuits are tested to ground by opening distribution panel switches, fuses, or circuit breakers and testing each circuit in turn.

Multiconductor cables may be tested in several ways. For instance, measurement of insulation resistance can be made between the wire and lead sheath. Various other measurements can be made, such as wire to ground, wire to wire, wire to braid, and wire to sheath.

Keep in mind that when testing wiring that is connected to any panelboard or equipment there may be appreciable leakage between terminals, which will show in tests as lowered insulation resistance. If previous test and record cards were made with the panels connected, continue any future test in the same manner.

Testing Circuit Breakers

Circuit breakers may be tested with the megger by first disconnecting the circuit breaker from the line and connect the megger black lead to the frame or ground. Check the insulation resistance of each terminal to ground by connecting the red (positive) lead to each terminal in turn and making the measurements. Next open the breaker and measure the insulation resistance between terminals by putting one lead on one terminal and the other on the second for a two-terminal breaker; for a three-pole breaker, check between poles 1 and 2, 2 and 3, and 1 and 3, in turn.

If the breakers are of the oil type, dirty oil may cause leakage currents between the breaker contacts even when open. In dry types of breakers, dirt or grease in the mounting may cause leakage. The measurement of insulation resistance can be made between either circuit breaker terminal to ground and should also be made between terminals.

Testing Safety Switches and Switchgear

Switches with safe insulation are a vital part of any electrical installation and so deserve careful attention. Switches should be completely disconnected from the line and relay wiring before testing. When manual switches are being tested, measure the insulation resistance from ground to terminals and between terminals. When testing electrically operated switches, check the insulation resistance of the coil or coils and contacts. For coils, connect one megger lead to one of the coil leads and the other to ground. Next, test between coil lead and core iron or solenoid element.

If relays are involved, measure insulation resistance with one lead connected to the relay plate or contact and the other test lead connected to the coil, core, or solenoid contact.

Although the suggested tests may appear to be excessive in view of the usually superior performance of most switches over long periods of time, these recommendations are made with the knowledge that one inoperative closed switch can literally wreck a whole plant system. Thorough testing can help to ensure against such an occurrence.

Frequency Meter

Frequency is the number of cycles completed each second by a given ac voltage; usually expressed in hertz; 1 Hz = 1 cycle/s.

The frequency meter is used in ac power-producing devices like generators to ensure that the correct frequency is being produced. Failure to produce the correct frequency will result in heat and component damage.

Electrical Thermometers

For the measurement of temperatures, three basic electrical thermometer methods are used:

- The resistance method which makes use of the fact that the resistance of a metal varies in direct proportion to temperature. This method is normally used for temperatures up to approximately 1500°F.

- The thermocouple method which is based on the principle that a difference in temperature in different metals generates a voltage and is used for measuring temperatures up to about 3000°F.

- The radiation-pyrometer and optical-pyrometer are generally used for temperatures above 3000°F. They combine the principle of the thermocouple with the effect of radiation of heat and light.

Infrared Sensing Device

An infrared sensing device is an optical device that measures the infrared heat emitted from an object.

Practical Application

Most manufacturers of security/fire-alarm systems publish service manuals for their equipment which — in a simplified and systematic manner — troubleshooting and servicing procedures for their components and equipment. Their main objective is to direct technicians to the exact cause of a malfunction and assist in repairing the system. Each qualified technician not familiar with the system should be able to isolate the exact cause of nearly all possible malfunctions when using such manuals. Therefore, it is recommended that all service technicians obtain a service manual (including wiring diagrams, etc.) for the particular system in question.

Although the exact content of service manuals will vary from manufacturer to manufacturer, most are divided into three main sections:

- Theory of operation

- Troubleshooting

- Repair and adjustments

The section on theory of operation should give a thorough explanation of each circuit and should be accompanied by a schematic diagram — such as the one in Figure 8-24 — clearly identifying points that are referred to in the text. The purpose of this section is to give technicians an understanding of the proper operation of the system, which in turn will enable them to locate the causes of those problems not found by following the regular step-by-step troubleshooting procedures.

Troubleshooting tables, such as the one in Figure 8-25, lists the symptoms that may occur, along with the most likely causes and page numbers of the detailed troubleshooting procedures for the various circuits. The service technician will find that consulting this table, and checking the possible causes in the order give, will prove to be the most efficient procedure to follow. The possible causes are listed either in order of most probable cause or fastest to verfy cause, whichever has been found by the manufacturer's technicians to be the most efficient approach.

A repair and adjustment section usually is included to provide guidance in replacing defective components, or realigning components that have gotten out of adjustment. When such instructions are given, the service technician should follow them closely to ensure successful repair. Of course, technicians performing the repair must have a working knowledge of repair procedures and precautions that pertain to printed-circuit boards. They should also be equipped with the proper tools. Lack of ability and/or use of improper tools can lead to more damage rather than eliminate a problem.

There is really no substitute for the service manuals provided by the manufacturers, and all service technicians should obtain manuals for the equipment on which they are working as well as for equipment that they expect to be performing work on.

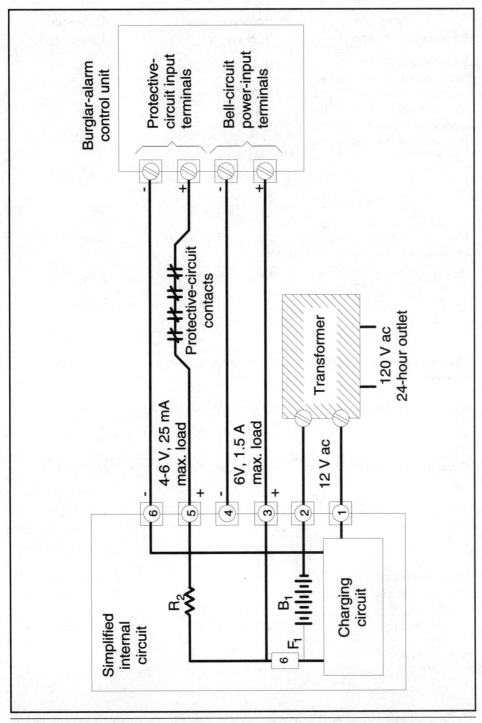

Figure 8-24: Schematic diagram accompanying the "Theory of Operation" section of a service manual.

Symptom	Possible causes	Reference
Resistors R54, R55 burnt	1. Power supply	1. Page 4B
Dialer does not trip Note: Make sure switch is in ON (center) position. Make sure potentiometer P4 is in extreme clockwise position as viewed from terminal strip end of alarm center	1. Batteries weak	1. Page 4B
	2. Power supply	2. Page 4B
	3. Trip circuits	3. Page 5B
	4. Start-delay and battery cutout circuit	4. Page 7B
	5. Channel switch and logic	5. Page 9B
Motor does not run on both channels and lamp does not light	1. Start-delay and battery cutout	1. Page 7B
	2. Motor supply	2. Page 8B
	3. Channel switch and logic	3. Page 9B
Motor does not run but lamp comes on	1. Motor supply	1. Page 8B
Motor runs but lamp does not light	1. Dialing filter and relay control	1. Page 12B
Dialer trips but does not shut off	1. Memory circuit	1. Page 6B
	2. Trip circuit	2. Page 5B
	3. Channel switch and logic	3. Page 9B
Dialer cannot switch from one channel to the other	1. Memory circuit	1. Page 6B
Dialer cannot program, erase	1. Tape head, jacks	1. Page 10B

Figure 8-25: Typical troubleshooting table.

Chapter 9
ESTIMATING INSTALLATION COSTS

Sound cost estimating of security/fire-alarm systems consists of a complete takeoff (or quantity survey) of all materials and equipment required for a complete installation, and then the calculation of the total labor required to install equipment and materials. To the cost of materials, equipment, and labor are added all direct expenses, variable job factors, taxes, overhead, and profit to determine a "selling price" for the project. If these procedures are intelligently performed and combined with good job management, the estimate should compare very favorably with the actual construction cost.

The steps necessary to prepare a cost estimate for a given security-system installation will normally run as follows:

- *Takeoff:* The count of all security devices, smoke detectors, magnetic contact devices, and similar items, and the measurement of all perimeter wiring, feeders to security control panels, anchors and fasteners, etc.

- *Listing the Material:* All items accounted for in the takeoff should be listed in an orderly sequence on a standard pricing sheet, as will be described later.

261

- *Applying Labor Units:* Determining the proper labor unit from proven labor-unit tables and applying them to the various materials or labor operation under the labor-unit column on the pricing sheet.

- *Finalizing:* The summation of material dollars and labor hours, the assignment of job factors and dollar values to labor hours, and the determination of overhead and profit.

Material Takeoff

A quantity survey or material takeoff consists of counting all the outlets and components by type (door contacts, bells, lockswitches, alarm panels, telephone dialers, etc.). These quantities are entered in their appropriate space on a material takeoff form such as shown in Figure 9-1. This form is intended to be presented to the customer when the detailed estimate has been completed. Each room or area of the building is listed in the columns marked "Location," and then the number of items per Location is entered in the squares below, "No. of Items Per Location." These items are totaled and priced. The total net price of material, labor costs, sales tax, etc. are totaled to obtain a selling price.

Some estimators make a very detailed material takeoff, listing all circuits separately and including such small items as wire connectors, fastenings, etc. Others will take off the major items of material for an entire building, listing only the different types of materials separately and giving a lump-sum dollar value for small incidentals. It really doesn't matter which procedure is used, as long as the estimator has sufficient information from which to make a complete list of all materials required to complete the installation. With this list it will be possible to apply labor units and thus have a means for pricing and ordering the materials.

A typical material takeoff begins with the counting of all magnetic contacts, glass-break detectors, smoke detectors, heat sensors, sounding devices, etc. The estimator continues by counting all alarm panels, telephone dialers, and all other major equipment. With this material out of the way, the measuring of all wiring, window foil, etc., takes place, using a rotameter or architect's scale.

The actual mechanics of a material takeoff procedure is comparatively simple and will become almost routine in a very short time. The sooner the estimating procedures become routine, the sooner the estimator will be able to make rapid and accurate takeoffs.

The estimator should remember that the circuit lines on floor plans represent only the horizontal portion of the various runs. To accumulate the vertical runs in the system, a scaled section of the building, showing the various floors and ceilings, should be used. Then the mounting heights of alarm stations, sounding devices, etc. can be marked to scale on the drawing of the building section. During the measuring

ALARM SYSTEM PROPOSAL

FOR: Name _____ Date _____

Street _____ City _____ Phone _____

PREPARED BY:

LOCATION

NAME _____

ADDRESS _____

CITY _____ STATE _____ ZIP _____

PHONE _____

NUMBER OF ITEMS PER LOCATION	ITEM	TOTAL QTY	MODEL NO.	UNIT PRICE	TOTAL PRICE
	CONTROL PANEL				
	POWER SUPPLY				
	EXIT/ENTRY DELAY				
	INDOOR REMOTE STATION				
	OUTDOOR REMOTE STATION				
	PREALARM STATION				
	OUTDOOR SOUNDING DEVICE				
	INDOOR SOUNDING DEVICE				
	DIALER				
	DIALER POWER SUPPLY				
	DIALER SWITCHING MODULE				
	DIALER CONNECTOR CORD				
	DIALER TAPE CARTRIDGE				
	ULTRASONIC DETECTOR				
	PHOTOELECTRIC SYSTEM				
	SMOKE DETECTORS				
	HEAT SENSORS				
	MAGNETIC CONTACTS				
	GLASS BREAK DETECTORS				
	SWITCH MAT				
	MISC. WIRING SUPPLIES				

TOTAL NET PRICE	
INSTALLATION	
SALES TAX	
TOTAL PRICE	
DEPOSIT	
BALANCE	

Figure 9-1: Alarm system proposal.

process, whenever a point is reached where there is a vertical section of the run, the rotameter or other measuring device is run over the proper vertical distance on the scaled cross section. This will continually accumulate the vertical distances along with the horizontal distances on the floor plans.

There are several other aids that will help the estimator make an accurate takeoff. One is to use different colored pencils in checking off runs of cable as they are measured — a different color for each wire size, cable type, or section of the runs. For example, black could be used to indicate the detection circuits, blue for control circuits, and red for annunciation circuits.

Listing The Material

While taking off the various alarm components from drawings, the estimator must list the items on pricing sheet forms so that pricing may be obtained for the various items and labor units added and extended. To help make this operation easier for both the estimator and the purchasing agent, the listings should be made in an orderly sequence on the pricing sheets.

When the takeoff has been done properly, the estimator will immediately have two items of valuable information: a brief description of each outlet, component circuit run, equipment, etc., and the quantity of each item listed. From these descriptions, the estimator can determine the exact quantity of materials and the necessary labor hours to completely install the system, provided that he or she has a good knowledge of actual security/fire-alarm installations and building construction.

Such incidentals as fastenings, hangers, wire connectors, etc. are rarely noted on drawings. Therefore, the estimator will be required to make an educated guess, based upon an understanding of the project's requirements, past experience with other projects, and the use of good judgment.

There is really no easy way to accomplish an exact material takeoff, but experienced estimators are able to produce very accurate estimates, rarely omitting important items, when a systematic method is used. The extent of the detail in which items of material are listed can vary to fit the contractor's particular method, but experience has shown that the more detailed the list, the better.

Applying Labor Units And Pricing

Determining the amount of labor that will be expended on a particular project is much more involved than the mere application of labor units. The pricing of materials also requires an intelligent analysis of the quotations by suppliers or price services. The majority of estimators obtain firm quotations from one or more security equipment suppliers, including the manufacturers of security/fire-alarm equipment.

Requests for quotations on special materials should be made as early as possible, although suppliers make it a habit to wait until the last few minutes prior to bid openings before giving out the quotation. This, of course, is done to prevent underbidding by another supplier.

When the quotation is received, the contractor or installer should check over the list of items on the quotation carefully. Suppliers do not normally guarantee that the items will meet with the project's specifications, nor will they take any responsibility for errors. Substitutions are common these days, and it is the contractor's responsibility to make certain that all items quoted will meet with the architect's or engineer's specifications. The contractor should also check the quantities of the quotation against those obtained from the takeoff to make sure they are correct.

Whenever possible, the contractor should obtain a guarantee of the quoted price for a definite period of time. Most suppliers will stand by their quotations for approximately 30 days. But what happens if it takes 6 weeks to award the contract? There is a good chance that the material quote will go up, and the contractor will have to pay more for the material than the price used in estimating. Therefore, the contractor should try to determine exactly when a particular job will be awarded (this is not necessarily the date of the bid opening) and then obtain a guarantee that the quote will be good until at least that time.

While waiting for a quotation from suppliers, labor units should be applied to the takeoff. A labor unit is a time figure indicating the time required to install, connect, or otherwise make usable a given item of material or a given labor operation. These units are used by the majority of contractors who must quote a firm lump-sum price to obtain security/fire-systems work. The units are normally based upon worker-hours or a percentage of a worker-hour. For example, 1.50 worker-hours indicates $1\frac{1}{2}$ worker-hours; that is, the labor required for a particular operation will take one worker $1\frac{1}{2}$ hours to accomplish.

Labor units are applied to each item of material and then extended and totaled to give the total worker-hours required to complete the project. The value of the labor in dollars and cents is then determined by multiplying the total computed worker-hours by the installer's average hourly rate of pay.

A separate unit of labor should be provided for the installation of each item of material or labor operation performed. This unit should be broken down further to apply to varying working conditions. For example, if a labor unit is given for installing 100 ft of two-conductor no. 22 cable at ground level, it stands to reason that installing the same amount of cable 20 ft above the floor will require more worker-hours. Scaffolding would have to be set up and moved into the area, and the workers would be required to spend more time carrying reels of wire to the scaffold platform. See Figure 9-2. Even if the work could be done with a ladder, some additional time would be required to move the ladder and climb up and down as the movement takes place.

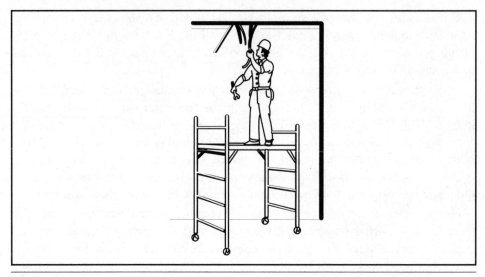

Figure 9-2: Working at heights requires more worker-hours than working at ground or floor level.

There are several other conditions affecting the labor operation that must be given consideration in preparing any and all bids:

1. The type of building construction
2. Height of the installation above normal working areas
3. The weight of the material or equipment
4. Performance of the general contractor (if any)
5. The availability and proficiency of the workers
6. Whether the wiring is to be concealed or exposed
7. Whether the installation is installed in new or existing buildings

The basic labor operation for any security/fire-alarm system installation must take into consideration several factors often overlooked by the inexperienced contractor or estimator. For example, the labor unit must include layout instructions, material handling, the actual installation of the material, coffee breaks, visits to the rest room, etc. If the labor units used do not include all of these items, the contract must make allowances to cover them. From the above statements, we can see that the amount of time required for a worker to install a given item may not be an adequate basis for determining an accurate labor unit.

The contractor or estimator is continually faced with having to use good judgment (and educated guesses) when dealing with labor units. At first, the selection of the proper labor units may seem to be a difficult task, but after some experience in the field, the estimator will be able to choose the labor units most applicable to the particular project or portion of a job.

The first step in arriving at the most accurate total estimated labor for a given job is to take off and list the material items on the pricing sheets, segregated in accordance with the installation and building conditions. On larger and more complex jobs, the different categories applicable to each type of material can be expanded in line with the different specific installation conditions.

The second step is to apply the labor unit specifically related to that particular installation condition for the size and type of material involved, depending on the extent of segregated listing of the material and the extent of segregation of the available labor data. However, there is no point in listing the materials on a segregated basis if segregated labor data are not available or if the estimator does not adjust the existing data to account for the specific conditions. Anything less than a segregated listing of the materials in accordance with the varying installation conditions and the application of related labor data reduces the accuracy of the total estimated labor.

Once the choice of labor unit has been made, the mechanics of labor-unit entry consist of merely copying the appropriate labor units from whatever source is available and entering the units in the labor-unit column on the pricing sheet opposite the proper item of material or labor operation.

After all of the labor units have been applied on the pricing sheet, they should be extended and totaled. This operation involves little more than elementary mathematics, but many errors can be made. The estimator, therefore, should be extremely careful at this point. One decimal point in the wrong place can mean the difference between a profit and a loss on a project. It is recommended that a good electronic calculator be used in making all extensions and totals.

No bid should ever be turned in without a check of the figures. Preferably, the person making the initial takeoff should check through the figures; then someone else should quickly check them over. One method of checking column totals is to add them first from top to bottom and then from bottom to top.

In any case, sufficient time should be allowed for checking the figures, as errors often result from hasty last-minute efforts to complete an estimate to meet a specific bid time.

Summarizing the Estimate

Summarizing the estimate is the final accumulation of all estimated costs such as labor, material, job factors, direct cost, overhead, and profit. Determination of the final quotation is one of the most important steps in preparing the estimate, because one mistake in the final summarizing can affect all of the accuracy with which the previous steps have been handled.

A typical bid summary sheet (Figure 9-3) includes the following basic sections or groups of cost data:

- Description of the project

- Cost of listed material and labor

- Nonproductive labor

- Direct job expenses

- Taxes, bonds, etc.

- Overhead

- Profit

Such a form serves as a sound guide to accurately summarize the estimate for practically any security/fire-alarm system installation.

Direct Job Expense and Overhead

A thorough understanding of both direct job expense and overhead is necessary so that they may be included in the final estimate to defray such costs. In general, direct job expenses are those costs (in addition to labor and materials) that have to be paid for as a direct result of performing the job. In other words, if the job was not performed, these costs would not occur. Overhead expense, on the other hand, is all costs that have to be paid whether the particular job is being done or not.

An estimate is not complete until all direct job and overhead expenses have been added to the other items entering into the cost of the project. Direct job expenses are relatively simple to calculate if the contractor is fair with the firm and includes all items of expense that relate directly to the job at hand. Calculating overhead, however, is a different picture altogether. Many contractors take their previous overhead figures and apply them to work which will be performed in the future. This may result in an accurate estimate, but in most cases, the overhead will change during the performance of the work being bid. Therefore, the contractor should analyze the anticipated future overhead for all jobs being bid at the present.

Another consideration is the size of the job. It is a fact that, in most cases, a small job will cause a higher percentage of overhead than a large job. However, the contractor cannot assume that this will always be true, especially in the case of specialized projects.

BID SUMMARY SHEET

JOB _____ PAGE _____
_____ OF _____
_____
_____

ESTIMATED BY _____ CHECKED BY _____ DATE _____

DESCRIPTION	MATERIAL				LABOR		
	Quantity	Unit Price	Per	Amount	Unit	Per	Amount
		TOTAL					

MISCELLANEOUS		RECAPITULATION	
		Material Cost	
		Hours Labor @	
		Hours Labor @	
		Direct Job Expense	
		Total Prime Cost	
		Overhead Expense	
		TOTAL COST	
		Profit	
		Selling Price	
		BID SUBMITTED	

Figure 9-3: Typical bid summary sheet.

When the estimate has been completed to the point of adding the overhead, the known data should include cost of materials, cost of labor, and direct job expense. The overhead is then determined by one of the following methods:

1. The overhead for the year may be divided by the gross sales volume for the year to find the overhead as a percentage of the gross sales volume. This percentage is then applied to the prime cost of the job.

2. The overhead expense for the year may be divided by the total cost of labor, material, and job expense for the year to find the overhead as a percentage of the prime cost.

When the estimated annual volume differs from the past annual volume for which an overhead based upon accounting records is obtainable and when, for some reason, the same total dollar cost of overhead expenses must be maintained, the estimator must determine by simple proportion the applicable average overhead percentage of prime cost and apply this percentage using the job-size scale. This is done by estimating the overhead percentage on the basis of past recorded data, adjusted to future volume and size of work. If the job being estimated represents a change in general work pattern or is a special type of job, the estimator must make an intelligent analysis of all the conditions and further adjust the estimated overhead percentage to be applied as accurately as possible.

Completing the Summary

Completing the summary involves only the inclusion of such miscellaneous items as wire connectors, tape, and fasteners as shown in Figure 9-4. Most contractors feel

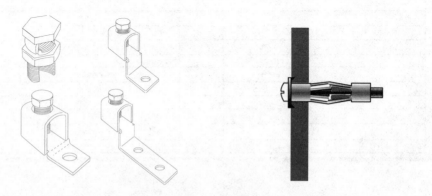

Figure 9-4: With the exception of very specialized projects, wire connectors, fasteners, and similar items are lumped together and figured as a certain percentage of the total installation cost.

that the listing of these items serves no purpose. Therefore, on most projects, an allowance for these items is made rather than a list with the price of each individual item. This allowance is usually in the form of a lump-sum figure, a percentage gained from experience, or an educated guess. As a rule, $\frac{1}{2}$ of 1 percent is sufficient for all projects except highly specialized ones. Once this figure has been determined, the dollar value should be entered in the appropriate space on the summarizing form.

The contractor also will be required to calculate miscellaneous labor costs on many projects. Conditions such as overtime (required to complete the project within a specified time), labor disputes, and special installations will make the inclusion of extra labor necessary. There is no set rule for calculating this figure exactly. It is a matter of experience and good judgment.

The subtotals of the dollar value of the labor, material, subcontractors (if any), and direct job expense are totaled to give the total prime cost. The percentage of applicable estimated overhead determined as previously discussed is applied, and the dollar value of the overhead expense is calculated. This, added to the prime cost, gives the total gross cost.

The percentage of profit to be included in the estimate is either determined by the contractor alone or after consultation between the contractor and the estimator, taking into consideration the type and size of the job, the character of the competition on the job, and the desirability of obtaining the job.

Some contractors prefer to apply a fixed percentage of profit to all estimates. Others vary the percentage in accordance with the factors indicated above. Some do not use a percentage adder, but determine the dollar value of the profit desired on the basis of a certain amount for each worker-day required by the job or by allowing a flat sum.

There are certain items of cost that in a true sense are direct job expenses but against which it may not be desirable to assess a profit. Such items may be sales taxes, excise taxes, and payment and performance bonds. If these items have not been included previously in the estimate, they must be added into the final price.

The total estimated price is calculated by totaling the gross cost, profit, and other items. Normally the total estimated price or the nearest even figure is determined to be the amount of the bid. In too many instances, when the contractor or estimator becomes uneasy over the competition on the job, the amount of the bid bears little resemblance to the total estimated price.

Too much emphasis cannot be put on the necessity of including in the summary the proper allowances for direct job expense, job factor, nonproductive labor, labor productivity factor, overhead expenses, and profit. Any estimate properly summarized will more nearly provide enough income from that job to pay for all costs, both direct and indirect, caused by that job than if the final price is established on a hit-or-miss basis. When each job proves to be reasonably profitable, the entire business operation is successful.

Labor Units

The labor units in Figure 9-5 are the result of averaging the figures of several proven estimating manuals. Bear in mind that these units are based on workers experienced in the security/fire-alarm field and, furthermore, that modern handheld power tools, wire strippers, and other time-saving devices are assumed to be used in the installation.

Needless to say, labor units are the most important factor in estimating, and no one list of units will accurately forecast the work of all contractors. Worker-hour values are given in Figure 9-5 for the most commonly used items of security/fire-alarm systems. Interested contractors may adopt these units and modify them appropriately to suit their own operations.

Remember, these labor units reflect the work of experienced contractors. If it is necessary to increase any of them drastically, there must be a reason for time-consuming work habits, use of devices or materials that slow down installation, etc. It would be advantageous to seek out these reasons and find ways to improve operating efficiencies. Labor units are given for several groups of difficulty for installations using low-voltage cable, since all degrees of working conditions are likely to be encountered.

There are many installation variables that can affect the labor cost for any given type of outlet, contact installation, wire-pulling operation, etc. A large number of these conditions can be divided into four installation situation groups for all practical purposes. These groups may be designated 1, 2, 3, and 4, with group 1 representing the least amount of work and group 4 requiring the greatest number of worker-hours for the same labor operation.

Group 1: All working areas are open and readily accessible to workers. Work above grade levels requires no scaffolding, only stepladders.

Group 2: Includes the installation of security/fire-alarm equipment, contacts, and wiring in areas that are partially accessible but require minor fishing of cables in concealed partitions. Installation of surface molding to conceal wiring also will fall into this group.

Group 3: These wiring situations usually involve the installation of concealed wiring in partially inaccessible areas, such as crawl spaces, limiting the working room. Other situations include notching of firestops or diagonal bracing to get cables in finished wall spaces, installing wiring on masonry walls where furring strips have been applied, and installing wiring in attics or basements where both horizontal and vertical surfaces have been closed in

Group 4: The most difficult situations include cutting through masonry walls, removal of finished floor boards to route wiring, removal of baseboards and door/window trim to permit routing of new wiring, or cutting and patching of finished surfaces to conceal new wiring.

Items to be Installed	Group			
	1	2	3	4
Alarm bells	0.50	0.70	0.90	1.10
Alarm panels	1.75	2.00	2.25	2.50
Door cords	0.70	1.00	1.30	1.65
Exit/entry delay module	0.45	0.50	0.70	0.85
Fire-alarm station	0.50	0.70	0.90	1.10
Foil blocks	0.40	0.75	1.00	1.25
Heat sensors	0.80	1.00	1.25	1.50
Horns	0.70	1.00	1.25	1.50
Indoor remote stations	2.50	3.30	5.50	7.70
Indoor mounting devices	0.70	1.00	1.30	1.65
Lockswitches	1.00	1.50	2.00	2.50
Low-voltage cable, 2/c (per 1000 ft)	8.50	12.00	14.00	16.00
Low-voltage cable, 3/c (per 1000 ft)	9.50	14.00	16.00	18.00
Low-voltage cable, 4/c (per 1000 ft)	10.50	15.50	17.50	19.50
Magnetic contacts, pair	0.40	0.75	1.00	1.25
Mechanical contacts	0.30	0.50	0.70	0.90
Motion detectors	1.30	1.80	2.10	2.30
Outdoor alarm bells	1.25	1.75	2.00	2.30
Outdoor remote stations	3.00	3.50	4.00	4.50
Photoelectric cells, recessed	1.20	1.75	2.00	2.30
Photoelectric cells, wall-mounted	1.00	1.30	1.75	2.00
Power supplies	0.30	1.50	2.00	2.50
Relays	1.20	1.70	2.10	2.50
Sirens	1.00	1.50	2.00	2.30
Smoke detectors	0.80	1.00	1.25	1.50
Telephone dialers	2.00	2.50	3.00	3.50
Transformers	0.45	0.50	0.70	0.85
Windows foil (per 100 ft)	4.50	5.00	5.50	6.00
Window sensors	0.70	1.00	1.30	1.65

Figure 9-5: Security/fire-alarm system labor units (worker-hours).

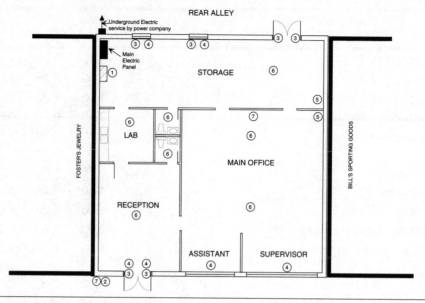

Figure 9-6: Floor plan of a small commercial building.

Practical Application

To illustrate how a typical estimate is performed, take the commercial building shown in Figure 9-6. The design criteria are as follows:

1. Security- and fire-alarm system is to be provided.

2. System is to be local type.

3. Distance to street is 12 ft.

4. Distance to tenants on each side is approximately 1 ft.

5. There is a dimly lighted alley in the rear of the building.

6. Front and rear doors are used for egress and entry.

7. All control stations are to be inside.

8. There are no watchdogs in the building.

9. Security system is to be armed only with windows closed.

10. Rear alley is to be lighted during a security alarm.

11. Window types:
    a. Front: fixed plate glass
    b. Rear: double-hung

12. Door types:
    a. Front: double plate glass with steel casing
    b. Rear: double steel

The security/fire-alarm system was laid out as shown in Figure 9-6. The large numbers correspond to the following equipment:

1. Control panel
2. Remote station (siren speakers above acoustical ceiling)
3. Magnetic contacts
4. Glass-break detectors
5. Photoelectric detector
6. Smoke detector
7. Fire horn

Begin the material takeoff by listing all major components by catalog number, quantity, and price of each item. Use a rotameter or scale and calculate the total footage of wire. Then use a lump-sum figure for miscellaneous items like connectors, fastenings, etc. When completed, extend the figures as in Figure 9-7.

Refer to the labor units in Figure 9-5 and enter proper units in the appropriate column. Extend the labor units, then total both the material and labor columns. Enter the material dollar value and labor worker-hours under the recapitulation columns.

Multiply the worker-hours by the average hourly rate, calculate the labor adder and other direct job expenses (if any), and enter them in the proper spaces. Total the dollar value of material, labor, and direct job expense to obtain a total prime cost. Finish the estimate by adding overhead and profit to obtain a selling price. Figure 9-7 shows that the total selling price is $4056.42.

COMPUTERIZED ESTIMATING

In the quest to shorten the lengthy process of estimating the installation costs of security fire-alarm systems, two major developments have occurred: the assembly concept and computerized estimating. Both developments have the potential of providing great benefits to installation contractors, although reaping the full benefits of these improvements takes a bit of effort, particularly because it is difficult to tailor the systems to meet the specific needs of each contractor.

The assembly method was first popularized by the Estimatic Corp. in the 1950s. (Estimatic was also a pioneer in computerized estimating long before anyone else was doing it.) The company used the concept that virtually every type of electrical/electronic symbol used in construction drawings could be summarized as a specific list of materials.

For example, the assembly for a common duplex receptacle would include the receptacle, the finish plate, a box, a plaster ring, screws for fastening the box to the

BID SUMMARY SHEET

JOB Page Health Dept.
611 Mossy Oak Drive
Overall, Virginia 22658

PAGE 1
OF 1

ESTIMATED BY __JET__ CHECKED BY __RRU__ DATE __10/7/95__

DESCRIPTION	MATERIAL				LABOR		
	Quantity	Unit Price	Per	Amount	Unit	Per	Amount
051 Control Panel	1	360.00	ea.	360.00	1.75	ea.	1.75
413 Battery	1	36.60		36.60	0.30		0.30
216R Indoor Remote Station	3	39.00		117.00	2.50		9.50
290 Prealarm Station	3	27.00		81.00	0.50		0.50
581 Outdoor Sounding Device	2	40.00		80.00	1.25		2.50
205 Indoor Sounding Device	1	20.00		20.00	0.70		0.70
550 Siren Driver	2	60.00		120.00	1.00		2.00
304 Relay	1	15.00		15.00	1.20		1.20
2025 Photoelectric System	2	300.00		600.00	1.20		2.40
295A Smoke Detectors	7	60.00		420.00	0.80		5.60
441 Magnetic Contacts	6	4.00		24.00	0.40		2.40
170 Glass Break Detectors	6	45.00		270.00	0.70		4.20
171 Adapter (delay)	1	27.00		27.00	1.00		1.00
217 Emergency Switch	2	3.00		6.00	1.00		2.00
221 Transformer	1	20.00		20.00	0.45		0.45
18/2 Wire	700 ft	0.20		140.00	8.60	M	6.02
Misc. (fasteners, connectors)	Lot	27.00		27.00	4.00		4.00
TOTAL				$2363.60			42.36

MISCELLANEOUS	RECAPITULATION	
	Material Cost	$2363.60
	42.36 Hours Labor @ $20.00	847.20
	3 Hours Labor @ $25.00	75.00
	Direct Job Expense	250.00
	Total Prime Cost	$3535.80
	Overhead Expense 15%	530.37
	TOTAL COST	$4066.17
	Profit 15%	609.22
	Selling Price	$4676.09
	BID SUBMITTED	$4676.09

Figure 9-7: Completed estimate sheet.

framing, a grounding pigtail, a couple ft of No. 12 wire in the box, an average of two wire nuts, and two $\frac{1}{2}$-in EMT connectors. Thus the assembly includes everything indicated by the duplex receptacle symbol on the plans.

This is typical of all assemblies, where there could be many thousands of combinations of different types of receptacles with different types of finish plates, different types of plaster rings, and so on. Even raceways or cable assemblies can be broken down into assemblies: for example, three no. 12 THHNs in $\frac{3}{4}$-in EMT, three no. 6s, and one no. 10 in 1-in EMT, and so on.

Thus the contractor develops a full set of assemblies and prices them all, so that when the estimator takes on a job, the estimator counts all the symbols and raceways on the plans, and then prices the list as assemblies (so many type XYZ assemblies, so many type ABC assemblies, etc.). Because all the assemblies are prepriced and prelabled, the estimator no longer needs to count or price most individual parts. And when it is time to order material, the modern computer can take these assemblies and list how many of each individual item to order from suppliers.

Certainly computerized estimating (Figure 9-8) has made a noticeable impact on the trade, with the computer able to perform all the tedious mathematic functions. It can save an estimator a lot of work and at the same time eliminate the likelihood of errors in mathematics. These are the main benefits of computerized estimating. There are also other benefits to be reaped, but none nearly as important.

The takeoff remains difficult (even with the automatic takeoff tools). Then comes writing up the estimate; that is, entering it into the computer. At first glance this would seem far easier than the "old" method of writing down each item and assigning it a cost and labor rate, but other factors come into play with the computer that diminish the gain somewhat.

Figure 9-8: Computer estimating has made a noticeable impact on the trade.

First of all there are the computer codes. All the popular computerized estimating systems use a special code number for each particular type and size of material. For example, ¾-in EMT might be code number 27.7; 1-in EMT might be code number 27.11; no. 12 THHN solid could be code number 246.94, and so on. So now the estimator must enter not only a description of the item, but a code number also. (This is not always necessary, but almost all estimators enter a description so they can double-check their work.) And because there are so many different items in electrical construction that no one remembers all the code numbers, it is necessary for the estimator to look up code numbers for most of the items. Some estimating rooms have organized a large chart on the walls from which the estimator can obtain all the code numbers at a glance.

Thus far the best method developed for itemized estimating is to use a combination of assemblies and the computer. In the best of these systems the estimator does the standard type takeoff and enters the totals into the computer. Then the computer takes all these assemblies, breaks them down into their individual parts, and prints out one complete bill of material.

You get the best of the assembly system's benefits, and you don't have to update the prices of your assemblies continually, because all the computer needs is the quantities of materials that make up each assembly, not the prices. After the whole job is broken down to a single material list, the computer will give a material price and labor hour figure to each item, and not to entire assemblies.

Of course, the task of updating the material prices in the computer remains; but given the makeup of the industry at this time, there is no worthwhile alternative to spending some time doing this.

Although computerized estimating systems have been around for a number of years, only in the past decade have the prices of both the computer equipment and the programs decreased to where the average contractor can afford them. Actually, computers for the past few years have been making the transition from a "nice tool" to "standard equipment" in electrical contractors' offices.

Remember when purchasing any computer system (but especially for estimating) that flexibility is critically important, as is proper training in the use of the system. Any computer system that you use for estimating should be capable of being fully integrated with computer programs your company may be using for accounting and management.

ESTIMATING SYSTEMS

There are so many different computerized estimating systems on the market that it is difficult for the new user to know which to choose. The only practical method is to to obtain descriptive literature on the available systems, study this literature thoroughly, and then ask for a demonstration of the ones that seem best suited for your business. After weighing cost, ease of use, and other factors, choose the one that suits you the best.

However, if you are new at computer estimating, Craftsman Book Company of 6058 Corte Del Cedro, Carlsbad, CA 92018 has several estimating manuals that sell for very reasonable prices. Many of these manuals also include free computer software suitable for the IBM PC computer. The manuals are updated annually and include both labor units and material costs. It is recommended that you give the Craftsman estimating manuals a try before purchasing more sophisticated software.

The following firms specialize in computerized estimating systems. It is suggested that you write to each for descriptive literature:

Calculated Industries, Inc.
4840 Hytech Drive
Carson City, NV 89706-2408
1-800-854-8075

Deluxe Business Systems
PO Box 64046
St. Paul, MN 55164-9968

Litning Software
250 Peralta Blvd. Suite 119
Fremont, CA 94536

Scalex Corporation
2794 Loker Avenue West, Suite 105
Carlsbad, CA 92008-9609

SDSI Business Systems
27475 Ynez Road, Suite 385
Temecula, CA 92591
909-677-6785

Appendix I
Glossary

AA (Aluminum Association): A manufacturers' association that promotes the use of aluminum.

AAC: All aluminum conductor.

ASC: Aluminum alloy stranded conductors.

Abrasion: The process of rubbing, grinding, or wearing away by friction.

Abrasion resistance: Ability to resist surface wear.

Abrasive paper: Paper or cloth on which flint, garnet, emery, aluminum oxide, or corundum has been fastened with glue or some other adhesive. One use in the electrical field is to clean conductors, contacts, or terminals.

ac (alternating current): 1) A periodic current, the average of which is zero over a period; normally the current reverses after given time intervals and has alternately positive and negative values. 2) The type of electrical current actually produced in a rotating generator (alternator).

Accelerated life tests: Subjecting a product to operating conditions more severe than normal to expedite deterioration, affording some measure of probable life at normal conditions.

Accelerator: 1) A substance that increases the speed of a chemical reaction. 2) Something to increase velocity.

Accent lighting: Lighting used to emphasize an object or specific area.

Acceptable (nuclear power): Demonstrated to be adequate by the safety analysis of the station.

Acceptance test: Made to demonstrate the degree of compliance with specified requirements.

Accepted: Approval for a specific installation or arrangement of equipment or materials.

Accessible: Capable of being removed or exposed without damaging the building structure or finish, or not permanently closed in by the structure or finish of the building. See *readily accessible*.

ACSR (aluminum, conductor, steel reinforced): A bare composite of aluminum and steel wires, usually aluminum around steel.

Actuated equipment (nuclear power): Component(s) that perform a protective function.

Administrative authority: An organization exercising jurisdiction over the National Electrical Safety Code.

AEIC: Association of Edison Illuminating Companies.

Aggregate: Material mixed with cement and water to produce concrete.

Aging: The irreversible change of material properties after exposure to an environment for an interval of time.

AIA: 1) American Institute of Architects. 2) Aircraft Industries Association.

Air cleaner: Device used for removal of airborne impurities.

Air diffuser: Air distribution outlet designed to direct airflow into desired patterns.

Air entrained concrete: Concrete in which a small amount of air is trapped by addition of a special material to produce greater durability.

Air flow: The distribution or movement of air.

Air gap: A small gap that is deliberately left in the magnetic core of an electromagnetic device. When the coil becomes deenergized, some magnetic flux (residual magnetism) always remains, and if it were not for the air gap in the magnetic core, the residual magnetism might be sufficient to hold the armature in the sealed-in position.

Air horsepower (AHP):Work done in moving a given volume or weight of air at a given speed.

Air oven: A lab oven used to heat by convection of hot air.

Al: Aluminum.

Alarm indicating appliance:An appliance that produces an audible or visible alarm signal, or both, in response to a fire emergency.

Alarm initiating device: A device which, when actuated, initiates an alarm. Such devices, depending on their type, can be operated manually or actuated automatically in response to smoke, flame, heat, or waterflow.

Alarm signal: A signal indicating an emergency requiring immediate action, such as an alarm for fire from a manual station, a waterflow alarm, or an alarm from an automatic fire-alarm system.

Alarm system: A combination of compatible initiating devices, control panels and indicating appliances designed and installed to produce an alarm signal in the event of fire, intrusion, or other similar action.

Al-Cu: An abbreviation for aluminum and copper, commonly marked on terminals, lugs, and other electrical connectors to indicate that the device is suitable for use with either aluminum conductors or copper conductors.

Alive: Energized; having voltage applied.

Alligator wrench: A wrench with toothed V-shaped jaws fixed in position.

Alloy: A substance having metallic properties and being composed of elemental metal and one or more chemical elements.

Alternator: A device to produce alternating current. Alternators range in size from small automotive types to huge types used in power plants to produce electricity for cross-country distribution.

Alumoweld®: An aluminum clad steel wire by Copperweld Steel Corp.

Ambient: Surrounding on all sides, such as air or noise.

Ambient temperature: Temperature of fluid (usually air) that surrounds an object on all sides.

Ambient temperature compensated: A device, such as an overload relay, which is not affected by the temperature surrounding it.

American bond: Brickwork pattern consisting of five courses of stretchers followed by one bonding course of headers.

Ammeter: An electric meter used to measure current, calibrated in amperes.

Ampacity: The current-carrying capacity of conductors or equipment, expressed in amperes.

Ampere (A): The basic SI unit measuring the quantity of electricity.

Ampere-hour: The quantity of electricity that passes any point in a circuit in one hour.

Ampere rating: The current-carrying capacity of an overcurrent protective device. When a fuse or circuit breaker is subjected to a current above its ampere rating, it will open the circuit after a predetermined period of time.

Ampere squared seconds (I^2t): The measure of heat energy developed within a circuit during the fuse's clearing. It can be expressed as "melting I^2t," or "racing I^2t," or the sum of them as "clearing I^2t." I stands for effective let-through current (RMS), which is squared, and the t stands for time of opening in seconds.

Ampere-turn: The product of amperes times the number of turns in a coil.

Amplification: Procedure of expanding the strength of a signal.

Amplifier: 1) A device that enables an input signal to directly control a larger energy flow. 2) The process of increasing the strength of an input.

Amplitude: The maximum value of a wave.

Analog: Pertaining to data from continuously varying physical quantities.

Analog device: A device that can be adjusted to different states. A simple example is the dimmer control for a conventional lighting fixture. This type of control can turn the light on or off, or adjusted to any position between. Thus, a dimmer control is an analog device as opposed to a digital device such as a common on-off snap switch.

Angle bracket: A form of support having two faces generally at right angles to each other. A web is often added to increase strength.

Angle, roll over (overhead): The sum of the vertical angles between the conductor and the horizontal on both sides of the traveler, excessive roll over angles can cause premature splice failures.

Angular velocity: The average time rate of change of angular position; in electrical circuits = 2f, and f equals frequency.

ANI (American Nuclear Insurers): A voluntary unincorporated association of companies providing property and liability insurance for U.S. nuclear power plants; formerly NELPIA.

Annealing: The process of preventing or removing objectional stresses in materials by controlled cooling from a heated state; measured by tensile strength.

annealing, bright: Annealing in a protective environment to prevent discoloration of the surface.

Annunciator: An electrically or mechanically operated visible signaling device having one or more target or lamp indictors to display the status of a security/fire-alarm system.

Anode: 1) Positive electrode through which current enters a nonmetallic conductor such as an electrolytic cell. 2) The negative pole of a storage battery.

ANSI (American National Standards Institute): An organization that publishes nationally recognized standards.

Antenna: A device for transmission or reception of electromagnetic waves.

Anti-dogleg methods: Any method used to secure or strap conduit in place while bending is taking place.

Antioxidant: Retards or prevents degradation of materials exposed to oxygen (air) or peroxides.

Antisiphon trap: Trap in a drainage system designed to preserve a water seal by defeating siphonage.

Aperture seal (nuclear): A seal between containment aperture and the electrical penetration assembly.

Appendix, NEC: The National Electrical Code (NEC) Appendices A and B are located at the end of the code book. Appendix A includes material extracted from other NFPA documents. Appendix B is not part of the requirements of the NEC and contains additional material for informational purposes only.

Appliance: Equipment designed for a particular purpose, using electricity to produce heat, light, mechanical motion, etc.; usually complete in itself, generally other than industrial use, normally in standard sizes or types.

Approved: 1) Acceptable to the authority having legal enforcement. 2) Per Occupational Safety and Health Act. A product that has been tested to standards and found suitable for general application, subject to limitations outlined in the nationally recognized testing lab's listing.

Apron: Piece of horizontal wood trim under the sill of the interior casing of a window.

Arc: A flow of current across an insulating medium.

Arc furnace: Heats by heavy current flow through the material to be heated.

Arcing time: The amount of time from the instant the fuse link has melted until the overcurrent is interrupted or cleared.

Arc resistance: The time required for an arc to establish a conductive path in or across a material.

Area (A): The square measurement of any plane surface or cross section of a conduit, air duct, etc., or the circular plane of a propeller.

Areaway: Open space below the ground level immediately outside a building. It is enclosed by substantial walls.

Armature: 1) Rotating machine: the member in which alternating voltage is generated. 2) Electromagnet: the member that is moved by magnetic force.

Armor: Mechanical protector for cables; usually a helical winding of metal tape, formed so that each convolution locks mechanically upon the previous one (interlocked armor); may be a formed metal tube or a helical wrap of wires.

Arrester: 1) A circuit device designed to check and limit voltage surges caused by lightning. 2) Wire screen secured to the top of an incinerator to confine sparks and other products of burning.

Ashlar: Squared and dressed stones used for facing a masonry wall; short upright wood pieces extending from the attic floor to the rafters forming a dwarf wall.

Article, NEC: The National Electrical Code (NEC) is organized into nine chapters. The main body of the NEC text begins with Article 90 — Introduction, and ends with Article 820 — Community Antenna Television and Radio Distribution Systems.

Askarel: A synthetic insulating oil that is nonflammable but very toxic — being replaced by silicone oils.

ASME: American Society of Mechanical Engineers.

Associated circuits (nuclear power): Nonclass 1E circuits that share power supplies or are not physically separated from Class 1E circuits.

ASTM (American Society for Testing and Materials): A group writing standards for testing materials and specifications for materials.

Asymmetrical: Not identical on both sides of a central line; unsymmetrical.

Atom: The smallest particle to which an element may be divided and still retain the properties of the element. According to our present understanding, the atom is believed to consist of a central nucleus composed of protons and neutrons, surrounded by orbiting electrons.

Attachment plug or cap: The male connector for electrical cords.

Attenuation: A decrease in energy magnitude during transmission.

Audible: Capable of being heard by humans.

Auditable data: Technical information that is documented and organized to be readily understandable and traceable to independently verify inferences or conclusions based on these records.

Auger: A wood-boring tool of large size with handle attached at right angles to the tool line. Several types are made for different purposes.

Autoclave: A heated pressure vessel used to bond, cure, seal, or used for environmental testing.

Automatic: Operating by own mechanism when actuated by some impersonal influence; nonmanual; self-acting.

Automatic transfer equipment: A device to transfer a load from one power source to another, usually from normal to emergency source and back.

Autotransformer: Any transformer where primary and secondary connections are made to a single cell. The application of an autotransformer is a good choice for some users where a 480Y/277- or 208Y/120-volt, three-phase, four-wire distribution system is utilized.

Auxiliary: A device or equipment that aids the main device or equipment.

AWG (American Wire Gage): The standard for measuring wires in America.

Awl: A small pointed tool for making holes for nails or screws. When used to mark metal objects, it is sometimes called "scratch awl."

Axial: Of or forming an axis; on or around an axis.

Axis: The line about which a rotating body turns.

Ballast: A device designed to stabilize current flow.

Battery: A device which changes chemical to electrical energy, used to store electricity.

Bimetal strip: Temperature regulating or indicating device that works on the principle that two dissimilar metals with unequal expansion rates, welded together, will bend as temperature changes.

Bonding bushing: A special conduit bushing equipped with a conductor terminal to take a bonding jumper; also has a screw or other sharp device to bite into the enclosure wall to bond the conduit to the enclosure without a jumper when there are no concentric knockouts left in the wall of the enclosure.

Bonding jumper: A bare or insulated conductor used to ensure the required electrical conductivity between metal parts required to be electrically connected. Frequently used from a bonding bushing to the service equipment enclosure to provide a path around concentric knockouts in an enclosure wall; also used to bond one raceway to another.

Bonding locknut: A threaded locknut for use on the end of a conduit terminal, but a locknut equipped with a screw through its lip. When the locknut is installed, the screw is tightened so its end bites into the wall of the enclosure close to the edge of the knockout.

Braid: An interwoven cylindrical covering of fiber or wire.

Branch circuit: That portion of a wiring system extending beyond the final overcurrent device protecting a circuit.

Bridge: A circuit which measures by balancing four impedances through which the same current flows:

- Wheatstone — resistance

- Kelvin — low resistance

- Schering — capacitance, dissipation factor, dielectric constant

- Wien — capacitance, dissipation factor

Bus: The conductor(s) serving as a common connection for two or more circuits.

Bus bars: The conductive bars used as the main current supplying elements of panel boards or switchboards; also the conductive bars duct; an assembly of bus bars within an enclosure which is designed for ease of installation, has no fixed electrical characteristics, and allows power to be taken off conveniently, usually without circuit interruption.

BX: A nickname for armored cable (wires with a spiral-wound, flexible steel outer jacketing); although used generically, BX is a registered tradename of the General Electric Company.

Bypass: Passage at one side of or around a regular passage.

Cable: An assembly of two or more wires which may be insulated or bare.

Cable, aerial: An assembly of one or more conductors and a supporting messenger.

Cable, armored: A cable having armor. *See* Armor.

Cable, belted: A multiconductor cable having a layer of insulation over the assembled insulated conductors.

Cable clamp: A device used to clamp around a cable to transmit mechanical strain to all elements of the cable.

Cable, coaxial: A cable used for high frequency, consisting of two cylindrical conductors with a common axis separated by a dielectric; normally the outer conductor is operated at ground potential for shielding.

Cable, control: Used to supply voltage (usually ON or OFF).

Cable, duplex: A twisted pair of cables.

Cable, power: Used to supply current (power).

Cable, pressure: A cable having a pressurized fluid (gas or oil) as part of the insulation; paper and oil are the most common insulators.

Cable, ribbon: A flat multiconductor cable.

Cable, service drop: The cable from the utility line to the customer's property.

Cable, signal: A cable used to transmit data.

Cable, spacer: An aerial distribution cable made of covered conductors held by insulated spacers; designed for wooded areas.

Cable tray: A rigid structure to support cables: a type of raceway: normally having the appearance of a ladder and open at the top to facilitate changes.

Cable, tray: A multiconductor having a nonmetallic jacket, designed for use in cable trays (not to be confused with type TC cable, for which the jacket must also be flame retardant).

Cable, triplexed d: Helical assembly of three insulated conductors and sometimes a bare grounding conductor.

Cable, unit: A cable having pairs of cables stranded into groups (units) of a given quantity; these groups then form the core.

Cable, vertical riser: Cables utilized in circuits of considerable elevation change; usually incorporate additional components for tensile strength.

Cabling: Helically wrapping together of two or more insulated wires.

Capacitance: The storage of electricity in a capacitor; the opposition to voltage change; the unit of measurement is the farad.

Capacitor: An apparatus consisting of two conducting surfaces separated by an insulating material. It stores energy, blocks the flow of direct current, and permits the flow of alternating current to a degree depending on the capacitance and frequency.

Capillary action: The traveling of liquid along a small interstice due to surface tension.

Capstan: A rotating drum used to pull cables or ropes by friction; the cables are wrapped around the drum.

Cathode: 1) The negative electrode through which current leaves a nonmetallic conductor, such as an electrolytic cell. 2) The positive pole of a storage battery. 3) Vacuum tube — the electrode that emits electrons.

Cathode-ray tube: The electronic tube which has a screen upon which a beam of elec trons from the cathode can be made to create images; for example, the television picture tube.

Cathodic protection: Reduction or prevention of corrosion by making the metal to be protected the cathode in a direct current circuit.

Cavity wall: Wall built of solid masonry units arranged to provide airspace within the wall.

CB: Pronounced "see bee." An expression used to refer to "circuit breaker," taken from the initial letters *C* and *B*.

C-C: Center to center.

CCA: *See* Customer Complaint Analysis.

CEE: *See* International Commission on Rules for the Approval of Electrical Equipment.

Centigrade scale Temperature: Scale used in metric system. Freezing point of water is 0°C; boiling point is 100°C.

CFR: *See* Code of Federal Regulations.

Choke coil: A coil used to limit the flow of alternating current while permitting direct current to pass.

Circuit: A closed path through which current flows from a generator, through various components, and back to the generator.

Circuit breaker: A resettable fuse-like device designed to protect a circuit against overloading.

Circuit foot: One foot of circuit; that is, if one has a three-conductor circuit, each lineal foot of circuit would have three circuit feet.

Circular mil: The non-SI unit for measuring the cross-sectional area of a conductor.

CL: Center line.

Clearance: The vertical space between a cable and its conduit.

Coaxial cable: A cable consisting of two conductors concentric with and insulated from each other.

Code: Short for National Electrical Code.

Code installation: An installation that conforms to the local code and/or the national code for safe and efficient installation.

Code of Federal Regulations (CFR): The general and permanent rules published in the Federal Register by the executive departments and agencies of the federal government. The Code is divided into 50 titles, which represent broad areas; titles are divided into chapters, which usually bear the name of the issuing agency; For example, Title 30 — Mineral Resources, Chapter I — MESA; Title 29 — Labor, Chapter XVII — OSHA; Title 10 — Energy, Chapter I — NRC.

Color code: Identifying conductors by the use of color.

Come along: A cable grip (usually of tubular basket-weave construction which tightens its grip on the cable as it is pulled) with a pulling "eye" on one end for attaching to a pull-rope for pulling conductors into a conduit or other raceway.

Computer: An electronic apparatus: 1) for solving complex and involved problems, usually mathematical or logical, rapidly, 2) for storing large amounts of data.

Concealed: Rendered inaccessible by the structure or finish of the building. Wires in concealed raceways are considered concealed, even though they may become accessible by being withdrawn.

Concentricity: The measurement of the center of the conductor with respect to the center of the insulation.

Conductance: The ability of material to carry an electric current.

Conductor: Any substance that allows energy flow through it, with the transfer being made by physical contact but excluding net mass flow.

Conductor, bare: Having no covering or insulation whatsoever.

Conductor, covered: A conductor having one or more layers of nonconducting materials that are not recognized as insulation under the National Electrical Code.

Conductor, insulated: A conductor covered with material recognized as insulation.

Conductor load: The mechanical load on an aerial conductor—wind, weight, ice, etc.

Conductor, plain: A conductor that consists of only one metal.

Conductor, segmental: A conductor that has sections isolated one from the other and connected in parallel; used to reduce ac resistance.

Conductor, solid: A single wire.

Conductor, stranded: Assembly of several wires, usually twisted or braided.

Conductor stress control: The conducting layer applied to make the conductor a smooth surface in intimate contact with the insulation; formerly called extruded strand shield (ESS).

Conduit: A tubular raceway.

Conduit fill: Amount of cross-sectional area used in a raceway.

Conduit, rigid metal: Conduit made of Schedule 40 pipe, normally 10-ft lengths.

Configuration, cradled: The geometric pattern which cables will take in a conduit when the cables are pulled in parallel and the ratio of the conduit ID to the I /C cable OD is greater than 3.0.

Configuration, triangular: The geometric pattern which cables will take in a conduit when the cables are triplexed or are pulled in parallel with the ratio of the conduit ID to the l/C cable OD less than 2.5.

Connection: 1) The part of a circuit which has negligible impedance and which joins components or devices. 2) A cable terminal, splice, or seal at the interface of the cable and equipment.

Connection, delta: Interconnection of three electrical equipment windings in delta (triangular) fashion.

Connection, star: Interconnection of three electrical equipment windings in star (wye) fashion.

Connector: A device used to physically and electrically connect two or more conductors.

Connector, pressure: A connector applied by using pressure to form a cold weld between the conductor and the connector.

Connector, reducing: A connector used to join two different size conductors.

Constant current: A type of power system in which the same amount of current flows through each utilization equipment, used for simplicity in street-lighting circuits.

Constant voltage: The common type of power in which all loads are connected in parallel, but different amounts of current flow through each load.

Contact: A device designed for repetitive connections.

Contactor: A type of relay.

Continuity: The state of being whole, unbroken.

Continuous load: 1) As stipulated by NEC—in operation 3 hours or more. 2) For nuclear power—8760 h/year (scheduled maintenance outages permitted).

Continuous vulcanization (CV): A system utilizing heat and pressure to vulcanize insulation after extrusion onto wire or cable; the curing tube may be in a horizontal or a vertical pole.

Control: Automatic or manual device used to stop, start, and/or regulate flow of gas, liquid, and/or electricity.

Copper: A word used by itself to refer to copper conductors. Examples: "A circuit of 500 kcmil copper" or "the copper cost of the circuit." It is a good conductor of electricity, easily formed, and easily connected to itself and other metals.

Cord: A small flexible conductor assembly, usually jacketed.

Cord set: A cord having a wiring connector on one or more ends.

Core: The portion of a foundry mold that shapes the interior of a hollow casting.

Core (cable): The portion of an insulated cable under a protective covering.

Counter emf: The voltage opposing the applied voltage and the current in a coil; caused by a flow of current in the coil; also known as back emf.

Coupling: The means by which signals are transferred from one circuit to another.

Coupon: A piece of metal for testing, of specified size; a piece of metal from which a test specimen may be prepared.

CT: Pronounced "see tee," refers to current transformer, taken from the initial letters *C* and *T*.

CU: Copper.

Current (I): The time rate of flow of electric charges; measured in amperes.

Current, charging: The current needed to bring the cable up to voltage; determined by capacitance of the cable; after withdrawal of voltage, the charging current returns to the circuit; the charging current will be 90° out of phase with the voltage.

Current density: The current per unit cross-sectional area.

Current-induced: Current in a conductor due to the application of a time-varying electromagnetic field.

Current, leakage: The small amount of current which flows through insulation whenever a voltage is present and heats the insulation because of the insulation's resistance; the leakage current is in phase with the voltage, and is a power loss.

Current limiting: A characteristic of short-circuit protective devices, such as fuses, by which the device operates so fast on high short-circuit currents that less than a quarter wave of the alternating cycle is permitted to flow before the circuit is opened, thereby limiting the thermal and magnetic energy to a certain maximum value, regardless of the current available.

Customer Complaint Analysis (CCA): A formal investigation of a cable defect or failure.

Cut in: The connection of electrical service to a building, from the power company line to the service equipment, for example, "the building was cut in" or "the power company cut in the service."

Cycle: 1) An interval of space or time in which one set of events or phenomena is completed. 2) A set of operations that are repeated regularly in the same sequence. 3) A number of different processes a system in a given state goes through before it finally returns to its initial state.

Dead: 1) Not having electrical charge. 2) Not having voltage applied.

Dead-end: A mechanical terminating device on a building or pole to provide support at the end of an overhead electric circuit. A *dead-end* is also the term used to refer to the last pole in the pole line. The pole at which the electric circuiting is brought down the pole to go underground or to the building served.

Dead-front: A switchboard or panel or other electrical apparatus without "live" energized terminals or parts exposed on the front, where personnel might make contact.

Demand: 1) The measure of the maximum load of a utility's customer over a short period of time. 2) The load integrated over a specified time interval.

Demand factor: For an electrical system or feeder circuit, a ratio of the amount of connected load (in kVA or amperes) which will be operating at the same time to the total amount of connected load on the circuit. An 80 percent demand factor, for instance, indicates that only 80 percent of the connected load on a circuit will ever be operating at the same time. Conductor capacity can be based on that amount of load.

Detection: The process of separating the modulation component from the received signal.

Device: An item intended to carry, or help carry, but not utilize electrical energy.

Dew point: The temperature at which vapor starts to condense (liquify) from a gas vapor mixture at constant pressure.

Dielectric strength: The maximum voltage which an insulation can withstand without breaking down; usually expressed as a gradient, in volts per mil (vpm).

Diode: A device having two electrodes, the cathode and the plate or anode, and which is used as a rectifier and detector.

Direct current (dc): 1) Electricity which flows in only one direction. 2) The type of electricity produced by a battery.

Disconnect: A switch for disconnecting an electrical circuit or load (motor, transformer, panel) from the conductors which supply power to it; for example, "He pulled the motor disconnect" means he opened the disconnect switch to the motor.

Disconnecting means: A device, a group of devices, or other means whereby the conductors of a circuit can be disconnected from their supply source.

Distribution, statistical analysis: A statistical method used to analyze data by correlating data to a theoretical curve in order to (a) test validity of data; (b) predict performance at conditions different from those used to produce the data. The normal distribution curve is most common.

Drawing, block diagram: A simplified drawing of a system showing major items as blocks; normally used to show how the system works and what the relationship between major items is.

Drawing, line schematic (diagram): Shows how a circuit works.

Drawing, plot or layout: Shows the "floor plan."

Drawing, wiring diagram: Shows how the devices are interconnected.

Drill: A circular tool used for machining a hole.

Drywall: Interior wall construction consisting of plasterboard, wood paneling, or plywood nailed directly to the studs without application of plaster.

Duty, continuous: A service requirement that demands operation at a substantially constant load for an indefinitely long time.

Duty, intermittent: A service requirement that demands operation for alternate intervals of load and no load, load and rest, or load, no load, and rest.

Duty, periodic: A type of intermittent duty in which the load conditions regularly reoccur.

Duty, short-time: A requirement of service that demands operations at loads and for intervals of time that may both be subject to wide variation.

Edison base: The standard screw base used for ordinary lamps.

EEI: Edison Electric Institute.

Efficiency: The ratio of the output to the input.

Elasticity: The property of recovery to original size and shape after deformation.

Electrolyte: A liquid or solid that conducts electricity by the flow of ions.

Electrolytic condenser-capacitor: Plate or surface capable of storing small electrical charges. Common electrolytic condensers are formed by rolling thin sheets of foil between insulating materials. Condenser capacity is expressed in microfarads.

Electromagnet: A device consisting of a ferromagnetic core and a coil that produces appreciable magnetic effects only when an electric current exists in the coil.

Electromotive force (emf) voltage: Electrical force that causes current (free electrons) to flow or move in an electrical circuit. The unit of measurement is the volt.

Electron: The subatomic particle that carries the unit negative charge of electricity.

Electron emission: The release of electrons from the surface of a material into sur rounding space due to heat, light, high voltage, or other causes.

Electronics: The science dealing with the development and application of devices and systems involving the flow of electrons in vacuum, gaseous media, and semiconductors.

Emitter: The part of a transistor that emits electrons.

Engine: An apparatus which converts heat to mechanical energy.

Environment: 1) The universe within which a system must operate. 2) All the elements over which the designer has no control and that affect a system or its inputs and outputs.

Equipment: A general term including material, fittings, devices, appliances, fixtures, apparatus, and the like used as part of, or in connection with, an electrical installation.

Farad: The basic unit of capacitance: one farad equals one coulomb per volt.

Fatigue: The weakening or breakdown of a material due to cyclic stress.

Fault: An abnormal connection in a circuit.

Fault, arcing: A fault having high impedance causing arcing.

Fault, bolting: A fault of very low impedance.

Fault, ground: A fault to ground.

Feedback: The process of transferring energy from the output circuit of a device back to its input.

Feeder: A circuit, such as conductors in conduit or a busway run, which carries a large block of power from the service equipment to a subfeeder panel or a branch circuit panel or to some point at which the block or power is broken down into smaller circuits.

Fish tape: A flexible metal tape for fishing through conduits or other raceway to pull in wires or cables; also made in nonmetallic form of "rigid rope" for hand fishing of raceways.

Fitting: An accessory such as a locknut, bushing, or other part of a wiring system that is intended primarily to perform a mechanical rather than an electrical function.

Flex: Common term used to refer to flexible metallic conduit.

Flexural strength: The strength of a material in bending, expressed as the tensile stress of the outermost fibers of a bent test sample at the instant of failure.

Frequency: The number of complete cycles an alternating electric current, sound wave, or vibrating object undergoes per second.

Friction tape: An insulating tape made of asphalt-impregnated cloth; used on 600-V cables.

Fuse: A protecting device which opens a circuit when the fusible element is severed by heating due to overcurrent passing through. Rating: voltage, normal current, maximum let-through current, time delay of interruption.

Fuse, dual element: A fuse having two fuse characteristics; the usual combination is having an overcurrent limit and a time delay before activation.

Fuse, nonrenewable or one-time: A fuse which must be replaced after it interrupts a circuit .

Fuse, renewable link: A fuse which may be reused after current interruption by replacing the meltable link.

Fusible plug: A plug or fitting made with a metal of a known low melting temperature; used as a safety device to release pressures in case of fire.

Galvanometer: An instrument for indicating or measuring a small electrical current by means of a mechanical motion derived from electromagnetic or dynamic forces.

Gauge: 1) Dimension expressed in terms of a system of arbitrary reference numbers; dimensions expressed in decimals are preferred. 2) To measure.

Generator: 1) A rotating machine to convert from mechanical to electrical energy. 2) A machine to convert automotive-mechanical to direct current. 3) General apparatus, equipment, etc. to convert or change energy from one form to another.

GFI: *See* Ground Fault Interrupter.

Greenfield: Another name for flexible metal conduit.

Grommet: A plastic, metal, or rubber doughnut-shaped protector for wires or tubing as they pass through a hole in an object.

Ground: A large conducting body (as the earth) used as a common return for an electric circuit and as an arbitrary zero of potential.

Ground check: A pilot wire in portable cables to monitor the grounding circuit.

Ground coil: A heat exchanger buried in the ground that may be used either as an evaporator or a condenser.

Grounded: Connected to earth.

Grounded conductor: A system or circuit conductor that is intentionally grounded.

Ground Fault Interrupter (GFI): A protective device that detects abnormal current flowing to ground and then interrupts the circuit.

Grounding: The device or conductor connected to ground designed to conduct only under abnormal conditions.

Grounding conductor: A conductor used to connect metal equipment enclosures and/or the system grounded conductor to a grounding electrode, such as the ground wire run to the water pipe at a service; also may be a bare or insulated conductor used to ground motor frames, panel boxes, and other metal equipment enclosures used throughout an electrical system. In most conduit systems, the conduit is used as the ground conductor.

Grounds: Narrow strips of wood nailed to walls as guides to plastering and as a nailing base for interior trim.

Guard: 1) A conductor situated so as to conduct interference to its source and prevent the interference from having an influence on the desired signal. 2) A mechanical barrier against physical contact.

Half effect: The changing of current density in a conductor due to a magnetic field extraneous to the conductor.

Half wave: Rectifying only half of a sinusoidal ac supply.

Handy box: The single-gang outlet box which is used for surface mounting to enclose wall switches or receptacles, on concrete or cinder block construction of industrial and commercial buildings; also made for recessed mounting; also known as a utility box.

Hard drawn: A relative measure of temper; drawn to obtain maximum strength.

Hardness: Resistance to plastic deformation; resistance to scratching, abrasion, or cutting.

Harmonic: An oscillation whose frequency is an integral multiple of the fundamental frequency.

Harness: A group of conductors laced or bundled in a given configuration, usually with many breakouts.

Heat dissipation: The flow of heat from a hot body to a cooler body by 1) convection, 2) radiation, or 3) conduction.

Helix: The path followed when winding a wire or strip around a tube at a constant angle.

Henry: The derived SI unit for inductance: one henry equals one weber per ampere.

Home run: The part of a branch circuit that goes from the panelboard housing the branch circuit fuse or CB and the first junction box at which the branch circuit is spliced to lighting or receptacle devices or to conductors which continue the branch circuit to the next outlet or junction box. The term "home run" is usually reserved for multioutlet lighting and appliance circuits.

Horsepower: The non-SI unit for power: 1 hp = 746 W (electric) = 9800 W (boiler).

Hot: Energized with electricity.

Hot junction: The part of the thermoelectric circuit which releases heat.

Hot leg: A circuit conductor which normally operates at a voltage above ground; the phase wires or energized circuit wires other than a grounded neutral wire or grounded phase leg.

IBEW: International Brotherhood of Electrical Workers.

IC: Pronounced "eye see." Refers to interrupting capacity of any device required to break current (switch, circuit breaker, fuse, etc.), taken from the initial letters I and C; it is the amount of current the device can interrupt without damage to itself.

ID: Inside diameter.

Identified: Marked to be recognized as grounded.

IEC: International Electrochemical Commission.

IEEE: Institute of Electrical and Electronics Engineers.

Ignition transformer: A transformer designed to provide a high voltage current.

Impedance (A): The opposition to current flow in an ac circuit; impedance includes resistance (R), capacitive reactance (xc), and inductive reactance (XL); it is measured in ohms.

Impedance matching: Matching source and load impedance for optimum energy transfer with minimum distortion.

Impulse: A surge of unidirectional polarity.

Inductance: The creation of a voltage from a time-varying current; the opposition to current change, causing current changes to lag behind voltage changes; the unit of measurement is the henry.

Infrared lamp: An electrical device that emits infrared rays, which are invisible rays just beyond red in the visible spectrum.

Infrared radiation: Radiant energy given off by heated bodies which transmits heat and will pass through glass.

In phase: The condition existing when waves pass through their maximum and minimum values of like polarity at the same instant.

Instrument: A device for measuring the value of the quantity under observation.

Insulated: Separated from other conducting surfaces by a substance permanently offering a high resistance to the passage of energy through the substance.

Insulated Power Cable Engineers Association (IPCEA): The association of cable manufacturing engineers who make nationally recognized specifications and tests for cables.

Insulation, class rating: A temperature rating descriptive of classes of insulations for which various tests are made to distinguish the materials; not necessarily related to operating temperatures.

Insulation dc resistance constant (IRK): A system to classify materials according to their resistance on a 1000-ft basis at 15.5°C (60°F).

Insulation, electrical: A medium in which it is possible to maintain an electrical field with little supply of energy from additional sources; the energy required to produce the electric field is fully recoverable only in a complete vacuum (the ideal dielectric) when the field or applied voltage is removed: used to (a) save space, (b) enhance safety, (c) improve appearance.

Insulation fall-in: The filling of strand interstices, especially the inner interstices, which may contribute to connection failures.

Insulation level (cable): The thickness of insulation for circuits having ground fault detectors which interrupt fault currents within 1) 1 minute = 100% level, 2) 1 hour = 133% level, (3) more than 1 hour = 173% level.

Insulation resistance (IR): The measurement of the dc resistance of insulating material; can be either volume or surface resistivity. Extremely temperature sensitive.

Insulation, thermal: Substance used to retard or slow the flow of heat through a wall or partition.

Integrated circuit: A circuit in which different types of devices such as resistors, capacitors, and transistors are made from a single piece of material and then connected to form a circuit.

Integrator: Any device producing an output proportionate to the integral of one variable with respect to a second variable; the second variable is usually time.

Intercalated tapes: Two or more tapes of different materials helically wound and overlapping on a cable to separate the materials.

Interconnected system: Operating with two or more power systems connected through the lines.

Interference: Extraneous signals which are undesired.

Interlock: A safety device to ensure that a piece of apparatus will not operate until certain conditions have been satisfied.

Inverter: An item which changes dc to ac.

Ion: An electrically charged atom or radical.

Ionization: 1) The process or the result of any process by which a neutral atom or molecule acquires charge. 2) A breakdown that occurs in gaseous parts of an insulation when the dielectric stress exceeds a critical value without initiating a complete break down of the insulation system; ionization is harmful to living tissue, and is detectable and measurable; may be evidenced by corona.

Ionization factor: The difference between the percentages of dissipation factors at two specified values of electrical stress; the lower of the two stresses is usually so selected that the effect of the ionization on the dissipation factor at this stress is negligible.

IPCEA: See *Insulated Power Cable Engineers Association*.

IR: *See* Insulation resistance.

IR drop: The voltage drop across a resistance due to the flow of current through the resistor.

IRK: *See* Insulation dc resistance constant.

Isolated: Not readily accessible to persons unless special means of access are used. Isolating With switches, means that the switch is not a loadbreak type and must be opened only when no current is flowing in the circuit. This term also refers to transformers (an isolating transformer) used to provide magnetic isolation of one circuit from another, thereby breaking a metallic conductive path between the circuits.

Jacket: A nonmetallic polymeric close-fitting protective covering over cable insulation; the cable may have one or more conductors.

Jacket, conducting: An electrically conducting polymeric covering over an insulation.

jumper: A short length of conductor, usually a temporary connection.

Junction: A connection of two or more conductors.

Junction box: Group of electrical terminals housed in a protective box or container.

Kilowatt: Unit of electrical power equal to 1000 W.

Kilowatt-foot: The product of load in kilowatts and the circuit's distance over which a load is carried in feet; used to compute voltage drop.

Kinetic energy: Energy by virtue of motion.

Kirchhoff's Laws: 1) The algebraic sum of the currents at any point in a circuit is zero. 2) The algebraic sum of the product of the current and the impedance in each conductor in a circuit is equal to the electromotive force in the circuit.

Knockout: A portion of an enclosure designed to be readily removed for installation of a raceway.

KO: Pronounced "kay oh," a knockout, the partially cut opening in boxes, panel cabinets, and other enclosures that can easily be knocked out with a screwdriver and hammer to provide a clean hole for connecting conduit, cable, or some fittings.

KVA: Kilovolts times ampere.

LA: Lightning arrestor.

Labeled Items: Carrying the trademark of a nationally recognized testing laboratory.

Leakage: Undesirable conduction of current.

Leakage distance: The shortest distance along an insulation surface between conductors.

Leg: A portion of a circuit.

Lighting outlet: An outlet intended for the direct connection of a lamp holder, lighting fixture, or pendant cord terminating in a lamp holder.

Lightning arrestor: A device designed to protect circuits and apparatus from high transient voltage by diverting the overvoltage to ground.

Limit control: Control used to open or close electrical circuits as temperature or pressure limits are reached.

Limiter: A device in which some characteristic of the output is automatically prevented from exceeding a predetermined value.

Line: 1) A circuit between two points. 2) Ropes used during overhead construction.

Live-front: Any panel or other switching and protection assembly, such as a switch board or motor control center, which has exposed electrically energized parts on its front, presenting the possibility of contact by personnel.

Live load: Any load on a structure other than a dead load; includes the weight of persons occupying the building and freestanding material.

Load: 1) A device that receives power. 2) The power delivered to such a device.

Load center: An assembly of circuit breakers or switches.

Load factor: The ratio of the average to the peak load over a period.

Load losses: Those losses incidental to providing power.

Lug: A device for terminating a conductor to facilitate the mechanical connection.

Magnet: A body that produces a magnetic field external to itself; magnets attract iron particles.

Magnetic field: 1) A magnetic field is said to exist at the point at which a force over and above any electrostatic force is exerted on a moving charge at that point. 2) The force field established by ac through a conductor, especially a coiled conductor.

Magnetic pole: Those portions of the magnet toward which the external magnetic induction appears to converge (south) or diverge (north).

MCM: An expression referring to conductors of sizes from 250 MCM, which stands for thousand circular mils, up to 2000 MCM. The most recent term for expressing thousand circular mils is kcmil.

Medium hard: A relative measure of conductor temper.

Megger: The term used to identify a test instrument for measuring the insulation resistance of conductors and other electrical equipment; specifically, a megohm (million ohms) meter; but Megger is a registered trade name of the James Biddle Co.

Megohmmeter: An instrument for measuring extremely high resistance.

Metal clad (MC): The cable core is enclosed in a flexible metal covering.

Mica: A silicate which separates into layers and has high insulation resistance, dielectric strength, and heat resistance.

MI cable: Mineral-insulated, metal-sheathed cabie.

Microwave: Radio waves of frequencies above one gigahertz.

Mil: A unit used in measuring the diameter of wire, equal to 0.001 in (25.4 cm).

MIL: Military specification.

Millimeter (mm): One-thousandth of a meter.

Mil scale: The heavy oxide layer formed during hot fabrication or heat treatment of metals.

Modem: Equipment that connects data transmitting/receiving equipment to telephone lines: a word contraction of modulator-demodulator.

Modulation: The varying of a "carrier" wave characteristic by a characteristic of a second "modulating" wave.

Moisture-resistance: So constructed or treated that moisture will not readily injure.

Molded case breaker: A circuit breaker enclosed in an insulating housing.

Motor: An apparatus to convert from electrical to mechanical energy.

Motor, capacitor: A single-phase induction motor with an auxiliary starting winding connected in series with a condenser for better starting characteristics.

Motor control: Device to start and/or stop a motor at certain temperature or pressure conditions.

Mutual inductance: The condition of voltage in a second conductor because of a change in current in another, adjacent conductor.

National Electrical Code (NEC): A national consensus standard for the installation of electrical systems.

National Fire Protection Association (NFPA): An organization to promote the science and improve the methods of fire protection; it sponsors various codes, including the National Code.

Natural convection: Movement of a fluid or air caused by temperature change.

Negative: Connected to the negative terminal of a power supply.

NEMA: National Electrical Manufacturers Association.

Neoprene: An oil-resistant synthetic rubber used for jackets; originally a DuPont trade name, now a generic term for polychloroprene.

Neutral: The element of a circuit from which other voltages are referenced with respect to magnitude and time displacement in steady-state conditions.

Neutral block: The neutral terminal block in a panelboard, meter enclosure, gutter, or other enclosure in which circuit conductors are terminated or subdivided.

Neutral wire: A circuit conductor which is common to the other conductors of the circuit, having the same voltage between it and each of the other circuit wires and usually operating grounded; such as the neutral of three-wire, single-phase, or three-phase, four-wire wye systems.

NFPA: *See* National Fire Protection Association.

Nineteen hundred box: A commonly used term to refer to any two-gang 4-in square outlet box used for two wiring devices or for one wiring device with a single-gang cover where the number of wires requires this box capacity.

Nipple: A threaded pipe or conduit less than 2 ft long.

Occupational Safety and Health Act (OSHA): Federal Law #91-59G of 1970 charging all employers engaged in business affecting interstate commerce to be responsible for providing a safe working place: it is administered by the Department of Labor. The OSHA regulations are published in Title 29, Chapter XVII, Part 1910 of the CFR and the *Federal Register*.

Ohmmeter: An instrument for measuring resistance in ohms.

Ohm's law: Mathematical relationship between voltage, current, and resistance in an electric circuit.

Oscillation: The variation, usually with time, of the magnitude of a quantity which is alternately greater and smaller than a reference.

Oscillator: A device that produces an alternating or pulsating current or voltage electronically.

Oscillograph: An instrument primarily for producing a graph of rapidly varying electrical quantities.

Oscilloscope: An instrument primarily for making visible rapidly varying electrical quantities: oscilloscopes function similarly to TV sets.

OSHA: *See* Occupational Safety and Health Act.

Outlet: A point on the wiring system at which current is taken to supply utilization equipment.

Outline lighting: An arrangement of incandescent lamps or gaseous tubes to outline and call attention to certain features, such as the shape of a building or the decoration of a window.

Output: 1) The energy delivered by a circuit or device. 2) The terminals for such delivery.

Overload: Load greater than the load for which the system or mechanism was intended.

Overvoltage (cable): Voltage above normal operating voltage, usually due to: (a) switching loads on/off, (b) lighting, (c) single phasing.

Pad-mounted: A shortened expression for "pad-mount transformer," which is a completely enclosed transformer mounted outdoors on a concrete pad, without need for a surrounding chain-link fence around the metal, boxlike transformer enclosure.

Panelboard: A single panel or group of panel units designed for assembly in the form of a single panel; includes buses and may come with or without switches and/or automatic overcurrent protective devices for the control of light, heat, or power circuits of individual as well as aggregate capacity. It is designed to be placed in a cabinet or cutout box that is in or against a wall or partition and is accessible only from the front.

Phase conductor: Any conductor other than the neutral one.

Phase leg: One of the phase conductors (an ungrounded or "hot" conductor) of a polyphase electrical system.

Phase out: A procedure by which the individual phases of a polyphase circuit or system are identified. Someone might "phase out" a three-phase circuit for a motor in order to identify phase A, phase B, and phase C. That person would then know how to connect them to the motor to get the correct phase rotation, causing the motor to rotate in the desired direction.

Phase sequence: The order in which the successive members of a periodic wave set reach their positive maximum values: (a) zero phase sequence — no phase shift; (b) plus/minus phase sequence — normal phase shift.

Phase shift: The absolute magnitude of the difference between two phase angles.

Photocell: A device in which the current-voltage characteristic is a function of incident radiation (light).

Photoelectric control: A control sensitive to incident light.

Photoelectricity: A physical action wherein an electrical flow is generated by light waves.

Photon: An elementary quantity (quantum) of radiant energy.

Pilot lamp: A lamp that indicates the condition of an associated circuit.

Pilot wire: An auxiliary insulated conductor in a power cable used for control or data.

Plating: Forming an adherent layer of metal on an object.

Plug: A male connector for insertion into an outlet or jack.

Polarity: 1) Distinguishing one conductor or terminal from another. 2) Identifying how devices are to be connected, such as plus (+) or minus (−) signs.

Polarization Index: Ratio of insulation resistance measured after 10 minutes to the measure at 1 minute with voltage continuously applied.

Pole: 1) That portion of a device associated exclusively with one electrically separated conducting path of the main circuit or device. 2) A supporting circular column.

Polyphase circuits: Circuits running on ac and having two or more interrelated voltages, usually of equal amplitudes, phase differences, and periods, etc. If a neutral conductor exists, the voltages referenced to the neutral conductor are equal in amplitude and phase. The most common version is that of three-phase, equal in amplitude with phases 120° apart.

Portable: Designed to be movable from one place to another, not necessarily while in operation.

Positive: Connected to the positive terminal of a power supply.

Potential: The difference in voltage between two points of a circuit. Frequently, one is assumed to be ground (zero potential).

Potential energy: Energy of a body or system with respect to the position of the body or the arrangement of the particles of the system.

Potentiometer: An instrument for measuring an unknown voltage or potential difference by balancing it, wholly or in part, by a known potential difference produced by the flow of known currents in a network of circuits of known electrical constants.

Power: 1) Work per unit of time. 2) The time rate of transferring energy. As an adjective, the word "power" is descriptive of the energy used to perform useful work: pound feet per second, watts.

Power, active: In a three-phase symmetrical circuit, $p = 3 \, Vl \cos \theta$; in a one-phase, two-wire circuit, $p = Vl \cos \theta$.

Power, apparent: The product of rms volts times rms amperes.

Power element: Sensitive element of a temperature-operated control.

Power factor: Correction coefficient for ac power necessary because of changing current and voltage values.

Power loss (cable): Loss due to internal cable impedance, mainly l2R: the loss causes heating.

Pressure motor control: A device that opens and closes an electrical circuit as pressures change.

Primary: Normaily referring to the part of a device or equipment connected to the power supply circuit.

Primary control: Device that directly controls operation of a heating system.

Printed circuit: A board having interconnecting wiring printed on its surface and designed for mounting of electronic components.

Process: Path of succession of states through which a system passes.

Program, computer: The ordered listing of a sequence of events designed to direct the computer to accomplish a task.

Protector, circuit: An electrical device that will open an electrical circuit if excessive electrical conditions occur.

Proton: The hydrogen atom nucleus; it is electrically positive.

Prototype: The first full-size working model.

Proximity effect: The distortion of current density due to magnetic fields; increased by conductor diameter, close spacing, frequency, and magnetic materials such as steel conduit or beams.

Pull box: A sheet-metal boxlike enclosure used in conduit runs, either single conduits or multiple conduits, to facilitate pulling in of cables from point to point in long runs or to provide installation of conduit support bushings needed to support the weight of long riser cables or to provide for turns in multiple-conduit runs.

Pyrometer: Thermometer that measures the radiation from a heated body.

Raceway: Any channel designed expressly for holding wire, cables, or bars and used solely for that purpose.

Rack (cable): A device to support cables.

Radar: A radio detecting and ranging system.

Radiant energy: Energy traveling in the form of electromagnetic waves.

Radiant heating: Heating system in which warm or hot surfaces are used to radiate heat into the space to be conditioned.

Radiation: The process of emitting radiant energy in the form of waves or particles.

Radiation, blackbody: Energy given off by an ideal radiating surface at any temperature.

Radiation, nuclear: The release of particles and rays during disintegration or decay of an atom's nucleus. These rays — alpha particles, beta particles, and gamma rays — cause ionization.

Radius, bending: The radii around which cables are pulled.

Rated: Indicating the limits of operating characteristics for application under specified conditions.

Reactance: 1) The imaginary part of impedance. 2) The opposition to ac due to capacitance (Xc) and inductance (XL).

Reactor: A device to introduce capacitive or inductive reactance into a circuit.

Receptacle: A contact device installed at an outlet for the connection of an attachment plug and flexible cord to supply portable equipment.

Recorder: A device that makes a permanent record, usually visual, of varying signals.

Rectifiers: Devices used to change alternating current to unidirectional current.

Rectify: To change from ac to dc.

Red-leg: 1) The phase conductor of a three-phase, four-wire, delta-connected system that is not connected to the single-phase power supply. 2) The conductor with the highest voltage above ground, which must be identified (as per NEC) and is commonly painted red to provide such identification.

Relay: A device designed to change a circuit abruptly because of a specified control input.

Relay, overcurrent: A relay designed to open a circuit when current in excess of a particular setting flows through the sensor.

Remote-control circuits: The control of a circuit through relays and other means.

Resistance: The opposition in a conductor to current; the real part of impedance.

Resistor: A device whose primary purpose is to introduce resistance.

Resonance: In a circuit containing both inductance and capacitance, a condition in which the inductive reactance is equal to and cancels out the capacitance reactance.

Rheostat: A variable resistor that can be varied while energized; normally one used in a power circuit.

ROM: Read only memory.

Romex: General Cable's trade name for type NM cable; but used generically by electrical workers to refer to any nonmetallic sheathed cable.

Roughing in: The first stage of an electrical installation, when the raceway, cable, wires, boxes, and other equipment are installed; electrical work that must be done before any finishing or cover-up phases of building construction can be undertaken.

Self-inductance: Magnetic field induced in the conductor carrying the current.

Semiconductor: A material that has electrical properties of current flow between a conductor and an insulator.

Sensor: A material or device that goes through a physical change or an electronic characteristic change as conditions change.

Separable insulated connector: An insulated device to facilitate power cable connections and separations.

Service cable: The service conductors made up in the form of a cable.

Service conductors: The supply conductors that extend from the street main or transformers to the service equipment of the premises being supplied.

Service drop: Run of cables from the power company's aerial power lines to the point of connection on a customer's premises.

Service entrance: The point at which power is supplied to a building, including the equipment used for this purpose (service main switch or panel or switchboard, metering devices, overcurrent protective devices, conductors for connecting to the power company's conductors, and raceways for such conductors).

Service equipment: The necessary equipment, usually consisting of a circuit breaker or switch and fuses and their accessories, located near the point of entrance of supply conductors to a building and intended to constitute the main control and cutout means for the supply to the building.

Service lateral: The underground service conductors between the street main, including any risers at a pole or other structure or from transformers, and the first point of connection to the service-entrance conductors in a terminal box, meter, or other enclosure with adequate space, inside or outside the building wall. Where there is no terminal box, meter, or other enclosure with adequate space, the point of connection is the entrance point of the service conductors into the building.

Service raceway: The rigid metal conduit, electrical metallic tubing, or other raceway that encloses the service-entrance conductors.

Sheath: A metallic close-fitting protective covering.

Shield: The conducting barrier against electromagnetic fields.

Shield, braid: A shield of interwoven small wires.

Shield, insulation: An electrically conducting layer to provide a smooth surface in intimate contact with the insulation outer surface; used to eliminate electrostatic charges external to the shield and to provide a fixed known path to ground.

Shield, tape: The insulation shielding system whose current-carrying component is thin metallic tapes, now normally used in conjunction with a conducting layer of tapes or extruded polymer.

Short-circuit: An often unintended low-resistance path through which current flows around, rather than through, a component or circuit.

Shunt: A device having appreciable resistance or impedance connected in parallel across other devices or another apparatus to divert some of the current. Appreciable voltage exists across the shunt and appreciable current may exist in it.

Signal: A detectable physical quantity or impulse (such as a voltage, current, or magnetic field strength) by which messages or information can be transmitted.

Signal circuit: Any electrical circuit supplying energy to an appliance that gives a recognizable signal.

Single-phase motor: Electric motor that operates on single-phase alternating current.

Single-phasing: The abnormal operation of a three-phase machine when its supply is changed by accidental opening of one conductor.

Solenoid: Electric conductor wound as a helix with a small pitch; coil.

Solidly grounded: No intentional impedance in the grounding circuit.

Solid state: A device, circuit, or system which does not depend on the physical movement of solids, liquids, gases, or plasma.

SP: Single pole.

Specs: Abbreviation for the word "specifications," which is the written precise description of the scope and details of an electrical installation and the equipment to be used in the system.

Starter: 1) An electric controller for accelerating a motor from rest to normal speed and for stopping the motor. 2) A device used to start an electric discharge lamp.

Starting relay: An electrical device that connects and/or disconnects the starting winding of an electric motor.

Starting winding: Winding in an electric motor used only during the brief period when the motor is starting.

Static: Interference caused by electrical disturbances in the atmosphere.

Stator: The portion of a rotating machine that includes and supports the stationary active parts.

Steady state: When a characteristic exhibits only negligible change over a long period of time.

Strand: A group of wires, usually twisted or braided.

Supervised circuit: A closed circuit having a current-responsive device to indicate a break or ground.

Surge: 1) A sudden increase in voltage and current. 2) Transient condition.

Switch: A device for opening and closing or for changing the connection of a circuit.

Switch, ac general-use snap: A general-use snap switch suitable only for use on alternating-current circuits and for controlling resistive and inductive loads (including electric discharge lamps) not exceeding the ampere rating at the voltage involved.

Switchboard: A large single panel, frame, or assembly of panels having switches, overcurrent and other protective devices, buses, and usually instruments mounted on the face or back or both. Switchboards are generally accessible from the rear and from the front and are not intended to be installed in cabinets.

Switch, general-use: A switch intended for use in general distribution and branch circuits. It is rated in amperes and is capable of interrupting its rated voltage.

Switch, general-use snap: A type of general-use switch so constructed that it can be installed in flush device boxes or on outlet covers or otherwise used in conjunction with wiring systems recognized by the National Electrical Code.

Switch, isolating: A switch intended for isolating an electrical circuit from the source of power. It has no interrupting rating and is intended to be operated only after the circuit has been opened by some other means.

Switch, knife: A switch in which the circuit is closed by a moving blade engaging contact clips.

Switch-leg: The part of a circuit that runs from a lighting outlet box where a luminaire or lampholder is installed down to an outlet box which contains the wall switch that turns the light or other load on or off; it is a control leg of the branch circuit.

Switch, motor-circuit: A switch, rated in horsepower, capable of interrupting the maximum operating overload current of a motor having the same horsepower rating as the switch at the rated voltage.

Synchronous machine: A machine in which the average speed of normal operation is exactly proportional to the frequency of the system to which it is connected.

Synchronous speed: The speed of rotation of the magnetic flux produced by linking the primary winding.

Synchrotron: A device for accelerating charged particles to high energies in a vacuum; the particles are guided by a changing magnetic field while they are accelerated in a closed path.

System: A region of space or quantity of matter undergoing study.

Tachometer: An instrument for measuring revolutions per minute.

Tap: 1) A splice connection of a wire to another wire (such as a feeder conductor in an auxiliary gutter) where the smaller conductor runs a short distance (usually only a few feet, but can be as much as 25 ft) to supply a panelboard or motor controller or switch. Also called a "tap-off," indicating that energy is being taken from one circuit or piece of equipment to supply another circuit or load. 2) A tool that cuts or machines threads in the side of a round hole.

Telegraphy: Telecommunication by the use of a signal code.

Telemetering: Measurement with the aid of intermediate means that permits interpretation at a distance from the primary detector.

Telephone: The transmission and reception of sound by electronics.

Thermal cutout: An overcurrent protective device containing a heater element in addition to and affecting a renewable fusible member which opens the circuit. It is not designed to interrupt short-circuit currents.

Thermally protected: (as applied to motors) Refers to the words "thermally protected" appearing on the nameplate of a motor or motor-compressor and means that the motor is provided with a thermal protector.

Thermal protector (as applied to motors): A protective device that is assembled as an integral part of a motor or motor compressor and that, when properly applied, protects the motor against dangerous overheating due to overload and failure to start.

Three-phase system: A three-phase, alternating-current system containing three individual circuits or phases. Each phase is timed so that the current alternations of the first phase are one-third of a cycle (120°) ahead of the second and two-thirds of a cycle (240°) ahead of the third.

Transformer: A device used to transfer energy from one circuit to another. It is composed of two or more coils linked by magnetic lines of force.

Trusses: Framed structural pieces consisting of triangles in a single plane for supporting loads over spans.

Utilization equipment: Equipment that utilizes electric energy for mechanical, chemical, heating, lighting, or other similar useful purposes.

Ventilated: Provided with a means to permit enough circulation of air to remove an excess of heat fumes or vapors.

Volt: The practical unit of voltage of electromotive force. One volt sends a current of one ampere through a resistance of one ohm.

Voltage: Voltage is the force, pressure, or electromotive force (emf) which causes electric current to flow in an electric circuit. Its unit of measurement is the volt, which represents the amount of electrical pressure that causes current to flow at the rate of one ampere through a resistance of one ohm. Voltage in an electric circuit may be considered as being similar to water pressure in a pipe or water system.

Voltage drop: The voltage drop in an electric circuit is the difference between the voltage at the power source and the voltage at the point at which electricity is to be used. The voltage drop, or loss, is created by the resistance of the connecting conductors.

Voltage-to-ground: In grounded circuits the voltage between the given conductor and that point or conductor of the circuit which is grounded; in ungrounded circuits, the greatest voltage between the given conductor and any other conductor of the circuit.

Watertight: So constructed that moisture will not enter the enclosing case or housing.

Watt: The unit of measurement of electrical power or rate of work; 756 W is equivalent to 1 hp. The watt represents the rate at which power is expended when a pressure of 1 V causes current to flow at the rate of 1 A. In a dc circuit or in an ac circuit at unity

(100 percent) power factor, the number of watts equals the pressure (in volts) multiplied by the current (in amperes).

Weatherproof: So constructed or protected that exposure to the weather will not interfere with successful operation.

Web: Central portion of an I beam.

Index

Index